P9-BBT-378

READING ON THE RIVER:
A Literary Anthology

Chattanooga State Community College

FOUNTAINHEAD
PRESS

Our green initiatives include:

Electronic Products

We deliver products in non-paper form whenever possible. This includes pdf downloadables, flash drives, and CDs.

Electronic Samples

We use Xample, a new electronic sampling system. Instructor samples are sent via a personalized web page that links to pdf downloads.

FSC Certified Printers

All of our printers are certified by the Forest Service Council, which promotes environmentally and socially responsible management of the world's forests. This program allows consumer groups, individual consumers, and businesses to work together hand-in-hand to promote responsible use of the world's forests as a renewable and sustainable resource.

Recycled Paper

Most of our products are printed on a minimum of 30% post-consumer waste recycled paper.

Support of Green Causes

When we do print, we donate a portion of our revenue to green causes. Listed below are a few of the organizations that have received donations from Fountainhead Press. We welcome your feedback and suggestions for contributions, as we are always searching for worthy initiatives.

Rainforest 2 Reef

Environmental Working Group

Cover photo by Michael Holsomback, Associate Professor, Humanities and Fine Arts Division, Chattanooga State Community College.
Interior photos provided by Michael Holsomback, Mark Wood, and Ken Page.
Cover and text design by: Carol A. Hill

Copyright © 2017 Chattanooga State Community College Humanities Department
Copyrights and reading credits appear on pp. 313-314 which constitutes an extension of the copyright page. It is a violation of the law to reproduce these selections by any means whatsoever without written permission of the copyright holder. The publisher has made every attempt to secure the appropriate permissions for material reproduced in this book. If there has been any oversight, we will be happy to rectify the situation, and written submission should be made to the publisher.
All rights reserved. No part of this book may be reproduced or utilized in any form or by any means, electronic or mechanical, including photocopying and recording, or by any informational storage and retrieval system, without written permission from the publisher.

Books may be purchased for educational purposes. For information, please call or write:
1-800-586-0330
Fountainhead Press
Southlake, TX 76092
Web site: www.fountainheadpress.com
E-mail: customerservice@fountainheadpress.com

ISBN: 978-1-68036-388-3

Printed in the United States of America

Introduction

Contents by Page Order

Contents by Theme

Quick Reference for Primary Literary Elements and Devices:

Personification:

Rhyme:

Introduction

Welcome to ENGL 1020, Composition II, at Chattanooga State! The readings in your *Reading on the River: A Literary Anthology* have been specifically selected by English faculty at Chattanooga State to assist you in developing the ability to critically analyze the writings of others from around the world and across the centuries that will assist you in learning to interpret the contemporary world around you.

The skills you developed in Composition I will be expanded and refined in your Composition II course. These skills include thinking critically, understanding the writing process, and utilizing effective research techniques, but you will also discover why literature is meaningful in a civilized society and how reading and evaluating literature can benefit you throughout your life.

This reader provides an opportunity for you to broaden your knowledge of literature so that you might develop your own perspective on how meaning is achieved through reading, analysis, and critical thinking. You will discover rich literary traditions of people from around the world and across many eras, and you will be asked to enter into their experiences of life as a way to shape your own worldview. Your English faculty members at Chattanooga State invite you to join us on this journey!

> *"That is part of the beauty of all literature. You discover that your longings are universal longings, that you're not lonely and isolated from anyone. You belong."*
>
> — *F. Scott Fitzgerald*

Chattanooga State's
Reading on the River: A Literary Anthology

The purpose of an English course reader is to provide organized units of work through which students can develop critical thinking and effective writing skills. The selections in your *Reading on the River: A Literary Anthology* represent the texts of both great writers of the past and of contemporary writers who have written about many of the same thoughts and attitudes that we all share about life and our own existence. The reader is divided by genre: poetry, fiction, drama, and creative non-fiction. Each genre invites you into a different way of looking at the world and into a discovery of who each of us are within this world.

A final note: The beautiful art reproduced on these pages is the work of instructors in the Humanities and Fine Arts Department at Chattanooga State. They are expressing visually how they view the world around them just as you are asked to do through your writing in this course.

Michael Holsomback
Associate Professor
Humanities and Fine Arts
Department

Mark Wood
Professor
Humanities and Fine Arts
Department

Ken Page
Instructor of Art
Humanities and Fine Arts
Department

Chattanooga State Community College • English 1020: Composition II Departmental Syllabus

Class Hours: 3

Credit Hours: 3

Catalog Course Description: Research project required. Focus on reading and responding to short fiction, poetry, drama, and/or non-fiction prose. *Note:* course meets General Education Communication requirement.

Prerequisite: ENGL 1010

Competencies

Students will demonstrate the ability to:

- C1. Analyze and evaluate oral and written expression by listening and reading critically for elements that reflect an awareness of situation, audience, purpose, and diverse points of view.

- C2. Distill a primary purpose into a single, compelling statement and order and develop major points in a reasonable and convincing manner based on that purpose.

- C3. Develop appropriate rhetorical patterns (i.e. narration, example, process, comparison/contrast, classification, cause/effect, definition, argumentation) and other special functions (i.e., analysis or research), while demonstrating writing/speaking skills from process to product.

- C4. Understand that the writing and speaking processes include procedures such as planning, organizing, composing, revising, and editing.

- C5. Make written and oral presentations employing correct diction, syntax, usage, grammar, and mechanics.

- C6. Manage and coordinate basic information gathered from multiple sources for the purposes of problem solving and decision-making.

- C7. Recognize the use of evidence, analysis, and persuasive strategies, including basic distinctions among opinions, facts, and inferences.

Instructional Activities

1. Activities may include but are not limited to the following:

   - Assign readings based upon the following guidelines (C1, C6, C7): Because this course is skills-based, revolving around the completion of the five essays described below, assigned readings in the various genres will be regarded as the reading of primary sources which will form the basis of each essay, respectively. The genre of poetry plus at least two largely prose-based genres (short fiction, long fiction, drama, non-fiction) must be represented.

- Minimum coverage of poetry: fifteen or more poems.

- Minimum coverage of largely prose-based genres (short fiction, long fiction, drama, non-fiction): fifty or more pages. The minimum requirements for reading assignments (primary sources) described above give instructors the flexibility to organize their readings according to genre or to theme.

2. Assign weekly graded work to build student writing, researching, and analyzing skills. These may include journals, exercises, quizzes, revisions, workshops, drafts, exercises, attendance, participation, etc. (C1, C2, C3, C4, C5, C6)

3. Assign essay topics all of which will incorporate primary sources; several will incorporate secondary sources as well. (C1, C2, C3, C4, C5, C6)

   - **Unit 1 Essay:** write an MLA documented essay of at least 600 words applying one or more literary elements to one primary source.

   - **Unit 2 Essay:** write an MLA documented essay of at least 750 words applying one or more literary elements to at least two sources (whether primary or a combination of primary and secondary).

   - **Unit 3 Essay:** write an MLA documented essay of at least 600 words, applying one or more literary elements to at least three sources (combining primary and secondary).

   - **Unit 4 Essay:** write an MLA documented essay of at least 750 words, applying one or more literary elements to at least three sources (combining primary and secondary).

   - **Final Exam:** write an MLA documented essay of at least 600 words applying one or more literary elements to at least two sources (whether primary or a combination of primary and secondary).

Note: All four essays and the Final Exam Essay must be submitted in order to pass the class.

Student Outcomes

By the end of the semester, students will be able to:

- **SO1.** Critically read, analyze, interpret, and discuss literary texts by listening and reading critically for elements related to genre, human expression, situation, audience, purpose, and diverse points of view. (I1, I2, I3)

- **SO2.** Distill a primary purpose into a single, compelling statement, effectively developing supporting points demonstrating rhetorical patterns such as comparison/contrast, argumentation, definition, and so on. (I2, I3)

- **SO3.** Understand the value and capacity of literature to express human experience through close contact with primary literary texts as forms of cultural and creative expression. (I1, I2, I3)

- **SO4.** Locate, evaluate, and incorporate a variety of primary and secondary sources into essays, smoothly synthesizing the student's arguments with those of published sources. (I1, I2, I3)

- **SO5.** Employ standard MLA guidelines to correctly format, cite, and document all primary and secondary sources, whether paraphrased, summarized, and/or directly quoted. (I1, I2, I3)

- **SO6.** Continue to develop and apply critical skills in proofreading, correcting, and revising sentences, paragraphs, and essays in accordance with conventions of form (punctuation, mechanics, and grammar), clarity, and effectiveness. (I1, I2, I3)

Assessment

Note: All four essays and the Final Exam Essay must be submitted in order to pass the class.

Grade Percentages:

Assessment	Percentage	Points
Four essays	60%	600
Final examination essay	15%	150
Weekly graded work (e.g.: journals, exercises, quizzes, revisions, workshops, drafts, exercises, attendance, participation, etc.)	25%	250
TOTAL	100%:	1000

Missing work will receive a zero (0) that will be averaged into the final course grade.

Final Grades:

Final grades for ENGL 1020: Composition 2 will be given in accordance with the College's Grading Policy as follows:

- 90–100: A
- 80–89: B
- 70–79: C
- 65–69: D
- Below 65: F
- I (Incomplete) May be given at the instructor's discretion to students who have not fulfilled all course requirements at the end of the grading period.

Course Delivery Format

Faculty may require online activities and assignments to include online tests and submission of all written and online communications. The extent of online activities/assignments may vary by course, but will be specified on the syllabus.

Standard Format – This format is the traditional in-class format and may use an online format to provide access to "static" materials which include the syllabus, course material, contact information, and Power Points and presentations. Faculty must make available when requested a copy of syllabus and any other instructor provided course materials, including their contact information. Faculty may require online activities and assignments to include online tests and submission of all written and online communications. The extent of online activities/assignments may vary by course but will be specified on the syllabus.

Hybrid Format – This format requires significant online activity. Students in hybrid classes must access course content and assessments using the internet in order to pass the class, whether it meets full-time or part-time in the classroom. Faculty need not hand out a copy of the syllabus and any other required course material, including their contact information.

Online Format – This format requires that the entire class be conducted online. The syllabus, course material, contact information, and PowerPoints and presentations will be provided online through the course management system. Assessments may be conducted online or in a proctored environment.

College Policies

This class is governed by the policies and procedures stated in the current Chattanooga State Student Handbook. You are responsible for reading and understanding these policies which you can find at the following link:

http://www.pageturnpro.com/Chattanooga-State/19125-Student-Handbook/index. html#1

Tiger Guide to Writing

The companion text to your *River Reader: A Literary Anthology* is Chattanooga State's custom *Tiger Guide to Writing (TGW)* Writers Handbook. The TGW is a comprehensive writing guide that includes information on writing processes, research, revision, and editing. Following is a brief menu of some of the resources available to you in the *TGW* by topic:

Writing Contexts	Annotated Bibliographies	MLA/APA/Chicago Style
Academic Contexts	Reading Strategies	Sentence Grammar
Writing Processes	Doing Research	Language Use
Developing Paragraph	Evaluating Sources	Punctuation/Mechanics
Arguments	Integrating Sources	Peer Revision
Rhetorical Analyses	Avoiding Plagiarism	Self-Revision
Reports	Literary Analyses	Giving Presentations
Sample Essays	*They Say, I Say* writing templates	Index of Terms

Though the *Tiger Guide to Writing* contains much of the information below, having this key information available to you here as well may be helpful as you begin your writing journey. It is not intended, however, to replace your *Tiger Guide to Writing* as the *TGW* is a "must-have" guide for many courses across campus.

Standard Essay Structure

By using the guidelines for the writing process, writers will be able to put their ideas on paper in the form of an essay. In most writing, an academic essay follows a specific structure that makes for strong organization and development of ideas.

Introduction – The introduction includes a "hook" to begin, an orientation in the middle, and a thesis statement to end. The purposes of an introduction in writing are to stir interest in the topic and to inform the reader about what to expect in the body of the essay through the thesis statement. The thesis statement is typically the last sentence of the introduction, and it provides the position the writer has taken on the analysis to be performed as well as the main supporting points the author will address in the body.

Body – The body includes the main points listed in the thesis statement. The body is the heart of an essay and where the real work takes place. The body typically includes researched source information followed by the writer's voice explaining why and how those materials are used to support each of the main points.

Conclusion – The conclusion summarizes the main points addressed in the body and leaves the reader with something to remember. It is the final opportunity for the writer to present final reasoning for the analysis within the body. The conclusion, however, is only valuable if the main points were presented well and were sufficiently supported in the body.

Writing Process

Writing can be daunting for many students. The elements of writing are numerous: developing good ideas, using good grammar and word choice, making the writing interesting, organizing thoughts well, and so on. Trying to juggle all of these can be frustrating. Understanding that writing is a process, however, rather than a single action helps writers focus on one task at a time. As opposed to one action, writing can be broken down into a series of functions that assist the writer in producing a final work without all the frustration and despair. These functions can be divided as follows:

Prewriting: In this step, writers brainstorm ideas, freewrite everything that comes to mind, conduct some initial research to get more specific ideas about the topic, talk with others about the topic, and/or take notes on all readings associated with the topic. Prewriting is a crucial step in preparing a path for the writer to follow.

Drafting: Eventually, the writer begins to pull together everything from the prewriting stage and make some sense out of it. In this stage, the writer begins to organize main points, determine which sources are most useful and credible, and develop a thesis statement that will guide the remainder of the writing. After completing these steps, the writer puts a rough draft of the finished product on paper. While this is not the final draft of the essay, it should include an introduction, body, and conclusion to assist the writer in refining organization moving forward.

Integrating Sources: Once the writer has a rough draft, it is time to determine where source material best "fits" into the essay and supports its main points. If source material previously assessed and selected does not seem to "fit," the writer may need to conduct additional research to find sources more aligned with the main points. Once the final sources are selected, the writer will integrate the sources in the essay by introducing them and citing the source material at its conclusion.

Rewriting: Rewriting does *not* mean starting over; instead, it means to make both minor and major changes to content, language, punctuation, and organization in order to improve the flow and mechanics of the writing. There are three steps in the rewriting process:

- *Revision* means to broadly *re-see* the essay from the perspective of the audience. Ask questions about what is missing, what is confusing, and what elements of writing style need improvement.

- *Editing* means to revise the language, itself, for effectiveness. Writers should proceed sentence-by-sentence and word-by-word to check for language accuracy.

- *Proofreading* means to check for errors in punctuation, spelling, grammar, and format. After reading through an essay several times, the brain will insert missing words, will not note spelling errors, and will mentally insert commas. A good strategy to avoid this is to start at the end of the essay and read backwards, sentence-by-sentence.

Why Literature?

"Once you allow yourself to identify with the people in a story, then you might begin to see yourself in that story even if on the surface it's far removed from your situation. This is what I try to tell my students: this is one great thing that literature can do - it can make us identify with situations and people far away."

— *Chinua Achebe*

Literature helps us understand ourselves through a process of self-discovery. When we read fiction, we can encounter circumstances that echo our own, but we also learn about human experiences that are foreign to us. Literature crosses the divide of cultures and gives us shared experiences. By studying fiction, one learns more about the use of language and the power of words. We learn how to communicate with others in the outside world. In opposition to, yet combined with the facts of history, literature gives us the cultural responses to events of the time period in which each piece was written. Reading literature allows us to travel to places we've never gone with people we'll never meet to have experiences we otherwise never would. A good work of fiction does more than merely entertain: it gives the reader insights into the human condition and a wider lens to view the world. Simply put, literature *makes* us human.

Literature and the Humanities

The humanities can be described as the way in which people experience, process, and make record of the world in which they live. This experience is often recorded through music, art, language, philosophy, history, and literature as an archive of the way people have lived and what has been important to them over specific periods of time. By comparing these records, each to the others, we get a glimpse of an evolution of human existence across the centuries.

Literature is a particularly beautiful record of this human existence. Literature generally refers to writing with the creative imagination through specific forms—like poetry, fiction, drama, and creative nonfiction—that are intended to rouse passion in each of us and to move us toward critical thinking and self-discovery. It is meant to be enjoyed, and it often speaks to the reader of those experiences in life that are common to all of us like love, hate, anger, joy, betrayal, and jealousy. Reading and analyzing literature challenges our intellects in active ways and provides historical knowledge not otherwise easily gained. Literature enlightens us about culture, sociology, and even psychology, and it provides insight into most every branch of human knowledge.

Literature depicts people and concepts that symbolize our culture and society. Literature often functions like a mirror for society—reading stories or other works and under-standing them helps us develop meaning for the people, places, and events we encounter every day. Immersing ourselves in these works can help us interpret what happens in our lives and in our culture. Literature, then, helps us understand what it means to be human and what we value.

Literature and Identity

Your Composition I reader, *Writing on the River*, is centered on the theme of identity. In the Composition I course, you discovered that many seemingly innocent aspects of our daily lives influence who we are and who we are to become as well as our view of others. Our character and personality traits are developed, partially, as a result of our interactions with everything with which we engage in our environments. This is true of our interaction with literature as well.

The theme of identity is common to many works of literature. Katniss Everdeen in *The Hunger Games*, Holden Caulfield in *Catcher in the Rye*, and even Max in the popular children's book, *Where the Wild Things Are*, are searching for who they are and who they want to become. Characters in these and many other works of literature often find themselves in identity crises due to a conflict between who they are and who they want to be. Readers can easily connect to this conflict between one's awareness of true self and one's desire to be someone else because it is common to the human experience.

As readers, we come to know ourselves through literature. Through an awareness of growth and change in the characters we read about in literature, we are able to begin to recognize who we are and to start upon a path toward our own self-awareness. Through an observation of how culture impacts identity, we learn to view our own identities in relationship to other cultures. Through an understanding of how the physical locations in which characters live impact who they are, we see that the same is true for us. Literature reveals the many facets of identity as well as the choice we have to either ignore or embrace those aspects of ourselves that we discover through these beautiful works of literature.

Literary Elements

Literary elements are the primary structures that authors use to create interesting writing and to most effectively move the reader. They include plot, setting, characterization, point of view, theme, tone, and conflict. Literary devices are elements of writing from which authors choose to make the language and ideas within the work rich and compelling as well as to transmit a message more effectively. There are many, many literary devices, but some of the most common are these:

Using language: alliteration, personification, rhyme, syntax, and imagery.

Relating ideas: symbolism, allegory, foreshadowing, simile, metaphor, and irony.

What is Literary Analysis?

French philosopher Jacques Derrida contended that *everything* is a text, for everything can be analyzed within a particular *context*. A work of literature is a text—one that invites its audience to be active participants in its telling. Sometimes the text (whether a film, a novel, a play, a poem, or a short story) asks to be regarded aesthetically, valued for its beautiful form or style; sometimes it asks to be considered critically, examined for its deeper, more implied themes or meanings.

Engaging a literary text, then, is a unique and exciting opportunity to approach and appreciate it through various lenses [called contexts], to consider how and why the text may have been written. These approaches [contexts] provide parameters for interpreting possible meanings suggested by the work of literature, such as its structure, its use of elements, and its deeper meanings. Exploring and understanding a literary text through one or more particular approaches [contexts] is the basis of literary analysis. And literary analysis can heighten critical thinking, enrich discussions, and afford us (as readers) diverse insights into not only the writer's but also our own perspectives on life.

Rhetorical Approach

In a ***rhetorical*** approach to literature, a reader examines the relationship between the author, narrator (fictional author), subject, narratee (fictional reader), and reader. The reader asks particular questions.

- Who is the author? What does he or she want from the reader(s)?

- Who is the narrator? What does he or she want from the narratee(s)?

- What is the subject? What is the author's attitude toward the subject? What is the narrator's attitude toward the subject? How, if at all, does the author's attitude differ from the narrator's?

- Who is the narratee? (i.e. Who does the narrator imagine the audience is?)

- Who is the reader? What do the author and the narrator do to change the reader's worldview?

Structural Approach

In a structural approach to literature, a reader divides the writing into pieces and compares and contrasts those pieces with one another to reveal patterns of development. This approach works well in conjunction with the elements of fiction.

Plot: Divide the plot into acts and scenes, as in a play, and discuss how each scene moves the plot forward. Look especially for misapprehensions and misunderstandings, revelations of truth, and reversals of fortune and circumstance.

Character: Identify the major characteristics and desires of a character. Divide the story into scenes, according to when a particular character appears. Note how the character changes in each scene from the beginning to the end of the story. Use opposites—for example: docile versus dominant, sane versus insane, virtuous versus vicious.

Setting: Divide the story into scenes according to changes in time and place. Compare and contrast the times and places. Look for patterns of change. For example, a writer illustrating the downfall of a character might describe how a character's bedroom changes from neatness to clutter and finally to complete trashiness, or a writer may trace the natural progression of seasons in a character's life by setting the scenes in spring, summer, autumn, then winter as the character ages.

Conflict: Identify what the characters want and how their desires influence or interfere with each other. Divide the struggle according to alliances when one character sides with another and reversals when one character gains the upper hand, and consider what leads characters to success and/or failure.

Theme: Identify the ideas the narrator and characters use to order their lives. Divide the story according to how those ideas change. For example, a father may tell his child never to lie; then the child may catch the father lying, and the father may have to alter his view on honesty to include a policy about when lying is fine and when it is not.

Point of View: Identify the narrator as first person, second person, or third person. Consider whether the narrator is omniscient, limited omniscient, or objective. Consider whether the narrator is trustworthy or not. Consider how the story would be told differently if it were told by a different narrator or with a different level of knowledge.

Then determine why the author might have chosen to tell the story from a particular perspective rather than from an alternate perspective.

Critical Approach

In a *critical* approach to literature, a reader uses criteria offered by one or more critical theories to explore the possible meanings of a literary text. These theories, then, provide context through which a text can be interpreted.

Some theories lead the reader beyond the text to consider how extrinsic forces—aspects of the writer's society (class, gender, race, etc.)—may have influenced the text. Some theories hold the reader within the text to consider how intrinsic features—aspects of the text itself (literary elements, form, tension)—may lead to deeper meaning(s). Some theories suggest that the meanings of a literary text can only be discovered from within the reader's own experiences, knowledge, or perceptions.

Although there are numerous critical theories that can be applied to literature, the following are some of the more popular:

Gender Studies

Gender studies focuses on the atypical or stereotypical depiction of men/women in a text:

- the way(s) in which men/women are misrepresented, treated unequally, and misunderstood by matriarchal/patriarchal systems (literature, social traditions, government—systems in which a particular gender is empowered)

- whether or not the text gives equal voice or consideration to the role or perspectives of men/women within the text

- how men and women seek equality with the opposite gender

TEXT IN CONTEXT:

- In regard to gender, how is the man/woman represented typically? Atypically?

- Would the man/woman be considered strong or weak? How might this strength or weakness be determined economically? Politically? socially? historically? culturally?

- In what way is the man/woman denied accurate representation/voice?

- In what way does the man/woman struggle for dominance?—equality?

Historical Context

An historical context considers certain events (social, political, etc.) that occurred (regionally, nationally, or globally) during the writer's lifetime that may have had a direct influence on the writing of the text. *Note:* With this approach, the reader should consider the history within a reasonable frame of time prior to the writing/publication/ release of the text. The reader also should consider the text's use of symbols as means of conveying/representing these influences. To use this approach successfully, the historical event seemingly represented in the text (symbolically or otherwise) must fit convincingly within the framework of the literary story.

TEXT IN CONTEXT:

- What is happening with the character(s) in the story that may correlate with what people like them were experiencing at the time the text was written/published/released?

- What was stereotypic of these people during this time? How do the characters fulfill or reject these stereotypes?

- How could the setting in which the story takes place reflect the political, social, and/or economic climate in which the text was written/published/released?

Psychoanalytic Context

A psychoanalytic context focuses on a character's actions and behavior, the motives for which may be rooted in the character's unconscious. This approach also explores the connection between the desires of the characters in the work, the desire of the author in writing the work, and the desire of the reader in reading the work.

Popular psychoanalytic approaches:

- Sigmund Freud's *Oedipus Complex* suggests that a boy possesses an unconscious desire for the exclusive love of his mother; this desire includes jealousy toward the father and the unconscious wish for the father's death.

- *Electra Complex* suggests that a girl possesses an unconscious desire for the exclusive love of her father; this desire includes jealousy toward the mother and the unconscious wish for the mother's death.

- *Tripartite model of the mind*
  1. id: the unconscious part of the mind, irrational, instinctual (primitive) urges, contains our secret desires, darkest wishes, most intense fears, driven to fulfill the demands of the pleasure principle
  2. superego: the internal censor for the mind, based on societal control, makes moral judgments and is driven to fulfill the demands of the morality principle
  3. ego: the conscious part of the mind, rational, logical, thinking, regulates id and comes to terms with the superego (attempts to satisfy both), driven by reality principle

Note: With the tripartite model, each part (id, superego, and ego) can be represented within one character or by different characters:

Example of one character: Character A is faced with making choice. In the decision process, Character A considers both outcomes (one arguing from a purely irrational standpoint, the other from a purely rational standpoint) and decides accordingly.

Example of multiple characters: Character A must make a decision. In a conversation, Character A's friend, Character B, warns A of the social ramifications should A make the "wrong" decision. In a separate conversation, A's friend, Character C, advises A to seize the moment and do what feels best. Here, Character B represents A's superego, while Character C represents A's id (for A had considered both sides before talking to B and C). Freud's theory is much more complex than this; yet for literary analysis, this is a basic representation.

TEXT IN CONTEXT:

- What are the motives behind the character's actions (both explicit and implied)?
- What could be the author's "message" embedded in the story?
- How did the story's ending shape your attitude toward the characters?
- Which of Freud's theories does the character seem to illustrate?
- How did the story shape your attitude toward any particular race, political, or social force within society?

Marxist Context

A Marxist context focuses on the economic struggle for power between the ruling "middle" class (bourgeoisie) and the working "lower" class (proletariat). *Note:* With this approach, the reader should consider the struggle for economic power between people/social classes; therefore, one should consider the characters' social and political standings in the story, for these social and political forces often determine (and inspire one's desire for) economic power. There is also an irony to consider: while the bourgeoisie often holds and attempts to retain power over the proletariat, the bourgeoisie would be unable to hold/retain its power without the work of the proletariat, and the proletariat would be unable to work at all without the needs of the bourgeoisie. This relationship between the classes, then, is co-dependent, symbiotic. Nonetheless, what remains imperative to a Marxist approach is one person's class exploitation of another (X taking advantage of Y to the social, political, or economic advantage of X).

There are key terms employed when using a Marxist approach:

- *Commodification* is the act of using a relationship, knowledge, opportunity, etc., only for its monetary value or as a means of gaining economic power; thus, a relationship with another person can be deemed a commodity if one person uses the relationship for her /his own economic gain.

- *Hegemony* is the dominance that one class maintains over another by way of tradition, laws, politics, or any other means by which a dominant class can subjugate a weaker one.

TEXT IN CONTEXT:

- Based on what happens in the story, to which class might each character belong?
- How do the characters' words/actions demonstrate their class?
- How is one class/person being exploited by another?

Post-colonialist Context

The post-colonialist context examines issues of power, economics, politics, religion, and culture and how these elements work in relation to colonial hegemony (western colonizers controlling the colonized)

TEXT IN CONTEXT:

- In the story, who is the oppressor, and who is the oppressed?

- How does the story symbolically represent various aspects of colonial oppression?

- What person(s) or groups does the work identify as "other" or stranger? How are such persons/groups described and treated?

- How does the story suggest the (forced) conformity of the oppressed's culture and identity to that of the oppressor?

- What does the story reveal about the politics and/or psychology of anti-colonialist resistance?

Writing About Literature

Many people find that they are unfamiliar or uncomfortable with writing about literature. Often students have had to write an opinion piece about a contemporary issue or a proposal to solve a problem on their college campus or in the nearby community, but they may not ever have written an analytical essay on a piece of literature. Writing about literature typically means setting one's personal experiences aside. It's not that these experiences are not valuable; they are, and they may have even allowed us to more fully understand a literary piece. However, when we analyze literature, we typically do so separately from our personal experiences.

There is, however, one notable exception called reader-response criticism, which is a kind of writing that does focus directly on how one has experienced and interacted with a literary work. When you write about literature in your Composition II course, though, you will likely need to write an essay that suggests an objective and academic way to view or understand the piece(s) you are analyzing. You'll typically want to avoid informal language and slang, and you'll need to adopt a more formal tone.

One technique you can use for an academic literary analysis is called "close reading." Critic I.A. Richards coined this term, which means to focus on particular details, patterns, and ideas throughout a text in order to better understand the overall literary piece. In other words, you must often break a text apart and look at its smaller pieces in correlation with each other in order to better understand the whole. Considering the literary elements that the author has used intentionally or that you have noted in your analysis is one helpful way to go about your "close reading." One may also consider the relevant historical or biographical context of a work when working on a written analysis.

The important thing to remember as you write about literature is that you are essentially making an argument for the way one should view the text you are analyzing. Think about how you want your reader to understand the piece you are writing about. Does the personification of certain inanimate objects in a play reveal important information about a character's devious motivations? Do the details of the setting of a short story allow the reader to understand that a work's narrator is unreliable? Consider questions like these as you work to build your argument.

Once you have made your argument, you'll want to support it with plenty of evidence from the text itself. You may also want to bring in researched evidence, either from literary critics or other reliable sources. These sources, along with quotations from the text itself, will lend credibility to your argument. Make sure, however, that it is your academic voice taking center stage in your essay. Save quotations from the text and researched evidence for supporting details.

Writing About Literary Elements

In your Composition II course, you will be asked to analyze one or more literary elements from works of literature. This analysis will require critical thinking in understanding your own reaction to the works, as well as the way the authors have used literary elements within the works. In the front of your *Reading on the River: A Literary Anthology,* you will find a Table of Contents dividing the works in this anthology by their predominant literary elements. This Table of Contents should assist you in determining which literary elements might be best suited for analysis in each work.

Analyzing a piece of literature encourages you to think about why the work was written and why the author chose particular literary elements to enhance the experiences that he hoped to share through his work. Your analysis asks you to consider why the author chose to use particular elements to impact you and to create a reaction in you. If you are not moved at all, why not? What did you learn from the experience of reading this literature?

In order to analyze and write successfully about literary elements, you must first be sure that you understand the elements themselves. A working knowledge of plot, character, theme, and setting within a work, for example, will help you further analyze the author's use of style and language as well as her use of literary devices such as metaphor and imagery. While there is much to know, you have been learning these elements and devices through reading and listening to people speak for most of your life. In this course, you will simply learn how to label these elements and how authors and speakers use them to influence the perception of their audiences.

Guiding questions for analysis:

- How would this text be less impactful if [element] were changed or eliminated?

- How does [element 1] impact [element 2]? Where do they overlap and rely on each other?

- What kind of emotional response is this text meant to elicit from the reader? What elements most significantly contribute to that response?

Historic Literary Timeline

The timeline on the following pages offer a visual perspective of how the works in this text relate to each other, both culturally and chronologically. Plato's "Allegory of the Cave" (around 350 B.C.) and Sophocles's "Oediupus Rex" (430 B.C.), however, were written so much earlier than the other pieces that they have been omitted from this view.

Year	Reading	Author
1593	"The Passionate Shepherd to His Love"	Christopher Marlowe
1596	"The Nymph's Reply to the Shepherd"	Sir Walter Raleigh
1609	"Sonnet XVIII" and "Sonnet CXVI"	William Shakespeare
1787	"The Indian Burying Ground"	Philip Freneau
1789	"The Lamb"	William Blake
1794	"The Tyger" and "The Sick Rose"	William Blake
1818	"Ozymandias"	Percy Bysshe Shelley
1820	"Ode on a Grecian Urn"	John Keats
1835	"Young Goodman Brown"	Nathaniel Hawthorne
1841	"The Snow-Storm"	Ralph Waldo Emerson
1842	"The Masque of the Red Death"	Edgar Allan Poe
1845	"The Raven"	Edgar Allan Poe
1855	"Childe Roland to the Dark Tower Came"	Robert Browning
1862	"I heard a Fly buzz – when I died"	Emily Dickinson
1871	"Jabberwocky"	Lewis Carroll
1892	"The Yellow Wallpaper"	Charlotte Perkins Gilman
1894	"The Story of an Hour"	Kate Chopin
1902	"The Panther"	Rainer Maria Rilke
1905	"Paul's Case"	Willa Cather
1916	*Trifles*	Susan Glaspell
1919	"The Negro Speaks of Rivers"	Langston Hughes
1920	"The Second Coming"	William Butler Yeats
1922	*The Waste Land*, "The Burial of the Dead"	T.S. Eliot
1924	"Love Sonnet XVII"	Pablo Neruda
1926	"The Rocking-Horse Winner"	D.H. Lawrence
1927	"Hills Like White Elephants"	Ernest Hemingway
1939	"Barn Burning"	William Faulkner
1941	"A Worn Path"	Eudora Welty
1942	"My Papa's Waltz"	Theodore Roethke
1948	"The Lottery"	Shirley Jackson
1950	"The Veldt"	Ray Bradbury
1951	"Aunt Jennifer's Tigers"	Adrienne Rich

1500
1600
1700
1800
1850
1900
1920
1930
1940
1950

Year		Reading	Author
1960	1960	"Metaphors"	Sylvia Plath
	1962	"Lady Lazarus"	Sylvia Plath
	1965	"Revelation"	Flannery O'Connor
	1966	"Digging"	Seamus Heaney
	1967	"Sisters of Mercy"	Leonard Cohen
1970	1973	"Everyday Use"	Alice Walker
	1978	"Phenomenal Woman"	Maya Angelou
1980	1980	"Chattanooga"	Ishmael Reed
	1981	"Conjoined, a marriage poem"	Judith Minty
	1984	"Navajo Night Chant"	
	1988	"The Writer"	Richard Wilbur
1990	1990	"Mother Tongue"	Amy Tan
	1991	"Woman Hollering Creek"	Sandra Cisneros
	1991	*To Dance with the White Dog*	Terry Kay
	1993	"On the Amtrak From Boston to New York"	Sherman Alexie
	1994	"Cold Summer"	Charles Bukowski
	1995	"Workshop"	Billy Collins
	1995	"Sticks"	George Saunders
	1997	*All Over But the Shoutin'*	Rick Bragg
2000	2001	"A Death in Texas"	Steve Earle
	2001	*Creatures of Habit*	Jill McCorkle
	2001	*"As Freezing Persons Recollect the Snow. Hypothermia."*	Peter Stark
	2004	"Church Dust"	Robert Morgan
	2004	"Gentleness Stirred"	Nimah Nawwab
	2007	"11:20"	Michael Paterniti
	2008	*Serena*	Ron Rash
2010	2011	*Silver Sparrow*	Tayari Jones
	2012	*Darkroom: A Memoir in Black and White*	Lila Quintero Weaver
	2013	"1.7 to Tennessee"	Jamie Quatro

	Creative Nonfiction		Poetry
	Drama		Writers @ Work
	Short Story		

The term "creative nonfiction" may seem oxymoronic. Fiction is a term that implies that an author has created a work that is entirely invented, whereas nonfiction implies that the work is a true account of reality. The goal of creative nonfiction, however, is to create a story based in the reality of actual people or events, but change elements of the story for the sake of style or theme. This may include inventing dialogue, condensing time, or rearranging details to convey the author's intended meaning—all while preserving the spirit of what actually occurred. In this sense, a story might not be absolutely factual and literal, but maintain what critics call *narrative truth*.

It has been said that if five people witness a car accident, there will be five different truthful accounts of it, since each person processes details and reality differently. So it is with literature: there are many ways of telling a "true" story using elements of fiction and nonfiction. Creative nonfiction manipulates facts to create insight about the human condition, and in doing so has become a unique art form all its own.

"As Freezing Persons Recollect the Snow: *Hypothermia*"

Peter Stark

Author Biography: Peter Stark is a travel and adventure writer whose work has appeared in many national magazines, including as a correspondent for *Outside* magazine. Born in Wisconsin, Stark's family loved the outdoors and adventure, and Stark continued that into adulthood. Though his home is in Montana, Stark frequently travels to corners of the world not seen by many people. He is the author of six books.

Context: As a journalist and author writing about travel and adventure to remote parts of the world, Stark is interested in human experience in these environments where they don't naturally belong. Much of his work explores the ways in which humans survive—or don't—in extreme environments and situations.

Point of View: Second person narration is considered informal usage and not to be used in academic writing, but Stark uses it to create the experience of hypothermia for the reader. "You" become the main character of the work. While reading this text, focus on how point of view is used both to convey information and describe the experience of hypothermia.

When your Jeep spins lazily off the mountain road and slams backward into a snowbank, you don't worry immediately about the cold. Your first thought is that you've just dented your bumper. Your second is that you've failed to bring a shovel. Your third is that you'll be late for dinner. Friends are expecting you at their cabin around eight for a moonlight ski, a late dinner, a sauna. Nothing can keep you from that.

Driving out of town, defroster roaring, you barely noted the bank thermometer on the town square: minus 27 degrees at 6:36. The radio weather report warned of a deep mass of arctic air settling over the region. The man who took your money at the Conoco station shook his head at the register and said he wouldn't be going anywhere tonight if he were you. You smiled. A little chill never hurt anybody with enough fleece and a good four-wheel-drive.

But now you're stuck. Jamming the gearshift into low, you try to muscle out of the drift. The tires whine on ice-slicked snow as headlights dance on the curtain of frosted firs across the road. Shoving the lever back into park, you shoulder open the door and step from your heated capsule. Cold slaps your naked face, squeezes tears from your eyes.

You check your watch: 7:18. You consult your map: A thin, switchbacking line snakes up the mountain to the penciled square that marks the cabin.

Breath rolls from you in short frosted puffs. The Jeep lies cocked sideways in the snowbank like an empty turtle shell. You think of firelight and saunas and warm food and wine. You look again at the map. It's maybe five or six miles more to that penciled square. You run that far every day before breakfast. You'll just put on your skis. No problem.

There is no precise core temperature at which the human body perishes from cold. At Dachau's cold-water immersion baths, Nazi doctors calculated death to arrive at around 77 degrees Fahrenheit. The lowest recorded core temperature in a surviving adult is 60.8 degrees. For a child it's lower: In 1994, a two-year-old girl in Saskatchewan wandered out of her house into a minus-40 night. She was found near her doorstep the next morning, limbs frozen solid, her core temperature 57 degrees. She lived.

Others are less fortunate, even in much milder conditions. One of Europe's worst weather disasters occurred during a 1964 competitive walk on a windy, rainy English moor; three of the racers died from hypothermia, though temperatures never fell below freezing and ranged as high as 45.

But for all scientists and statisticians now know of freezing and its physiology, no one can yet predict exactly how quickly and in whom hypothermia will strike—and whether it will kill when it does. The cold remains a mystery, more prone to fell men than women, more lethal to the thin and well muscled than to those with avoirdupois, and least forgiving to the arrogant and the unaware.

The process begins even before you leave the car, when you remove your gloves to squeeze a loose bail back into one of your ski bindings. The freezing metal bites your flesh. Your skin temperature drops.

Within a few seconds, the palms of your hands are a chilly, painful 60 degrees. Instinctively, the web of surface capillaries on your hands constrict, sending blood coursing away from your skin and deeper into your torso. Your body is allowing your fingers to chill in order to keep its vital organs warm.

You replace your gloves, noticing only that your fingers have numbed slightly. Then you kick boots into bindings and start up the road.

Were you a Norwegian fisherman or Inuit hunter, both of whom frequently work gloveless in the cold, your chilled hands would open their surface capillaries periodically to allow surges of warm blood to pass into them and maintain their flexibility. This phenomenon, known as the hunter's response, can elevate a 35-degree skin temperature to 50 degrees within seven or eight minutes.

Other human adaptations to the cold are more mysterious. Tibetan Buddhist monks can raise the skin temperature of their hands and feet by 15 degrees through meditation. Australian aborigines, who once slept on the ground, unclothed, on near-freezing nights, would slip into a light hypothermic state, suppressing shivering until the rising sun rewarmed them.

You have no such defenses, having spent your days at a keyboard in a climate-controlled office. Only after about ten minutes of hard climbing, as your body temperature rises, does blood start seeping back into your fingers. Sweat trickles down your sternum and spine.

By now you've left the road and decided to shortcut up the forested mountainside to the road's next switchback. Treading slowly through deep, soft snow as the full moon hefts over a spiny ridgetop, throwing silvery bands of moonlight and shadow, you think your friends were right: It's a beautiful night for skiing—though you admit, feeling the minus-30 air bite at your face, it's also cold.

After an hour, there's still no sign of the switchback, and you've begun to worry. You pause to check the map. At this moment, your core temperature reaches its high: 100.8. Climbing in deep snow, you've generated nearly ten times as much body heat as you do when you are resting.

As you step around to orient map to forest, you hear a metallic pop. You look down. The loose bail has disappeared from your binding. You lift your foot and your ski falls from your boot.

You twist on your flashlight, and its cold-weakened batteries throw a yellowish circle in the snow. It's right around here somewhere, you think, as you sift the snow through gloved fingers. Focused so intently on finding the bail, you hardly notice the frigid air pressing against your tired body and sweat-soaked clothes.

The exertion that warmed you on the way uphill now works against you: Your exercise-dilated capillaries carry the excess heat of your core to your skin, and your wet clothing dispels it rapidly into the night. The lack of insulating fat over your muscles allows the cold to creep that much closer to your warm blood.

Your temperature begins to plummet. Within 17 minutes it reaches the normal 98.6. Then it slips below.

At 97 degrees, hunched over in your slow search, the muscles along your neck and shoulders tighten in what's known as pre-shivering muscle tone. Sensors have signaled the temperature control center in your hypothalamus, which in turn has ordered the constriction of the entire web of surface capillaries. Your hands and feet begin to ache with cold. Ignoring the pain, you dig carefully through the snow; another ten minutes pass. Without the bail you know you're in deep trouble.

Finally, nearly 45 minutes later, you find the bail. You even manage to pop it back into its socket and clamp your boot into the binding. But the clammy chill that started around your skin has now wrapped deep into your body's core.

At 95, you've entered the zone of mild hypothermia. You're now trembling violently as your body attains its maximum shivering response, an involuntary condition in which your muscles contract rapidly to generate additional body heat.

It was a mistake, you realize, to come out on a night this cold. You should turn back. Fishing into the front pocket of your shell parka, you fumble out the map. You consulted it to get here; it should be able to guide you back to the warm car. It doesn't occur to you in your increasingly clouded and panicky mental state that you could simply follow your tracks down the way you came.

And after this long stop, the skiing itself has become more difficult. By the time you push off downhill, your muscles have cooled and tightened so dramatically that they no longer contract easily, and once contracted, they won't relax. You're locked into an ungainly, spread-armed, weak-kneed snowplow.

Still, you manage to maneuver between stands of fir, swishing down through silvery light and pools of shadow. You're too cold to think of the beautiful night or of the friends you had meant to see. You think only of the warm Jeep that waits for you somewhere at the bottom of the hill. Its gleaming shell is centered in your mind's eye as you come over the crest of a small knoll. You hear the sudden whistle of wind in your ears as you gain speed. Then, before your mind can quite process what the sight means, you notice a lump in the snow ahead.

Recognizing, slowly, the danger that you are in, you try to jam your skis to a stop. But in your panic, your balance and judgment are poor. Moments later, your ski tips plow into the buried log and you sail headfirst through the air and bellyflop into the snow.

You lie still. There's a dead silence in the forest, broken by the pumping of blood in your ears. Your ankle is throbbing with pain and you've hit your head. You've also lost your hat and a glove. Scratchy snow is packed down your shirt. Meltwater trickles down your neck and spine, joined soon by a thin line of blood from a small cut on your head.

This situation, you realize with an immediate sense of panic, is serious. Scrambling to rise, you collapse in pain, your ankle crumpling beneath you.

As you sink back into the snow, shaken, your heat begins to drain away at an alarming rate, your head alone accounting for 50 percent of the loss. The pain of the cold soon pierces your ears so sharply that you root about in the snow until you find your hat and mash it back onto your head.

But even that little activity has been exhausting. You know you should find your glove as well, and yet you're becoming too weary to feel any urgency. You decide to have a short rest before going on.

An hour passes. at one point, a stray thought says you should start being scared, but fear is a concept that floats somewhere beyond your immediate reach, like that numb hand lying naked in the snow. You've slid into the temperature range at which cold renders the enzymes in your brain less efficient. With every one-degree drop in body temperature below 95, your cerebral metabolic rate falls off by 3 to 5 percent. When your core temperature reaches 93, amnesia nibbles at your consciousness. You check your watch: 12:58. Maybe someone will come looking for you soon. Moments later, you check again. You can't keep the numbers in your head. You'll remember little of what happens next.

Your head drops back. The snow crunches softly in your ear. In the minus-35-degree air, your core temperature falls about one degree every 30 to 40 minutes, your body heat leaching out into the soft, enveloping snow. Apathy at 91 degrees. Stupor at 90.

You've now crossed the boundary into profound hypothermia. By the time your core temperature has fallen to 88 degrees, your body has abandoned the urge to warm itself by shivering. Your blood is thickening like crankcase oil in a cold engine. Your oxygen consumption, a measure of your metabolic rate, has fallen by more than a quarter. Your kidneys, however, work overtime to process the fluid overload that occurred when the blood vessels in your extremities constricted and squeezed fluids toward your center. You feel a powerful urge to urinate, the only thing you feel at all.

By 87 degrees you've lost the ability to recognize a familiar face, should one suddenly appear from the woods.

At 86 degrees, your heart, its electrical impulses hampered by chilled nerve tissues, becomes arrhythmic. It now pumps less than two-thirds the normal amount of blood. The lack of oxygen and the slowing metabolism of your brain, meanwhile, begin to trigger visual and auditory hallucinations.

You hear jingle bells. Lifting your face from your snow pillow, you realize with a surge of gladness that they're not sleigh bells; they're welcoming bells hanging from the door of your friends' cabin. You knew it had to be close by. The jingling is the sound of the cabin door opening, just through the fir trees.

Attempting to stand, you collapse in a tangle of skis and poles. That's OK. You can crawl. It's so close.

Hours later, or maybe it's minutes, you realize the cabin still sits beyond the grove of trees. You've crawled only a few feet. The light on your wristwatch pulses in the darkness: 5:20. Exhausted, you decide to rest your head for a moment.

When you lift it again, you're inside, lying on the floor before the woodstove. The fire throws off a red glow. First it's warm; then it's hot; then it's searing your flesh. Your clothing has caught fire.

At 85 degrees, those freezing to death, in a strange, anguished paroxysm, often rip off their clothes. This phenomenon, known as paradoxical undressing, is common enough that urban hypothermia victims are sometimes initially diagnosed as victims of sexual assault. Though researchers are uncertain of the cause, the most logical explanation is that shortly before loss of consciousness, the constricted blood vessels near the body's surface suddenly dilate and produce a sensation of extreme heat against the skin.

All you know is that you're burning. You claw off your shell and pile sweater and fling them away.

But then, in a final moment of clarity, you realize there's no stove, no cabin, no friends. You're lying alone in the bitter cold, naked from the waist up. You grasp your terrible misunderstanding, a whole series of misunderstandings, like a dream ratcheting into wrongness. You've shed your clothes, your car, your oil-heated house in town. Without this ingenious technology you're simply a delicate, tropical organism whose range is restricted to a narrow sunlit band that girds the earth at the equator.

And you've now ventured way beyond it.

There's an adage about hypothermia: "You aren't dead until you're warm and dead."

At about 6:00 the next morning, his friends, having discovered the stalled Jeep, find him, still huddled inches from the buried log, his gloveless hand shoved into his armpit. The flesh of his limbs is waxy and stiff as old putty, his pulse nonexistent, his pupils unresponsive to light. Dead.

But those who understand cold know that even as it deadens, it offers perverse salvation. Heat is a presence: the rapid vibrating of molecules. Cold is an absence: the damping of the vibrations. At absolute zero, minus 459.67 degrees Fahrenheit, molecular motion ceases altogether. It is this slowing that converts gases to liquids, liquids to solids, and renders solids harder. It slows bacterial growth and chemical reactions. In the human body, cold shuts down metabolism. The lungs take in less oxygen, the heart pumps less blood. Under normal temperatures, this would produce brain damage. But the chilled brain, having slowed its own metabolism, needs far less oxygen-rich blood and can, under the right circumstances, survive intact.

Setting her ear to his chest, one of his rescuers listens intently. Seconds pass. Then, faintly, she hears a tiny sound—a single thump, so slight that it might be the sound of her own blood. She presses her ear harder to the cold flesh. Another faint thump, then another.

The slowing that accompanies freezing is, in its way, so beneficial that it is even induced at times. Cardiologists today often use deep chilling to slow a patient's metabolism in preparation for heart or brain surgery. In this state of near suspension, the patient's blood flows slowly, his heart rarely beats—or in the case of those on heart-lung machines, doesn't beat at all; death seems near. But carefully monitored, a patient can remain in this cold stasis, undamaged, for hours.

The rescuers quickly wrap their friend's naked torso with a spare parka, his hands with mittens, his entire body with a bivy sack. They brush snow from his pasty, frozen face. Then one snakes down through the forest to the nearest cabin. The others, left in the pre-dawn darkness, huddle against him as silence closes around them. For a moment, the woman imagines she can hear the scurrying, breathing, snoring of a world of creatures that have taken cover this frigid night beneath the thick quilt of snow.

With a "one, two, three," the doctor and nurses slide the man's stiff, curled form onto a table fitted with a mattress filled with warm water which will be regularly reheated. They'd been warned that they had a profound hypothermia case coming in. Usually such victims can be straightened from their tortured fetal positions. This one can't.

Technicians scissor with stainless-steel shears at the man's urine-soaked long underwear and shell pants, frozen together like corrugated cardboard. They attach heart-monitor electrodes to his chest and insert a low-temperature electronic thermometer into his rectum. Digital readings flash: 24 beats per minute and a core temperature of 79.2 degrees.

The doctor shakes his head. He can't remember seeing numbers so low. He's not quite sure how to revive this man without killing him.

In fact, many hypothermia victims die each year in the process of being rescued. In "rewarming shock," the constricted capillaries reopen almost all at once, causing a sudden drop in blood pressure. The slightest movement can send a victim's heart muscle into wild spasms of ventricular fibrillation. In 1980, 16 shipwrecked Danish fishermen were hauled to safety after an hour and a half in the frigid North Sea. They then walked across the deck of the rescue ship, stepped below for a hot drink, and dropped dead, all 16 of them.

"78.9," a technician calls out. "That's three-tenths down."

The patient is now experiencing "afterdrop," in which residual cold close to the body's surface continues to cool the core even after the victim is removed from the outdoors.

The doctor rapidly issues orders to his staff: intravenous administration of warm saline, the bag first heated in the microwave to 110 degrees. Elevating the core temperature of an average-size male one degree requires adding about 60 kilocalories of heat. A kilocalorie is the amount of heat needed to raise the temperature of one liter of water one degree Celsius. Since a quart of hot soup at 140 degrees offers about 30 kilocalories, the patient curled on the table would need to consume 40 quarts of chicken broth to push his core temperature up to normal. Even the warm saline, infused directly into his blood, will add only 30 kilocalories.

Ideally, the doctor would have access to a cardiopulmonary bypass machine, with which he could pump out the victim's blood, rewarm and oxygenate it, and pump it back in again, safely raising the core temperature as much as one degree every three minutes. But such machines are rarely available outside major urban hospitals. Here, without such equipment, the doctor must rely on other options.

"Let's scrub for surgery," he calls out.

Moments later, he's sliding a large catheter into an incision in the man's abdominal cavity. Warm fluid begins to flow from a suspended bag, washing through his abdomen, and draining out through another catheter placed in another incision. Prosaically, this lavage operates much like a car radiator in reverse: The solution warms the internal organs, and the warm blood in the organs is then pumped by the heart throughout the body.

The patient's stiff limbs begin to relax. His pulse edges up. But even so the jagged line of his heartbeat flashing across the EKG screen shows the curious dip known as a J wave, common to hypothermia patients.

"Be ready to defibrillate," the doctor warns the EMTs.

For another hour, nurses and EMTs hover around the edges of the table where the patient lies centered in a warm pool of light, as if offered up to the sun god. They check his heart. They check the heat of the mattress beneath him. They whisper to one another about the foolishness of having gone out alone tonight.

And slowly the patient responds. Another liter of saline is added to the IV. The man's blood pressure remains far too low, brought down by the blood flowing out to the fast-opening capillaries of his limbs. Fluid lost through perspiration and urination has reduced his blood volume. But every 15 or 20 minutes, his temperature rises another degree. The immediate danger of cardiac fibrillation lessens, as the heart and thinning blood warms. Frostbite could still cost him fingers or an earlobe. But he appears to have beaten back the worst of the frigidity.

For the next half hour, an EMT quietly calls the readouts of the thermometer, a mantra that marks the progress of this cold-blooded proto-organism toward a state of warmer, higher consciousness.

"90.4 . . . "92.2 . . ."

From somewhere far away in the immense, cold darkness, you hear a faint, insistent hum. Quickly it mushrooms into a ball of sound, like a planet rushing toward you, and then it becomes a stream of words.

A voice is calling your name.

You don't want to open your eyes. You sense heat and light playing against your eyelids, but beneath their warm dance a chill wells up inside you from the sunless ocean bottoms and the farthest depths of space. You are too tired even to shiver. You want only to sleep.

"Can you hear me?"

You force open your eyes. Lights glare overhead. Around the lights faces hover atop uniformed bodies. You try to think: You've been away a very long time, but where have you been?

"You're at the hospital. You got caught in the cold."

You try to nod. Your neck muscles feel rusted shut, unused for years. They respond to your command with only a slight twitch.

"You'll probably have amnesia," the voice says.

You remember the moon rising over the spiky ridgetop and skiing up toward it, toward someplace warm beneath the frozen moon. After that, nothing—only that immense coldness lodged inside you.

"We're trying to get a little warmth back into you," the voice says.

You'd nod if you could. But you can't move. All you can feel is throbbing discomfort everywhere. Glancing down to where the pain is most biting, you notice blisters filled with clear fluid dotting your fingers, once gloveless in the snow. During the long, cold hours the tissue froze and ice crystals formed in the tiny spaces between your cells, sucking water from them, blocking the blood supply. You stare at them absently.

"I think they'll be fine," a voice from overhead says. "The damage looks superficial. We expect that the blisters will break in a week or so, and the tissue should revive after that."

If not, you know that your fingers will eventually turn black, the color of bloodless, dead tissue. And then they will be amputated.

But worry slips from you as another wave of exhaustion sweeps in. Slowly you drift off, dreaming of warmth, of tropical ocean wavelets breaking across your chest, of warm sand beneath you.

Hours later, still logy and numb, you surface, as if from deep under water. A warm tide seems to be flooding your midsection. Focusing your eyes down there with difficulty, you see tubes running into you, their heat mingling with your abdomen's depthless cold like a churned-up river. You follow the tubes to the bag that hangs suspended beneath the electric light.

And with a lurch that would be a sob if you could make a sound, you begin to understand: The bag contains all that you had so nearly lost. These people huddled around you have brought you sunlight and warmth, things you once so cavalierly dismissed as constant, available, yours, summoned by the simple twisting of a knob or tossing on of a layer.

But in the hours since you last believed that, you've traveled to a place where there is no sun. You've seen that in the infinite reaches of the universe, heat is as glorious and ephemeral as the light of the stars. Heat exists only where matter exists, where particles can vibrate and jump. In the infinite winter of space, heat is tiny; it is the cold that is huge.

Someone speaks. Your eyes move from bright lights to shadowy forms in the dim outer reaches of the room. You recognize the voice of one of the friends you set out to visit, so long ago now. She's smiling down at you crookedly.

"It's cold out there," she says. "Isn't it?"

Questions for Discussion:

1. What are the elements of a short story that Stark uses in the piece? Discuss why it is characterized as creative nonfiction.
2. Explain how historical accounts of hypothermia are used within the story. Do you think these accounts add or detract from the reading?
3. Discuss the importance of *imagery* and *setting* here. Why is vivid description important for this particular work?

"Mother Tongue"

Amy Tan

Author Biography: Amy Tan was born in 1952 in Oakland, California to Chinese immigrant parents. Tan dropped out of a Baptist college before earning her B.A. and M.A. in English at San Jose State University. Tan achieved great success with her first novel, *The Joy Luck Club*, which was a finalist for the National Book Award in 1989 and was adapted into a feature-length film. Tan has written several other novels, nonfiction pieces, and children's books as well.

Context: As an American-born daughter of Chinese immigrants, looming large in Tan's work is the push and pull between American and Chinese cultures and the conflict between generations raised in different places with different sets of values. Tan's mother plays a significant role in many of her works.

Diction: We all have various levels of language we use for different situations. For example, we use one type of English when we address family and friends, or send a text message—but we elevate our language when interviewing for a job or giving a formal speech. Notice how Tan uses *informal, formal,* and *colloquial* diction in the story as she defines her mother's tongue.

I am not a scholar of English or literature. I cannot give you much more than personal opinions on the English language and its variations in this country or others.

I am a writer. And by that definition, I am someone who has always loved language. I am fascinated by language in daily life. I spend a great deal of my time thinking about the power of language—the way it can evoke an emotion, a visual image, a complex idea, or a simple truth. Language is the tool of my trade. And I use them all—all the Englishes I grew up with.

Recently, I was made keenly aware of the different Englishes I do use. I was giving a talk to a large group of people, the same talk I had already given to half a dozen other groups. The nature of the talk was about my writing, my life, and my book, *The Joy Luck Club*. The talk was going along well enough, until I remembered one major difference that made the whole talk sound wrong. My mother was in the room. And it was perhaps the first time she had heard me give a lengthy speech, using the kind of English I have never used with her. I was saying things like, "The intersection of memory upon imagination" and "There is an aspect of my fiction that relates to thus-and-thus"—a speech filled with carefully wrought grammatical phrases, burdened, it suddenly seemed to me, with nominalized forms, past perfect tenses, conditional phrases, all the forms of standard English that I had learned in school and through books, the forms of English I did not use at home with my mother.

Just last week, I was walking down the street with my mother, and I again found myself conscious of the English I was using, the English I do use with her. We were talking about the price of new and used furniture and I heard myself saying this: "Not waste money that way." My husband was with us as well, and he didn't notice any switch in my English. And then I realized why. It's because over the twenty years we've been together I've often used that same kind of English with him, and sometimes he even uses it with me. It has become our language of intimacy, a different sort of English that relates to family talk, the language I grew up with.

So you'll have some idea of what this family talk I heard sounds like, I'll quote what my mother said during a recent conversation which I videotaped and then transcribed. During this conversation, my mother was talking about a political gangster in Shanghai who had the same last name as her family's, Du, and how the gangster in his early years wanted to be adopted by her family, which was rich by comparison. Later, the gangster became more powerful, far richer than my mother's family, and one day showed up at my mother's wedding to pay his respects. Here's what she said in part: "Du Yusong having business like fruit stand. Like off the street kind. He is Du like Du Zong—but not Tsung-ming Island people. The local people call putong, the river east side, he belong to that side local people. That man want to ask Du Zong father take him in like become own family. Du Zong father wasn't look down on him, but didn't take seriously, until that man big like become a mafia. Now important person, very hard to inviting him. Chinese way, came only to show respect, don't stay for dinner. Respect for making big celebration, he shows up. Mean gives lots of respect. Chinese custom. Chinese social life that way. If too important won't have to stay too long. He come to my wedding. I didn't see, I heard it. I gone to boy's side, they have YMCA dinner. Chinese age I was nineteen."

You should know that my mother's expressive command of English belies how much she actually understands. She reads the Forbes report, listens to Wall Street Week, converses daily with her stockbroker, reads all of Shirley MacLaine's books with ease—all kinds of things I can't begin to understand. Yet some of my friends tell me they understand 50 percent of what my mother says. Some say they understand 80 to 90 percent. Some say they understand none of it, as if she were speaking pure Chinese. But to me, my mother's English is perfectly clear, perfectly natural. It's my mother tongue. Her language, as I hear it, is vivid, direct, full of observation and imagery. That was the language that helped shape the way I saw things, expressed things, made sense of the world.

Lately, I've been giving more thought to the kind of English my mother speaks. Like others, I have described it to people as "broken" or "fractured" English. But I wince when I say that. It has always bothered me that I can think of no way to describe it other than "broken," as if it were damaged and needed to be fixed, as if it lacked a certain wholeness and soundness. I've heard other terms used, "limited English," for example. But they seem just as bad, as if everything is limited, including people's perceptions of the limited English speaker.

I know this for a fact, because when I was growing up, my mother's "limited" English limited my perception of her. I was ashamed of her English. I believed that her English reflected the quality of what she had to say. That is, because she expressed them imperfectly her thoughts were imperfect. And I had plenty of empirical evidence to support me: the fact that people in department stores, at banks, and at restaurants did not take her seriously, did not give her good service, pretended not to understand her, or even acted as if they did not hear her.

My mother has long realized the limitations of her English as well. When I was fifteen, she used to have me call people on the phone to pretend I was she. In this guise, I was forced to ask for information or even to complain and yell at people who had been rude to her. One time it was a call to her stockbroker in New York. She had cashed out her small portfolio and it just so happened we were going to New York the next week, our very first trip outside California. I had to get on the phone and say in an adolescent voice that was not very convincing, "This is Mrs. Tan."

And my mother was standing in the back whispering loudly, "Why he don't send me check, already two weeks late. So mad he lie to me, losing me money."

And then I said in perfect English, "Yes, I'm getting rather concerned. You had agreed to send the check two weeks ago, but it hasn't arrived."

Then she began to talk more loudly. "What he want, I come to New York to tell him front of his boss, you cheating me?" And I was trying to calm her down, make her be quiet, while telling the stockbroker, "I can't tolerate any more excuses. If I don't receive the check immediately, I am going to have to speak to your manager when I'm in New York next week." And sure enough, the following week there we were in front of this astonished stockbroker, and I was sitting there red-faced and quiet, and my mother, the real Mrs. Tan, was shouting at his boss in her impeccable broken English.

We used a similar routine just five days ago, for a situation that was far less humorous. My mother had gone to the hospital for an appointment, to find out about a benign brain tumor a CAT scan had revealed a month ago. She said she had spoken very good English, her best English, no mistakes. Still, she said, the hospital did not apologize when they said they had lost the CAT scan and she had come for nothing. She said they did not seem to have any sympathy when she told them she was anxious to know the exact diagnosis, since her husband and son had both died of brain tumors. She said they would not give her any more information until the next time and she would have to make another appointment for that. So she said she would not leave until the doctor called her daughter. She wouldn't budge. And when the doctor finally called her daughter, me, who spoke in perfect English—lo and behold—we had assurances the CAT scan would be found, promises that a conference call on Monday would be held, and apologies for any suffering my mother had gone through for a most regrettable mistake.

I think my mother's English almost had an effect on limiting my possibilities in life as well. Sociologists and linguists probably will tell you that a person's developing language skills are more influenced by peers. But I do think that the language spoken in the family, especially in immigrant families which are more insular, plays a large role in shaping the language of the child. And I believe that it affected my results on achievement tests, I.Q. tests, and the SAT. While my English skills were never judged as poor, compared to math, English could not be considered my strong suit. In grade school I did moderately well, getting perhaps B's, sometimes B-pluses, in English and scoring perhaps in the sixtieth or seventieth percentile on achievement tests. But those scores were not good enough to override the opinion that my true abilities lay in math and science, because in those areas I achieved A's and scored in the ninetieth percentile or higher.

This was understandable. Math is precise; there is only one correct answer. Whereas, for me at least, the answers on English tests were always a judgment call, a matter of opinion and personal experience. Those tests were constructed around items like fill-in-the-blank sentence completion, such as, "Even though Tom was, Mary thought he was—." And the correct answer always seemed to be the most bland combinations of thoughts, for example, "Even though Tom was shy, Mary thought he was charming," with the grammatical structure "even though" limiting the correct answer to some sort of semantic opposites, so you wouldn't get answers like, "Even though Tom was foolish, Mary thought he was ridiculous." Well, according to my mother, there were very few limitations as to what Tom could have been and what Mary might have thought of him. So I never did well on tests like that.

The same was true with word analogies, pairs of words in which you were supposed to find some sort of logical, semantic relationship—for example, "Sunset is to nightfall as is to." And here you would be presented with a list of four possible pairs, one of which showed the same kind of relationship: red is to stoplight, bus is to arrival, chills is to fever, yawn is to boring. Well, I could never think that way. I knew what the tests were asking, but I could not block out of my mind the images already created by the first pair, "sunset is to nightfall"—and I would see a burst of colors against a darkening sky, the moon rising, the lowering of a curtain of stars. And all the other pairs of words—red, bus, stoplight, boring—just threw up a mass of confusing images, making it impossible for me to sort out something as logical as saying: "A sunset precedes nightfall" is the same as "a chill precedes a fever." The only way I would have gotten that answer right would have been to imagine an associative situation, for example, my being disobedient and staying out past sunset, catching a chill at night, which turns into feverish pneumonia as punishment, which indeed did happen to me.

I have been thinking about all this lately, about my mother's English, about achievement tests. Because lately I've been asked, as a writer, why there are not more Asian Americans represented in American literature. Why are there few Asian Americans enrolled in creative writing programs? Why do so many Chinese students go into engineering? Well, these are broad sociological questions I can't begin to answer. But I have noticed in surveys—in fact, just last week—that Asian students, as a whole, always do significantly better on math achievement tests than in English. And this makes me think that there are other Asian-American students whose English spoken in the home might also be described as "broken" or "limited." And perhaps they also have teachers who are steering them away from writing and into math and science, which is what happened to me.

Fortunately, I happen to be rebellious in nature and enjoy the challenge of disproving assumptions made about me. I became an English major my first year in college, after being enrolled as pre-med. I started writing nonfiction as a freelancer the week after I was told by my former boss that writing was my worst skill and I should hone my talents toward account management.

But it wasn't until 1985 that I finally began to write fiction. And at first I wrote using what I thought to be wittily crafted sentences, sentences that would finally prove

I had mastery over the English language. Here's an example from the first draft of a story that later made its way into *The Joy Luck Club*, but without this line: "That was my mental quandary in its nascent state." A terrible line, which I can barely pronounce.

Fortunately, for reasons I won't get into today, I later decided I should envision a reader for the stories I would write. And the reader I decided upon was my mother, because these were stories about mothers. So with this reader in mind—and in fact she did read my early drafts—I began to write stories using all the Englishes I grew up with: the English I spoke to my mother, which for lack of a better term might be described as "simple"; the English she used with me, which for lack of a better term might be described as "broken"; my translation of her Chinese, which could certainly be described as "watered down"; and what I imagined to be her translation of her Chinese if she could speak in perfect English, her internal language, and for that I sought to preserve the essence, but neither an English nor a Chinese structure. I wanted to capture what language ability tests can never reveal: her intent, her passion, her imagery, the rhythms of her speech and the nature of her thoughts.

Apart from what any critic had to say about my writing, I knew I had succeeded where it counted when my mother finished reading my book and gave me her verdict: "So easy to read."

Questions for Discussion:

1. Why is Tan classifying the different kinds of English she knows and uses? Is she conveying information, telling a story, arguing a point, or doing all of these? Explain.
2. Discuss the significance of the title of the story. How does the title connect with the theme of the piece?
3. Tan does not want to use "broken" or "fractured" as names for the kind of English her mother speaks. Why not?

"11:20"

Michael Paterniti

Author Biography: Michael Paterniti was born in Connecticut and graduated from the University of Michigan. He writes for a number of national magazines such as *GQ* and *Esquire*, and was awarded the National Magazine Award in 1998 for the piece "Driving Mr. Albert: A Trip across America with Einstein's Brain." He lives in Portland, ME.

Context: Paterniti is foremost a journalist and creative non-fiction writer. His subjects are contemporary and wide-ranging, having to do with politics, food, and much more.

Figurative Language: Writers often use figurative language as a means to enhance description and create vivid images within the reader's mind. In this work, Paterniti uses raw description and figurative language to give the account of the 1999 Columbine High School shooting. Pay attention to his use of *metaphor* and *simile* in the work.

Before it walked the parking lot, its crippled feet scraping the silence of that 70-in-April spring day, before it lurched past the saplings bent once in the breeze, and before the sun flooded the wide, emerald windows of the library in a featureless building as featureless as the instant Colorado landscape in which it rose. Before the glass front doors were drawn back, reflecting nothing—no face, no figure—and the low, reassuring, underwater sound of voices, students at lunch or in choir or suiting up for gym, was met by the voice of something else, something pitiless and blank. Before Patrick Ireland, a real boy, was shot in the head and lay paralyzed on the right side of his body under a table in the library, playing dead though he half was. Before Lance Kirklin, a real boy, had his jaw blown off and had to communicate by squeezing hands, and before Daniel Rohrbough, a real boy, lay sprawled on the stone walk among the saplings as students leaped over him like cows fleeing from some medieval abattoir.

Before the glass doors of that featureless building shattered and the pipes burst and alarms sounded and the sprinkler system went haywire, before freaked students packed oxygenless closets or scurried up into ceilings or hid in lockers. Before all the shirtless, hairless boys were herded out of Columbine High School, hands over their heads, looking pale and stricken and, well, like little boys streaked with blood, their shirts having been used as wraps and tourniquets on the bodies left inside. Before all the stunned, gasping girls huddled in trembling circles, holding each other, well, like little girls suddenly with no mother left in the world.

Before night fell and the dead still lay inside that booby-trapped high school as a final affront, lay like the pinions of a star around the killers—and what could the scene of that terrible midnight have looked like?—before the media horde arrived with its Aggreko generators and deep-space satellite dishes. Before the blame and the signed caskets and the psychedelic mountains of flowers, and before the angry, indignant promises for gun control, for safer schools, for policing the Internet, for really caring about our kids, there was 11:20 on a Tuesday morning. Eleven-twenty in Columbine valley, what used to be farmland rising to the Front Range of the Rocky Mountains, in a place where the American dream lives in strip malls and stucco-and-drywall housing developments. A new America with emerald, Oz-like glass windows. Eleven-twenty on a day when the season makes a turn: Columbine High School, its windows like microchips, its saplings showing first leaves. The wide baseball fields bursting green. A dog barking, a plane passing lazily overhead, leaving a contrail trace of its progress. And for one last time, at 11:20, everything in its place: goofy, pimply, smart, beautiful, heartbreaking, not-yet-grown kids writing papers on Thoreau.

Afterward the snow fell—for three days. It blew into the backstops like huge, broken moths. Two hundred investigators combed the sarcophagus; dozens of cameras trained on a hugging boy and girl like more guns; the uncle of a dead girl, in a leather coat and combed hair, searched out any journalist he could find for an interview. "Death by mayhem," he kept repeating into microphones. Afterward, in a local diner, two older patrons argued about Wyatt Earp and Doc Holliday—who the better gunfighter had been. At a convenience store, a boy in a green bib sat behind the counter, bawling.

I myself stood for a while at the memorial, stood before the stuffed animals and flowers and purple Magic Markered messages—all of them trying to call back 11:20— and walked the police line that surrounded Columbine High, walked out over the baseball fields, snow up to my shins, until I was a good peg from the front door. It was silent but for the whine of generators. The shattered emerald windows to the library had plywood planks fixed over them. And hundreds of cars sat in the lot: pickup trucks and Acuras, a motorcycle and someone's mom's old Dodge.

Inside that building, everything was exactly as it had been: computers and lights still on, lunches half eaten, books turned to the last page read, the college application of a girl who was shot, its final check mark made, the pencil lying next to it. That's what's most hard to imagine: how, in midsentence, in the throes of some idea, in the beginning of some meaningful life, that girl was entered by some dark, crippled thing and became a memory.

It was sometime after eleven, and, standing there, gazing out over the parking lot and beyond the school to the new houses with their new cars and the new living rooms with their new rugs, you could have actually imagined this as any other school day. Everything seemingly in its place. A dog barked and a plane passed overhead, but this time it sounded like the roar of a monster.

Questions for Discussion:

1. Discuss the images Paterniti uses in this work. How do they create contrast between the tragic event and innocence of the setting?
2. Discuss how the author manipulates time. How does it simultaneously stop and move forward in the work? Explain.
3. Why do you think the author does not name the perpetrators of the event, but names the victims? What is the significance of this choice?
4. Discuss the role of memory in this piece. How does the author memorialize the Columbine shooting?

"A Death in Texas"

Steve Earle

Author Biography: Steve Earle is a prolific singer, songwriter, producer, actor, and writer. Born in 1955 in Virginia, his family moved to Texas, where at age 16, Earle dropped out of school and moved to Houston to live with his uncle. After discovering his deep interest in music there, he moved to Nashville three years later to pursue music. Over his long career he has performed his own music as well as written songs for some of the biggest names in country music, earning three Grammy awards along the way.

Context: "A Death in Texas" is based on real events. In 1986, Jon Wayne Nobles broke into a home in north Austin, TX and fatally stabbed two women: Mitzi Johnson-Nalley and Kelly Farquhar. Given the death penalty, Nobles converted to Catholicism in jail and expressed remorse for his actions. Steve Earle was one of 5 witnesses that Nobles invited to his execution.

Character: Though it may be odd to think of nonfiction as having "characters," death row inmate Jonathan Wayne Nobles can be considered the protagonist of Steve Earle's piece. Earle uses character description, dialogue, and other traditional elements of fiction to put a human face on a difficult social issue.

"HEY, MAN."

Jonathan Wayne Nobles grins at me through inch-thick wire-reinforced glass, hunching over to speak in a deep, resonant voice through the steel grate below. A feeble "What's up?" is the best I can manage. The visiting area in Ellis One Unit is crowded with other folks who have traveled, in some cases thousands of miles, to visit relatives and correspondents on Texas' Death Row. They sit at intervals in wooden chairs surrounding a cinder block and steel cage that dominates the center of the room. There are cages within the cage as well, reserved for inmates under disciplinary action and "death watch" status. Falling into the latter category, Jon must squeeze his considerable bulk into one of these phone-booth-sized enclosures.

It's an awkward moment for both of us. In the 10 years we have corresponded, we have never met face to face. The occasion is auspicious. Jon and I will spend eight hours a day together for the next three days and another three days next week. Then the state of Texas will transport Jon, chained hand and foot, 11 miles to the Walls unit in downtown Huntsville. There he will be pumped full of chemicals that will collapse his lungs and stop his heart forever. This is not a worst-case scenario. It is a certainty. Jonathan Nobles has precisely 10 days to live. And I, at Jon's request, will attend the execution as one of his witnesses.

Over the next few days a routine develops. I arrive at Ellis at 8:30 in the morning. We usually spend the first two hours talking about music, politics, religion—subjects that we have covered thoroughly enough in letters over the years to know that we have widely divergent views and tastes. We fill the long awkward silences that seem inevitable in prison visiting areas with trips to the vending machines for soft drinks, candy, and potato chips. I pass Jon's goodies to the guard on duty through a small opening in the steel mesh.

Inevitably, we move on to life behind bars, drugs, and recovery—topics where we share considerably more common ground. We are both recovering addicts who got clean only when we were locked up. Jon began reading about recovery and attending 12-step meetings in prison years ago. I can remember a time, back when I was still using drugs, when the recovery-speak that filled his letters made me extremely uncomfortable. Now it is a language that we share—sort of a spiritual shorthand that cuts through the testosterone and affords us a convenient, if uncomfortable, segue to the business at hand.

There are arrangements to be made. If Jon's body were to go unclaimed, as is the case with half of the men executed in Texas, he would be buried in the prison cemetery on the outskirts of Huntsville. Called "Peckerwood Hill" by the locals, it is a lonely space filled with concrete crosses, adorned only with the interred inmates' prison numbers. Those executed by the state are easily identifiable by the "X" preceding their number. There are no names on the stones. Jon doesn't want to wind up there.

Instead, he wants to be buried in Oxford, England—a place he's never seen. One of his pen pals, a British woman named Pam Thomas, has described it to him in her letters. He likes the picture Pam paints of the springtime there, when the bluebells are in bloom. Jon says that Pam is working on permission from a landowner there. I have Plan B on the back burner. A Dominican community in Galway, Ireland, has offered Jon a final resting place. At some point in the proceedings, it dawns on me that I have spent the past hour helping a living, breathing man plan his own burial.

One thing Jon and I don't talk about much is the movement to abolish the death penalty. In fact, Jon is suspicious of abolitionists. We were "introduced" by a pen pal of his and an acquaintance of mine. She had heard that I sometimes corresponded with inmates and asked if she could give Jon my address. I said sure. Within a month, I received my first letter. It was a page and a half long in a beautiful flowing script. It contained a lot of the usual tough rhetoric and dark humor I had learned to expect in letters from inmates. After several readings, I realized that the jailhouse small talk was merely a medium, a vehicle for one pertinent piece of information—that Jonathan Wayne Nobles was guilty of the crimes he was charged with.

In 1986 Jon was convicted (almost entirely on the strength of his own confession) of stabbing Kelley Farquhar and Mitzi Johnson-Nalley to death. He also admitted stabbing Ron Ross, Nalley's boyfriend, who lost an eye in the attack. Jon never took the stand during his trial. He sat impassively as the guilty verdict was read and, according to newspaper accounts, only flinched slightly when District Judge Bob Jones sentenced him to death.

When Jon arrived at Ellis he quickly alienated all of the guards and most of the inmates. He once broke away from guards while returning to his cell from the exercise yard and climbed the exposed pipes and bars in the cell block, kicking down television sets suspended outside on the bottom tier. On another occasion he cut himself with a razor blade, knowing that the guards would have to open his cell to prevent him from bleeding to death. He just wanted to hit one officer before he passed out.

But somehow, somewhere along the line, in what is arguably the most inhumane environment in the "civilized" world, Jonathan Nobles began to change. He became interested in Catholicism and began to attend Mass. He befriended the Catholic clergy who ministered in the prison system, including members of the Dominican Order of Preachers. He eventually became a lay member of the order and ministered to his fellow inmates, even standing as godfather at inmate Cliff Boggess' baptism. He later helped officiate at the Mass that was celebrated the night before Boggess' execution. I watched this transformation in the letters that I received.

The Jonathan Nobles who sits on the other side of the glass from me in September 1998 is a different man from the one the state of Texas sentenced to die almost 12 years ago. The greatest evidence of this fact is the way Jon is treated by everyone he encounters. A prison clerk, displaying genuine regret, interrupts our visit. She needs Jon to sign some papers. Jon does so and then informs me that the documents allow me to pick up his personal property and distribute it to a list of people detailed in a note the clerk will hand me on my way out. Inmate James Beathard, on his way down the line to visit with a family member, stops to talk and Jon introduces us. The guard patiently waits until the exchange is over before escorting him to his assigned cubicle. Socialization during inmate transfer is a clear violation of policy, but a lot of the rules have relaxed for Jon. He says it's like the last week of the school year. I believe it's more likely that he has earned the genuine respect of everyone here.

I excuse myself to go to the bathroom. The truth is, I simply need a break. On the way back I run into Father Stephen Walsh, a Franciscan friar from Boston who travels regularly to minister to the Catholic inmates at Ellis. He will serve as Jonathan's spiritual adviser, waiting with Jon in the holding cell over at the Walls until he's escorted into the death chamber itself. There, he will administer the last rites.

Every visit ends the same way. A guard gives us a five-minute warning, and Jon hurriedly dictates a list of "things to do" that I must commit to memory, since visitors are not allowed to bring writing instruments and paper into the unit. Then Jon presses his palm against the glass and I mirror his with mine. Jon says, "I love you. I'll see you tomorrow."

OVER THE PAST FEW DAYS

The other witnesses have arrived in Huntsville. I had dinner with Dona Hucka, Jon's aunt. She is the only blood relative to make the trip and she has driven all night to be here. Pam Thomas is in from England. Both are already on the unit when I arrive. We take turns leaning close to the glass while a prison employee takes Polaroid snapshots of each of us with Jon. The prison provides this service for the fee of eight dollars each.

It's 10 o'clock in the morning. There isn't much time left. At 12:30 we will be asked to leave the unit and Jon will be transported to the Walls. In the death chamber, we will be able to hear Jon over a speaker in the witness room, but this is our last opportunity to speak to him. Jon divides the remaining time between us more or less equally. I go first. Jon looks tired; the stress is showing for the first time. He leans down and motions me closer. I realize he's assessing my condition as well. "You all right, man?" I tell him that I'm okay. Jon is not convinced.

"I'm worried about you. You don't have to be Superman or nothin'. This is insane shit that's goin' on here today. You don't have to be strong for the women if that's what you're thinkin'. They're big girls. You need to take care of yourself."

"I know, Jon. I'm all right. I went to a meeting last night and my manager's here now. I've also got a couple of friends up from Houston who have done this before."

"Witnessed?"

"Yeah." That seemed to make him feel better. "Okay, but if you need to cry, it's all right. Go ahead and cry."

"When this is all over, I'll cry."

"Promise?"

"I promise."

Jon shifts gears suddenly. Back to business. He looks both ways to make sure the guard isn't watching. "Take this." With much effort he pushes a tiny slip of tightly rolled paper, the diameter of a toothpick, through the impossibly tight mesh. Somehow he pulls it off. "That's my daughter's phone number in California. My sister read it to me over the phone last night. They're going to strip search me and I can't take anything to the Walls and I'm afraid I'll forget it. Give it to Father Walsh. Then I'll have it when I make my last phone calls."

I poke the paper in the watch pocket of my Levi's. There are a few other requests. He wants me to call his foster mother and his sister after the execution, and send flowers to two women who worked for the prison who were kind to him over the years. I promise that I won't forget. "All right, bro. Take care of yourself and your kids. Tell Dona to come back." Hands against the glass one last time.

"I love you, Jonathan."

"I love you too, bro."

NOON I head back into Huntsville. My manager, Dan Gillis, arrived last night and not a moment too soon. Suddenly, driving has become difficult. The world has taken on a kind of surrealistic patina. I need someone to drive for the rest of the day. Also waiting at the hotel are two friends from the abolition movement, Karen Sebung and Ward Larkin. Both have witnessed executions, and they have made the trip to assist in any way they can. We talk over arrangements for the transportation and cremation of Jon's body, which, as it turns out, Dan has already taken care of. I make a couple of phone calls and check my messages. Then I shower, shave, and put on a pair of black jeans, a blue short-sleeve shirt, and a black linen sport coat.

4:00 We leave the hotel. Dan drives us to Hospitality House, a guest residence operated by the Baptist Church for the families of in-mates. Dona and Pam, as well as Pam's friend Caroline, are staying there. The two other witnesses, Bishop Carmody of the East Texas diocese and the Reverend Richard Lopez of the Texas Department of Corrections, are already there when we arrive. We are assembled here for an orientation session to be conducted by the Reverend Jim Brazzil, the chaplain at the Walls unit. He and the warden will be the only two people inside the chamber with Jon when he dies. He goes through the execution process step-by-step so that we will know what to expect and, though it's obvious he speaks with authority, I'm not listening. I can't concentrate, so I just nod a lot. It doesn't matter. No matter how well or poorly the witnesses are prepared, they are going to kill Jon anyway.

5:05 Reverend Brazzil answers his cell phone. It's Father Walsh, who's over at the Walls with Jon and wants the phone number, the one that Jon passed me through the

. . . oh my God. I can't find it. I was sure that I transferred the slip from my other jeans into my wallet when I changed clothes, but it's simply not there. Dan runs to the motel and checks my room, but it's hopeless. Reverend Brazzil relays the bad news to Father Walsh. I feel awful.

5:30 We arrive at the visitors' center across the street from the Walls unit. Karen Sebung accompanies me as far as the waiting area, where we witnesses are searched, then Dona and Pam are escorted to another room by a female officer. When they return, a large man enters the room and introduces himself as an officer of the prison's internal affairs division. If we should feel faint, he says, medical attention is available. He also warns us that anyone who in any way attempts to disrupt the "process," as he calls it, will be removed from the witness area immediately. Nothing about my body is working right. My feet and hands are cold and the side of my neck is numb.

5:55 The corrections officer returns. "Follow me, please." We walk across the street and through the front door of the old Gothic prison administration building. We turn left as soon as we enter and find ourselves in the waiting area of the governor's office, where we are asked to wait once again. There are two reporters there. The other three members of the press pool, along with the victims' family members, have already been escorted to the witness area, which is divided by a cinder block wall. The two sets of witnesses will never come in contact with each other.

6:00 We're led through a visiting area similar to the one at Ellis, then out into the bright evening sun for a moment and turn left down a short sidewalk. Another left and we enter a small brick building built into the side of the perimeter wall. We enter the tiny room in single file. Father Walsh appears from somewhere inside the death chamber to join us. The reporters enter last, and the door is locked behind us. I can hear the reporters scratching on their notepads with their pencils. There is only room for three of us—Dona, me, and Pam—in the front row. Dona grabs my left hand and squeezes it hard. She already has tears in her eyes.

Jon is strapped to a hospital gurney with heavy leather restraints across his chest, hips, thighs, ankles, and wrists.

His arms are wrapped in Ace bandages and extended at his sides on boards. At either wrist, clear plastic tubes protrude from the wrappings, snaking back under the gurney and disappearing through a plastic tube set in a bright blue cinder block wall. I think I see movement behind the one-way glass mirror on the opposite wall—the executioner getting into position. Jon is smiling at us, his great neck twisted uncomfortably sideways. A microphone suspended from the ceiling hangs a few inches above his head. The speaker above our heads crackles to life and Jon speaks, craning his head around to see the victims' witnesses in the room next door.

"I know some of you won't believe me, but I am truly sorry for what I have done. I wish that I could undo what happened back then and bring back your loved ones, but I can't." Jon begins to sob as he addresses Mitzi Nalley's mother. "I'm sorry. I'm so sorry. I wish I could bring her back to you. And Ron . . . I took so much from you. I'm sorry. I know you probably don't want my love, but you have it."

Turning to me, he seems to regain his composure somewhat. He even manages to smile again. "Steve, I can't believe that I had to go through all this to see you in a suit coat. Hey man, don't worry about the phone number, bro. You've done so much. I love you. Dona, thank you for being here. I know it was hard for you. I love you. Pam, thank you for coming from so far away. Thanks for all you have done. I love you. Bishop Carmody, thank you so much. Reverend Lopez and you, Father Walsh, I love you all. I have something I want to say. It comes from I Corinthians. It goes . . . " and Jon recites the lengthy piece of scripture that he agonized over for weeks, afraid he would forget when the time came. He remembers every word.

When he finishes reciting he takes a deep breath and says, "Father, into thy hands I commend my spirit." The warden, recognizing the prearranged signal he and Jon had agreed on, nods toward the unseen executioner and Jon begins to sing.

"Silent night/Holy night . . ."

He gets as far as "mother and child" and suddenly the air explodes from his lungs with a loud barking noise, deep and incongruous, like a child with whooping cough—"HUH!!!" His head pitches forward with such force that his heavy, prison-issue glasses fly off his face, bouncing from his chest and falling to the green tile floor below.

And then he doesn't move at all. I watch his eyes fix and glaze over, my heart pounding in my chest and Dona squeezing my hand. Dead men look . . . well, dead. Vacant. No longer human. But there is a protocol to be satisfied. The warden checks his watch several times during the longest five minutes of my life. When the time is up, he walks across the room and knocks on the door. The doctor enters, his stethoscope earpieces already in place. He listens first at Jon's neck, then at his chest, then at his side. He shines a small flashlight into Jon's eyes for an instant and then, glancing up at the clock on his way out, intones, "6:18."

We are ushered out the same way we came, but I don't think any of us are the same people who crossed the street to the prison that day. I know I'm not. I can't help but wonder what happens to the people who work at the Walls, who see this horrific thing happen as often as four times a week. What do they see when they turn out the lights? I can't imagine.

I do know that Jonathan Nobles changed profoundly while he was in prison. I know that the lives of people he came in contact with changed as well, including mine. Our criminal justice system isn't known for rehabilitation. I'm not sure that, as a society, we are even interested in that concept anymore. The problem is that most people who go to prison get out one day and walk among us. Given as many people as we lock up, we better learn to rehabilitate someone. I believe Jon might have been able to teach us how. Now we'll never know.

Questions for Discussion:

1. What techniques does Earle use to make Jon a sympathetic character, despite his crimes?
2. What is the significance of using timestamps in the second half of the piece?
3. With any controversial social issue, facts and research are important. But what is the additional value of writing creatively about this topic? What does it add to our understanding or perspective that facts alone cannot?

Drama

ust like literature and short fiction, we analyze drama by breaking it down into parts. Unlike literature and short fiction, drama is intentionally written to be a performance. Hence, it is important to analyze all of these elements and tropes to understand the theme and meaning of the dramatic piece. Readers and audience members should always ask "what major ideas about human nature or culture are represented in the story and on the stage?". Also, ask "what appears natural in this play?". Regardless, this analysis has to critically examine how it looks on the stage as well as analyze how it looks on the page. This "looks on the stage" aspect is called **the spectacle**. Part of the spectacle is being aware of the costumes, lighting, music, and setting. (Astute readers might also recognize these concepts as part of film and television!)

Drama also includes stage directions, which are important because they describe the spectacle of the play. They often provide **stage directions** and blocking to show how characters should move and gesture on stage, and they will describe how characters enter and leave the stage. While stage directions are often ignored, they are important to analyze because they describe how the play looks, which helps us understand what the play means.

Two tropes to look for when analyzing drama are **soliloquies** and **asides**. Since drama is often performed in front of an actual audience, characters may use these tropes to interact with the audience. A *soliloquy* represents a character's inner thoughts, and is usually given by one character who is alone on the stage (although, sometimes other characters on stage "freeze" to represent these internal thoughts). *Asides* are remarks made directly to the audience and not considered "heard" by other characters on stage.

Oedipus Rex

Sophocles

Author Biography: Sophocles, born around the year 497 BC into a wealthy family, was an ancient Greek playwright. Of the three playwrights of his time whose work still survives, Sophocles was the most awarded, winning not only more competitions than any other, but also being chosen to lead a number of important Greek cultural moments for the nation. He died at the age of 90 or 91.

Context: Sophocles wrote three plays about the ancient Greek city of Thebes, one of which is *Oedipus Rex* ("Rex" meaning "the king"). The play is based on the story of Oedipus, of whom it was said a prophecy fated him to kill his father and marry his mother on his way to becoming king of Thebes. Like much of Greek literature, the play concerns itself with fate, the right order of civilization, and the legacies of those who transgress.

Literary Terms:
Hamartia: A flaw that causes a person to lose something of value, usually his/her life.
Hubris: Excessive pride in oneself or one's actions.
Chorus: A group of characters that often explain and comment on the actions of a play.
Catharsis: A sense of relief felt by the audience that is created by the actions of characters in a drama

[Scene: outside, in front of the palace of Oedipus. There is also a shrine to Apollo at which are seated many suppliants. Oedipus enters the stage from the palace.]

OEDIPUS:
    My children, new-sprung race of old Cadmus,
    why do you sit at my shrines, wearing garlands
    of the suppliants' olive? All around
    the city is filled with the smell of incense,
5   all around filled with the sound of hymns and groans.
    These things I did not think it right to learn
    from messengers, and so I have come here myself,
    who am called Oedipus and known to all.
    But you, old man, tell me, since it is fitting
10   for you to speak on their behalf, why you
    sit out here, afraid of something or wanting it?
    So I would be willing to help you
    in any way, for he would be hardhearted
    who did not pity such an assembly.

PRIEST:

15 Oedipus, you who rule my land, you see
how many of us sit here at your altars;
some do not yet have the strength to fly far;
others are heavy with age. I am the priest
of Zeus, and these were chosen from the young men.
20 There is another group wreathed as suppliants
sitting in the marketplace and another
at the double-gated temple of Athena
and at the smoke-filled oracle of Ismenus.
For the city, as you yourself can see,
25 is badly shaken already and from the waves
can no longer lift her head above this
bloody tossing; there is death in the fruitful buds
from the earth and in the pasturing herds,
and even in the childless births of women.
30 Falling upon us, the fire-bringing god,
most hateful disease, drives the city,
and by him the house of Cadmus is drained,
and dark Hades grows rich with groans and wails.
Now, I do not hold you equal to the gods,
35 nor do these children who sit at your hearth,
but we judge you the first of men both
in the ordinary chances of life
and in the contingencies of the divine.
It was you who came and released Cadmus' town
40 from the tribute we paid to the cruel songstress,
and these things you did knowing nothing from us,
nor instructed at all, but with help from god
you spoke and knew how to set our lives straight.
And now, Oedipus, greatest in the eyes of all,
45 we who are here as your suppliants beseech you
to find some defense for us, as you may have heard
the voice of one of the gods or have learned
something from a man—for I think that the ideas
of experienced men most often succeed.
50 Come, o best of mortals, and save our city;
come, but be careful, since now this land
calls you her savior for your former zeal,
and let us never recall of your reign
that we first stood straight, but stumbled later.
55 Rather, then, restore this city to safety.
For at that time you gave us great fortune,
be now equal to what you were then.
Since, if indeed you would rule this land,
just as you do now, it is far better

60 to rule over men than a wasteland;
nothing matters, neither tower nor ship,
if it is empty of men to dwell within it.
OEDIPUS:
My poor children, what you desire is
known and not unknown to me, for I see well
65 that everyone is sick, and being sick,
still, not one of you is as sick as I am.
For your pain comes upon the individual,
one by one, to each man alone and no other,
but my soul groans for the city, for me and you
70 together. Hence, you do not wake me from sleep,
but know that I have been weeping much
and wandering many roads of the mind.
And that which my inquiry found our only cure
I have done, for I have sent Creon,
75 son of Menoeceus, my own brother-in-law,
to Apollo's home at Pytho, so that he may
learn what I should do or say to save this city.
And already enough time has passed that
I wonder what he is doing, for he has stayed
80 beyond the proper time. But whenever he comes,
I would surely be an evil man not to do
whatever the god reveals.
PRIEST:
Wonderful news! Both what you have said,
and what these have just pointed out to me:
85 Creon is approaching!
OEDIPUS:
Lord Apollo, if only he might come as bright
with redeeming fortune as shine his eyes!
PRIEST:
It seems he brings good news, for otherwise
he would not come crowned with berry-laden laurel.
OEDIPUS:
90 We shall know soon, for he is close enough to hear.
Lord, kinsman of my wife, child of Menoeceus,
what reply do you bring us from the god?
[Enter Creon from offstage.]
CREON:
A good one, for I say that even misfortunes,
if somehow put right, bring only good luck.
OEDIPUS:
95 What sort of reply is this? For what you say
gives me neither confidence nor fear.
CREON:
If you wish these people nearby to hear,

I am ready to speak, or should we go inside?

OEDIPUS:

Speak to everyone, for I consider their pain
100   more important even than that of my own soul.

CREON:

I shall say all I heard from the god.
Phoebus clearly ordered us, my lord,
to drive out the pollution being fostered
in this very land, not to nurture it unhealed.

OEDIPUS:

105   With what cleansing and for what type of disaster?

CREON:

By driving a man into exile,
or undoing murder with murder again,
since this blood shakes our city like a storm.

OEDIPUS:

And who is the man whose fate he decrees?

CREON:

110   My lord, once Laius was our leader in this land,
before you came to govern this city.

OEDIPUS:

So I have heard, though I never saw him.

CREON:

He died, and the god now orders us clearly
to take violent vengeance on the murderers.

OEDIPUS:

115   Where on earth are they? Where will be found
this indistinct track of ancient guilt?

CREON:

In this very land, he said. What is sought
can be captured, but what is ignored escapes.

OEDIPUS:

Did Laius meet his bloody fate in his home
120   or estate or in some other land?

CREON:

He left home to consult an oracle, he said,
and never returned again, once he had set out.

OEDIPUS:

Did no messenger or fellow traveler see,
whom we might use to find something out?

CREON:

125   No, they died, except one, who, fleeing in fear
of those he saw had nothing to say but one thing.

OEDIPUS:

What? For one thing could lead us to learn many,
if from hope might come a small beginning.

CREON:
  He said that bandits fell upon them and killed him,
130 not with one man's strength, but the hands of many.
OEDIPUS:
  How did a bandit come to dare so much,
  unless he acted with money from here?
CREON:
  This was suspected. But with Laius fallen,
  we had no helper in our troubles.
OEDIPUS:
135 What kind of trouble, when your kingship had
  fallen thus, made you see to this so poorly?
CREON:
  The riddle-singing Sphinx compelled us to look
  at what lay at hand, forgetting things unseen.
OEDIPUS:
  Then I shall reveal these things anew,
140 for justly did Phoebus, and justly did you
  assign me this case on behalf of the dead,
  so that you will rightly see me as an ally,
  avenging both this land and the god together.
  For not on behalf of more distant friends,
145 but as if from myself I shall dispel the stain.
  For whoever he was who killed that man
  would as soon kill me with that same violent hand.
  Helping that one, therefore, I am helping myself.
  But you, my children, as soon as you can, rise
150 from these seats, stopping these suppliant wails.
  Someone, muster here the people of Cadmus,
  as I will leave nothing undone. For with God's help
  we shall see whether we are saved or lost.
PRIEST:
  Let us stand up, my children; those things for which
155 we came here this man himself has promised.
  But may Phoebus who sent these prophecies
  come at once as savior and stayer of disease!
  [Exeunt omnes.]
  [The Chorus marches into the orchestra.]
CHORUS:
  Str 1 O sweetly worded voice of Zeus, who are you
  who come from all-gold Pytho to glorious Thebes?
160 My frightened mind shakes in fear, quivering,
  o healing Delian Paean,
  in awe before you. What is it you will achieve for me,
  something new or something known and coming back again?
  Tell me, o child of golden Hope,

165   immortal Utterance.
    Ant 1 First I call on you, daughter of Zeus, immortal Athena,
    and your earth-protecting sister, Artemis,
    who sit, famous, on your throne in the marketplace;
    and Phoebus the farshooter
170   I call: my threefold protection from death, shine forth on me.
    If ever when madness was set upon the city,
    you sent away our burning scourge,
    come also now.
    Str 2 Alas! for I bear countless woes;
175   disease falls upon my entire crew,
    and no mind's weapon can protect me,
    for the fruit of our famous land does not grow,
    nor do our women emerge from their
    mournful labors with offspring.
180   One upon another you might see each soul,
    like a well-winged bird, surer than irresistible fire,
    setting out for the promontory of the western god.
    Ant 2 Unable to count their number,
    the city is destroyed, and unpitied,
185   their generations lie upon the ground,
    spreading death, finding no mourners.
    While brides and white-haired mothers come together
    and groan as suppliants over their mournful labors,
    the hymn for healing and the lament ring loud together.
190   Because of these, o golden daughter of Zeus,
    send bright-eyed Strength.
    Str 3 Furious Ares, now without bronze shields,
    yet still surrounded by cries, confronts me and burns me;
    let him, in hurried running, turn his back
195   on our fatherland, either borne by a wind
    into the great chamber of Amphitrite
    or rushing to the inhospitable Thracian wave.
    For, if night ever leaves something undone,
    day comes along to complete it.
200   This one, o reverend lightning-bearer,
    father Zeus, make him perish with your thunderbolt.
    Ant 3 And you, lord of light, from your golden bow
    I would have your unconquered arrows fly
    as a guard set in front of me before my enemy,
205   and those of shining, fire-bringing Artemis,
    with which she darts across the hills of Lycia.
    And I call upon the one with the golden headband,
    eponym of this land, wine-faced Bacchus,
    hailed companion of the Maenads' throng,
210   to approach with a torch of shining pine,

against this god dishonored by the gods.

[Enter Oedipus from the palace.]

OEDIPUS:

You seek, and what you seek, if you are willing
to listen to my words and help in this sickness,
you may take as help and relief from your troubles.
215   Although a stranger to both report and victim,
I shall announce these things, for I would not be far
in tracking it, if I did not have some clue.
But now, since only later did I become
a citizen among citizens, I decree
220   the following to the people of Cadmus:
whoever among you knows at whose hands
Laius son of Labdacus was destroyed,
I order this man to tell it all to me.
And if the culprit fears this accusation,
225   he should lose his fear and come forward,
for he will suffer nothing worse than safe exile
from this land. But if someone knows that another
or one from some other land is the murderer,
let him not be silent! For I myself
230   shall complete his reward, and he will have
my favor. But if you are silent again,
and someone out of fear pushes away
responsibility from himself or a friend,
then you must hear from me what I intend to do.
235   I ban this man, whoever he is, from all land
over which I hold power and the throne.
I decree that no one shall receive him
or speak to him, nor make him partner
in prayers to the gods or sacrifices,
240   nor allow to him holy water;
but instead that everyone must expel him
from their homes, as this man is the source
of our pollution, as the oracle
of Pytho has just revealed to me.
245   And so I myself am become an ally
both to the god and the man who died.
And I curse the doer, whether he worked alone
or evaded us with accomplices,
that he wear out his unlucky life
250   as badly as he himself is bad.
And I pray, if he should be known to me
and share in my hearth among my family,
that I suffer all that I called upon these.
All these things I charge you to complete,

255 on my behalf and on the god's, and for this land,
wasted away, fruitless and godless.
But even if this problem were not put
before us by god, you should not suffer
this unclean thing, since the man lost was
260 both very noble and your king, so see this through.
Now, since I am ruler and hold this kingdom
that he held before—holding also the bed
and wife we have both sown; and children
of the same mother would have been born to us,
265 had his line not been ill-fated—since chance
has driven me into that one's powers,
therefore I shall fight for him in this matter,
as if for my own father, and I shall try
everything, seeking to find the one who
270 committed the murder, for Labdacus' son,
son of Polydorus, and before him
Cadmus and Agenor, kings of old.
I pray god that to those who do not do these things
no crop may spring up from the ground, nor children
274 from their wives, but they be destroyed in suffering
more hateful than that which holds us now.
But to you other people of Cadmus,
to however many approve what I say,
may Justice and all the gods stay with you
280 always as your ally.
CHORUS:
 Just as you adjured me under a curse, my lord,
so shall I speak. For neither did I kill
nor am I able to show the killer.
But it is the task of the one who sent it,
285 Phoebus, to say whoever has done this thing.
OEDIPUS:
 You have spoken justly, but no man can
compel the gods when they are unwilling.
CHORUS:
 I would say things secondary to this,
but things which, I think, ought to be said.
OEDIPUS:
290 And if there are matters tertiary to it,
do not fail to say them also.
CHORUS:
 I know that my lord Tiresias most always
sees the same as my lord Apollo; from him one
investigating this might learn the wisest things.
OEDIPUS:
295 But this has not been neglected! No,

even this I have done, for I sent two guides
after Creon mentioned him, and it is only
surprising that he is not already here.
CHORUS:
There are still other reports, though mute and old…
OEDIPUS:
300   What's this? I will investigate any story.
CHORUS:
It is said he died at the hands of bandits.
OEDIPUS:
So I have heard, but no one sees the one who saw.
CHORUS:
But if he has any fear at all, hearing
such curses as yours he will not remain here.
OEDIPUS:
305   But to a man who does not shrink from doing
the thing, a word will not be frightening.
CHORUS:
But the one to accuse him is here, for
already those men lead hither the godlike
seer, in whom alone of men lives the truth.
[Enter Tiresias, led by guides.]
OEDIPUS:
310   O Tiresias, who grasp all things,
both what can be learned and what is unspeakable,
both of heaven and treading the earth,
even if you cannot see, you still understand
what sickness plagues our city, and we find, lord,
315   you alone are our savior and defender.
For Phoebus, if you have not heard this also
from the messengers, in response to our question
said relief from this sickness would only come
if we should discover and punish well
320   the murderers of Laius or send them forth
as fugitives from this land. Therefore,
grudging nothing from the speech of birds
or something known from another sort
of divination, save yourself and the city,
325   and save me, and ward off all the pollution
from the dead man. We are in your hands,
and to help a man from troubles when you have
the power is the sweetest of labors.
TIRESIAS:
Alas, alas! How terrible to know
330   when it does not help the knower; for knowing this
well I let it slip—I should not have come here.

OEDIPUS:

What's this? How dispiritedly you have come!

TIRESIAS:

Send me home, for you will bear your lot easily
and I mine, if you will yield to me.

OEDIPUS:

335   You speak neither clearly nor helpfully
to this city, which raised you, if you guard your thoughts.

TIRESIAS:

For I see that your words come at the wrong time,
and since I would not suffer the same thing…

OEDIPUS:

No, by the gods, don't hold back what you know, when
340   all of us as suppliants bow down before you.

TIRESIAS:

None of you understand, but I shall never
reveal my own troubles, and so I shall not say yours.

OEDIPUS:

What are you saying? You will not explain
what you understand, but rather intend
345   to betray us and destroy the city.

TIRESIAS:

I cause no pain for you or myself. Why do you
vainly seek this? For you can learn nothing from me.

OEDIPUS:

You worst of wicked men! You would anger
a stone! Will you reveal nothing, but instead
350   show yourself unmovable and impractical?

TIRESIAS:

You have found fault with my anger, but your own,
living within you, you did not see, but blamed me.

OEDIPUS:

Who could hear such words and not grow angry,
words with which you dishonor the city?

TIRESIAS:

355   It will end the same, though I hide it in silence.

OEDIPUS:

Why not, then, tell me what will come anyway?

TIRESIAS:

I should explain no further. At these things,
if you wish, rage as much as your heart is able.

OEDIPUS:

Indeed, since I am so angry, I'll pass over none
360   of what I understand. Know that I think
you, too, had your hand in this deed and did it,
even though you did not kill with your own hands.
But if you could see, I would think the deed yours alone.

TIRESIAS:

    Really? I say to you: Abide by that decree
365   you made earlier, and from this day address
    neither these men here nor me, since you
    are the unholy polluter of this land.

OEDIPUS:

    Did you throw out this word so boldly?
    And where do you think you will escape it?

TIRESIAS:

370   I have escaped it, for I hold the potent truth.

OEDIPUS:

    Who told you to say this? It is no prophecy!

TIRESIAS:

    You did! For you forced me to speak unwillingly!

OEDIPUS:

    What do you mean? Speak again, that I may learn more.

TIRESIAS:

    Didn't understand before? Or do you test me?

OEDIPUS:

375   No, I don't know what you mean. Explain again.

TIRESIAS:

    I say that you slew the man whose slayer you seek.

OEDIPUS:

    You'll not rejoice to have said these evils twice.

TIRESIAS:

    Should I now say more, too, to anger you further?

OEDIPUS:

    Whatever you deem best; it will be said in vain.

TIRESIAS:

380   I say that you secretly have lived most foully
    with those who should be most dear, nor do you see
    to what extent of evil you have come.

OEDIPUS:

    Do you really think you can say this unpunished?

TIRESIAS:

    If there is any strength in the truth.

OEDIPUS:

385   There is, but not for you. You don't have this,
    since you are blind in your ears and mind and eyes.

TIRESIAS:

    You are truly pathetic, hurling these insults,
    which soon every man here will hurl at you.

OEDIPUS:

    You live in one single night, so that you can never
390   harm me or any other who sees the light.

TIRESIAS:

    No, for fate will not befall you at my doing;

.Apollo is enough, who works to see this done.
OEDIPUS:

Did Creon invent all this, or someone else?
TIRESIAS:

Creon is no burden on you, but you on yourself.
OEDIPUS:

395   O wealth and power and skill reaching
beyond skill, in a much-envied life
how much resentment gathers up inside you,
if for the sake of this realm, which the city put
into my hands as a gift, not something sought,
400   the trusted Creon, my friend from the beginning,
beguiles me and secretly desires to oust me,
engaging this craftily-working wizard,
this tricky beggar, who sees clearly only
for profit, but is blind when it comes to skill.
405   So tell me, when are you the wise seer?
How is it that, when the singing hound was here,
you never said how the citizens might be freed?
Even though the riddle could not be solved by
the first man who met it, but required prophecy.
410   But you did not come forth with this, knowing some clue
from birds or gods; instead I came along,
the idiot Oedipus! I stopped her,
working from intellect, not learning from birds.
The very man you're trying to overthrow,
415   thinking to stand beside Creon's throne.
I think you both—you and the one who framed these things—
will regret your urge to cleanse the land, but if you
were not so old, you'd learn now what such words earn.
CHORUS:

To us it seems that both this man's words
420   and your own, Oedipus, were said in anger.
But we must not dwell on such things. Only this:
how best we may fulfill the god's instructions.
TIRESIAS:

Even though you are a tyrant, I must at least
be granted an equal reply, for I, too,
425   have the right to speech. For I am no slave to you,
at all, but to Loxias, so I will not be
written off as Creon's client. I will reply,
since you reproach me as blind: You, even though you
see clearly, do not see the scope of your evil,
430   nor where you live, nor with whom you dwell.
Do you know your true descent? And secretly
you are an enemy to your own kin,

both under the earth and on it. Striking you
from both sides the terrible hounds of your mother's
435 and father's curse will drive you from this land;
though you see well enough now, then you will be blind.
What place will not be harbor to your shouting?
What Cithaeron will not echo back your cries,
when you truly understand that wedding?
440 You sailed home into it, no proper harbor
after such good sailing before! Nor do you
perceive the multitude of other evils,
which will make you the equal of your children.
Go ahead—insult Creon and this mouth of mine,
445 for of all mortals who will be destroyed
root and branch, there is not one sadder than you.
OEDIPUS:
    Am I to tolerate hearing this from this man?
    No, to hell with him! No! Turn around quickly
    and head back home, far away from here.
TIRESIAS:
450 I would not have come here, if you had not called me.
OEDIPUS:
    I did not know what nonsense you would speak,
    or I would hardly have sent for you.
TIRESIAS:
    Men like myself are born, to your eyes, fools,
    but to the parents who bore you we seem wise.
OEDIPUS:
455 To whom? Wait! Who on earth are my parents?
TIRESIAS:
    This very day will sire you and destroy you.
OEDIPUS:
    How riddling and foolish is all you say!
TIRESIAS:
    Then you of all people should understand it.
OEDIPUS:
    With these same taunts you now hurl, you will find me great.
TIRESIAS:
460 This same stroke, however, has destroyed you.
OEDIPUS:
    But if I saved this city, that doesn't matter.
TIRESIAS:
    Then I will leave. You, boy, lead me home.
OEDIPUS:
    Yes, go! When you are here, you are in the way,
    but rushing off you cannot pain us further.
TIRESIAS:
465 I will leave after I have said what I came to say,

not fearing your face, for you cannot destroy me.
I say to you: That man, whom you have long sought,
threatening him and naming as the murderer
of Laius, that man is here.

470 An immigrant in theory, soon he will be
revealed a native Theban, though he will not be
happy to learn it; for blind instead of seeing,
a beggar instead of rich he will travel
foreign earth, tapping it with his staff.

475 He will be revealed to live with his children
as brother and father both; and to his parents
he is both his wife's son and lord and his father's
fellow-sower and slayer. Go inside and
consider this. Should you find that I am lying,

480 you will prove I have no skill at prophecy.
[Exeunt omnes except Chorus]
CHORUS:
Str. 1 Who was it the oracle-speaking
rock of Delphi saw
committing the most unspeakable acts
with red hands?

485 Now, stronger than swift-footed horses,
he must deftly move his foot in flight.
For in arms against him leaps
the son of Zeus with fire and lightning
and, following after him,

490 the terrible, unerring Furies.
Ant. 1 For, recently from snowy Parnassus
shone clearly the call
to track by every possible method
the unknown man.

495 For he wanders through the wild wood
and up to caves like a bull upon the rocks,
miserable, with miserable foot, living alone,
seeking to escape the prophecies
of the prophetic navel of the world,

500 yet they forever hover, living, around him.
Str. 2 Therefore, terribly, terribly does
the wise bird-interpreter shake
me; I can neither approve nor deny,
but I am confused.

505 My heart hovers with expectation,
seeing neither here not in the future.
For never have I learned
that any quarrel lay between
the Labdacids and the son of Polybus,

510　neither before nor now,
　　which I could use as proof
　　or trust as touchstone
　　to go against the public fame of Oedipus
　　as I seek to help the Labdacids
515　in the undiscovered murder.
　　Ant. 2 But, though Zeus and Apollo know
　　the ways of mortals, among men,
　　there is no sure rule that a seer's opinion
　　counts more than mine,
520　though a man may surpass wisdom
　　with his own wisdom.
　　But, no, until I see an account
　　confirmed, never would I
　　agree when men are speaking slanders.
525　For once the winged maiden
　　came openly against him,
　　and he was seen wise
　　and found friendly to the city; therefore
　　by the judgment of my mind
530　never will he merit suspicion.
　　[Enter Creon from offstage.]

CREON:

　　Gentlemen of the city, I have learned that
　　the tyrant Oedipus has spoken terrible
　　words against me, so I am here, unable
　　to bear it. If in our present distress
535　he thinks he has suffered at my hands,
　　then I have no desire for long life
　　if I must bear this reputation, for
　　its damage affects no single part of my life,
　　rather the greatest part of it, if I am called
540　base in my city, base even by my friends.

CHORUS:

　　But, while this censure did come, it came quickly
　　and pushed out in anger, not from rational thoughts.

CREON:

　　Was it said that won over by advice
　　of mine the seer uttered false words?

CHORUS:

　　He said these things, but I do not know why.

545 CREON:

　　Did he make this accusation of me
　　with eyes set straight and from his right mind?

CHORUS:

　　I don't know, for what rulers do I do not see.

[Enter Oedipus from the palace.]
OEDIPUS:
  You there, how did you come here? Or do you have
550 so much daring that you approach my roof,
  although the patent murderer of this man
  and the manifest thief of my kingdom?
  Come then, say, by the gods, did you think me a fool
  or coward that you would weave these schemes?
555 That I would not discover this deed of yours
  creeping forth in treachery or, when I learned,
  I would not defend myself? Isn't this venture
  of yours foolish, to hunt tyranny
  without wealth or friends, a thing only captured
560 with a mob and cash?
CREON:
  Do you know what you should do? Hear an answer in
  response to your speech, then learn and judge for yourself.
OEDIPUS:
  You're a clever speaker, but I'm a bad student,
  for I have found you hostile and troubling to me.
CREON:
565 Hear now this one thing that I came to say.
OEDIPUS:
  'This one thing' should not be that you are not false.
CREON:
  If you think that stubbornness is of value
  apart from reason, you are a madman!
OEDIPUS:
  If you think a man who does his kinsman ill
570 will not pay the price, you are a fool.
CREON:
  I understand you think these things legitimate,
  but tell me what suffering you had at my hands.
OEDIPUS:
  Did you or did you not persuade me that I must
  send a man for the reverend seer?
CREON:
575 Even now I hold the same opinion.
OEDIPUS:
  How long a time has passed since Laius…
CREON:
  Did what deed? I do not understand.
OEDIPUS:
  … wanders invisible, conquered by death?
CREON:
  Many long years have been measured out since then.

OEDIPUS:

580   Next, was this seer in business at that time?

CREON:

Just as wise and revered as he is today.

OEDIPUS:

Did he say anything about me at the time?

CREON:

Never when I stood near and listened.

OEDIPUS:

Did you not hold an inquiry for the killer?

CREON:

585   We held one; how could we not? Yet we heard nothing.

OEDIPUS:

How, then, did this wise man not tell you anything?

CREON:

I don't know; I prefer to keep quiet
in matters when I don't comprehend them.

OEDIPUS:

There is one thing you could say with comprehension…

CREON:

590   What is it? If I know, I will not deny it.

OEDIPUS:

For whom, if he did not meet with you, did he say
that the death of Laius was my work?

CREON:

If he says that, then he himself knows, but I
would learn from you, as you now ask from me.

OEDIPUS:

595   Learn away! For I will not be caught as slayer.

CREON:

Well, then—are you still married to my sister?

OEDIPUS:

There is no denial of your question.

CREON:

Do you grant equal rule of this land to her?

OEDIPUS:

All that she desires she has from me.

CREON:

600   Am I not, then, the third, equal with you both?

OEDIPUS:

Indeed, for it's here you are proved a bad friend.

CREON:

Not if you would reckon with yourself as I do!
Consider this first: Would anyone choose
605   to rule with fear rather than to sleep untrembling,
if he could have the same power? And so I
myself was not born preferring to be tyrant

rather than do a tyrant's acts, nor was
any other who has good sense. For now I have
610   everything from you without fear; but if I
myself were ruler, I'd do much against my will.
How then could tyranny be sweeter to me
than trouble-free rule and sovereignty?
In no way will you find me so deceived
615   that I require fair things that hold no profit.
Now I can be with anyone; all salute me.
Now those wanting something from you call on me;
I am their whole path to success. How could I
exchange this life for the other? An evil mind
620   could not reason fairly. But I am no lover
of such schemes, anyway, nor would I ever
support it even if another did the deed.
And this will be the proof of it: go to Pytho
and learn the oracles, if I have
625   reported them correctly. Then, if you catch me
plotting something with the seer, don't kill me
with one vote, but with two, mine and yours.
But, don't blame me just like that, with mere suspicion.
For it is not just either to randomly
630   consider wicked men good or the good wicked.
I think that casting off a good friend is equal
even to throwing out one's own dear life.
In time, though, you will surely know these things, since
time alone shows that a man is just,
but you might learn he is bad in a single day.
635 CHORUS:
He spoke as one should to a man worried he will
fall, my lord, for quick thinkers are not safe ones.
OEDIPUS:
Whenever someone swiftly moves secret plots
against me, I must also counter-plot swiftly.
But if I wait in silence, these things will be
640   accomplished, not as his deeds, but my mistakes.
CREON:
What do you want? To cast me from this land?
OEDIPUS:
Hardly—I want you to die, not flee.
CREON:
You are the form of jealousy.
OEDIPUS:
You speak neither to concede nor to persuade?
CREON:
645   For I see well that you do not understand.

OEDIPUS:

I understand my own affairs well enough.

CREON:

You must know mine equally well.

OEDIPUS:

Not when they are false!

CREON:

Do you understand nothing?

OEDIPUS:

650   Yet, there must be rule.

CREON:

Not if ruled badly!

OEDIPUS:

O city, city!

CREON:

The city is mine, too, not yours alone!

CHORUS:

655   Stop, my lords! I see, at just the right moment,
Jocasta, coming from the house to you, with whom
you ought to settle this present quarrel.

[Enter Jocasta from the palace.]

JOCASTA:

Why, unhappy men, do you stir up this
unwelcome revolution of the tongue? Aren't you
660   ashamed to stir private evils when the land is
so sick? Come inside, and you, Creon, return home;
don't make this foolish grief into something big.

CREON:

Sister, this husband of yours, Oedipus, judges
terrible things for me, choosing two evils:
665   to forsake my fatherland or to die.

OEDIPUS:

I concede this, for, my lady, I caught him
basely conspiring against me with evil craft.

CREON:

May I live no more, but die accursed, if I have done
against you any of what you accuse me.

JOCASTA:

670   By the gods, Oedipus, believe this,
respecting this oath to the gods most of all,
then me and these who are here with you.

Str.

CHORUS:

Yield to these wishes and thoughts,
my lord, I pray.

OEDIPUS:

675   What would you have me yield?

CHORUS:
Respect a man who never before was foolish
and now is powerful from his oath.
OEDIPUS:
Do you know what you seek?
CHORUS:
I do.
OEDIPUS:
680   Then tell me why.
CHORUS:
Never should you cast out a friend who is bound with an oath,
dishonored, with only the charge of obscure words.
OEDIPUS:
Know well that when you seek this, you seek either
my destruction or exile from this land.
CHORUS:
685   No, by the foremost of all the gods,
the Sun! May I perish godless and friendless,
the worst fate, if I have this in mind!
But for me, the dying land eats away
at my ill-starred heart, if this fight between you two
690   will join itself to our old problems.
OEDIPUS:
Then let him go, since I must either die
or be driven by force from this land, dishonored.
For I pity your speech, since it is piteous,
not his. He will be hated wherever he goes.
CREON:
695   You are clearly hateful in yielding, and severe
when you pass from anger. But personalities
like yours are justly painful to themselves.
OEDIPUS:
Will you not let me be and go away?
CREON:
I'll go,
700   finding you ignorant, but just in their eyes.
[Exit Creon offstage.]
Ant.
CHORUS:
Lady, why do you hesitate
to take this man inside the house?
JOCASTA:
I would learn what has befallen.
CHORUS:
Suspicion through unknown words
705   came, and even an unjust word can bite.

JOCASTA:

From both of them?

CHORUS:

Yes.

JOCASTA:

But, what was the cause?

CHORUS:

It has done enough to me, enough when the land
710   already suffers so, that it should stay departed.

OEDIPUS:

Do you see where you've gotten, despite your good
intentions, trying to ease and blunt my anger?

CHORUS:

My lord, I've said it not only once,
but know that I am mad, helpless in rational thought,
715   if I forsake you,
who, when my dear country was lost in troubles,
set her upright again.
But now, become once more our guide to better things!

JOCASTA:

By the gods, tell me also, my lord,
720   what problem puts you in so much anger!

OEDIPUS:

Since I respect you, my wife, more than them, I shall
speak of Creon and what he plots against me.

JOCASTA:

Speak, if you will explain the quarrel clearly.

OEDIPUS:

He said I was the murderer of Laius.

JOCASTA:

725   Knowing this for himself, or learning from hearsay?

OEDIPUS:

He sent that criminal seer, since regarding
his own affairs, he keeps his tongue unstained.

JOCASTA:

You now, free yourself from these matters;
listen to me and learn why nothing mortal
730   can show you anything of prophecy.
I shall tell a quick tale to prove my words.
A prophecy came to Laius once—I won't say
from Apollo himself, but from his servants —
that death would come to him from his child,
735   whoever was born to him from me. But then,
just as the report is, some foreign brigands
slew him where the three wagon-roads meet.
Yet three days had not passed from the birth of my child,

when that man, binding his ankles together,
740 sent him in another's hands into the wild
of the mountain. And so Apollo brought about
neither that he slay his father nor that Laius
suffer the terrible thing he feared from his child.
Such things the speeches of seers predict,
745 you should ignore; for whatever the god
requires, he himself will easily reveal.
OEDIPUS:
Hearing you just now, my lady, how
my soul wanders, how my mind shakes me!
JOCASTA:
What care compels you to say such a thing?
OEDIPUS:
750 I thought I heard you say this: that Laius
was cut down where the three wagon-roads meet.
JOCASTA:
So it was announced, nor has it changed at all.
OEDIPUS:
And where is the place where he suffered this?
JOCASTA:
The land is called Phocis, and a split road
755 leads to it both from Delphi and from Daulia.
OEDIPUS:
And how long has passed since these things happened?
JOCASTA:
It was announced in the city just
before you took the rule of this land.
OEDIPUS:
O Zeus, why have you willed me to do this?
JOCASTA:
760 What is it, Oedipus, that grips your heart?
OEDIPUS:
Do not question me further, but tell me:
What did Laius look like, how old was he?
JOCASTA:
Tall, his hair just sprinkled with white like snow,
though his figure was not far from yours.
OEDIPUS:
765 Alas, alas! It seems that I have just cast
myself unknowing under terrible curses!
JOCASTA:
Why say that? I tremble to look at you, my lord!
OEDIPUS:
I am terribly afraid the prophet can see.
You will prove it, if you tell me one thing further.

JOCASTA:

770   Though I still tremble, I shall speak what you ask me.

OEDIPUS:

Did he go with a small escort, or having
a large bodyguard, as befits a prince?

JOCASTA:

There were five men in all, among them a herald,
and a single chariot that carried Laius.

OEDIPUS:

775   Alas! Already matters are clear! Who was it
who announced these matters to you, my lady?

JOCASTA:

A servant, who returned the sole survivor.

OEDIPUS:

And does he chance to still be at the palace?

JOCASTA:

No, indeed. For when he returned from there
780   and saw you holding power and Laius lost,
he grasped my hand and beseeched me to send
him to the country to tend the flocks, so that
he would be far from the sight of this city.
This I did, for he was worthy, although a slave,
785   to take even greater grace than this.

OEDIPUS:

How quickly could he return to us here?

JOCASTA:

He could be here now! But why do you order this?

OEDIPUS:

I fear myself, lady, lest I have
said too much, and so I wish to see him.

JOCASTA:

790   But he will come! Now, however, I deserve
to learn what holds so badly for you, my lord.

OEDIPUS:

Nor will you be deprived, when I am gone so far
into expectations. For how could I speak to one
more important than you as I meet such fortune?
795   My father is Polybus of Corinth,
my mother Merope of the line of Dorus.
I was thought the greatest of the citizens there,
before chance befell me, worthy of marvel,
but not worthy, at least, of my energy.
800   At a banquet a man overwhelmed by drink
called me a fraud in whom I claimed for my father.
That day I tried to hold in my anger,
but the next day I went home and asked

my mother and father, and they angrily
805 treated the insult as the speech of a drunkard.
I rejoiced with them both at this, but still
it chafed me always, for the rumor spread far.
Unknown to my mother and father I set out
to Delphi, and Phoebus sent me away
810 as unworthy of the answers I had sought,
but telling me other terrible, awful things—
that I must sleep with my mother, and
that I would bring to light a brood unbearable
for men to see, and that I must be the slayer
815 of the father who sired me. I heard and fled,
henceforth to share with Corinth only the stars,
where I would never see completed
the disgrace of those evil oracles of mine.
In my travels I came to that place
820 in which you say that your king was lost.
And to you, lady, I shall speak the truth.
When traveling near that very triple road,
a herald and a man riding there
in a chariot, like the man you described,
825 encountered me. Both the one in front
and the old man himself drove me from the road
with force. In my anger I struck the driver,
turning me off the road, and the old man,
when he saw, watched me as I passed the chariot
830 and struck me on the head with the two-pronged goad.
But he more than paid for it and soon was struck
by the scepter from this very hand, lying
on his back, at once thrown out of the car.
I killed them all. But if that stranger
835 had some connection with Laius,
who would be more wretched than this man you see?
What man would be more hateful to God,
the man whom no man, foreign or citizen,
may receive at home, nor anyone address,
840 but all must cast from their house? And no other
called down such curses on me than myself!
I even stain the dead man's bed with the hands
at which he perished. Am I so evil?
Not entirely unholy? If I must flee,
845 then in my flight I may neither see my own kin
nor step inside my fatherland, or I must
take my mother in marriage and kill my father
Polybus, who raised and sired me. Who would not,
judging these things, say truly in my case

850 that they come from a cruel divinity?
Never, o holy reverence of the gods,
never may I see this day, but I would rather
be blotted out from humanity before
I saw this stain of my doom arrive upon me.
CHORUS:
855 Although these things trouble us, my lord, until
you learn from the one who was present, have hope.
OEDIPUS:
Indeed, this much of hope is left to me:
only to await that man, the herdsman.
JOCASTA:
And what do you want of him, when he appears?
OEDIPUS:
860 I shall tell you; for if he is found saying
the same tale as you, I shall have escaped this woe.
JOCASTA:
What special tale did you hear from me?
OEDIPUS:
You said he reported that brigands
killed Laius. If, then, he still says the same
865 number, I did not kill him, for surely one man
could not be equal to many. But if he
clearly names a single man, a lone traveler,
then already this deed comes down upon me.
JOCASTA:
Yet, know that his account stood thus, and he cannot
870 take it back now, for the city heard these things,
not I alone. But even if he does alter
something from his previous story,
not even thus, my lord, will he bring to
light Laius' killer truly accomplished,
875 who, indeed, Loxias said must die at the hands
of my child. Yet my poor boy never slew
him, but rather perished himself long before.
And so I would not look to prophecies,
not here or anywhere else.
OEDIPUS:
880 You reason well, but, nevertheless, send someone
to fetch the servant, and don't neglect it.
JOCASTA:
And soon I shall, but let us go inside the house,
for I would do nothing but that it is your wish.
[Exeunt omnes.]
CHORUS:
Str. 1 If only fate may find me still acting

885 with reverent holiness in words
and all my deeds, for which lofty laws
are ordained, born
in heaven above, their only
father Olympus,
890 no mortal form of men
bore them, nor does
forgetfulness ever lull them to sleep.
In them is a great god, who does not grow old.
Ant. 1 Audacity sires the tyrant—audacity, if
895 filled up rashly with all excess,
neither timely nor useful,
scaling the highest eaves
rushes into precipitous necessity
where it suffers from its ill-placed foot.
900 I pray that God
will never end the struggle
that is good for the city.
I will never cease clinging to God as my protector.
Str. 2 But if someone goes
905 disdainful in hands or speech,
nor fearing Justice,
nor revering the seats of the holy gods,
let a bad fate take him,
the wages of unlucky insolence,
910 unless he reaps his profit justly
and retreats from impious acts,
or if he touches untouchable things in his folly.
What man can protect himself, warding
away the shafts of anger when such things happen?
915 For if deeds like this are honored,
why must I dance?
Ant. 2 No longer will I worship
at the inviolate navel of the world,
nor at Abae,
920 nor ever in the Olympian shrine,
unless these events are made
manifestly clear to all mortals.
But, o powerful one, if you are correctly called that,
Zeus, who rule all things, may they not elude
925 you and your eternal, deathless empire!
For already the old prophecies of Laius
are waning and being set aside.
Apollo does not seem to be honored;
faith wanders, lost.
[Enter Jocasta from the palace.]

JOCASTA:

930　Lords of this land, the thought came to me
to supplicate the shrines of the gods, taking
in my hands these wreaths and offerings of incense.
For Oedipus unduly twists his spirit
with every sort of grief, not like a man
935　of reason, judging new matters by the old,
but whoever talks has him, if he speaks his fears.
And so, since my assurances achieve nothing,
I have come as a suppliant with these tokens,
to you, Lycean Apollo, for you are nearest,
940　so that you will render us unpolluted,
since now we are all afraid, seeing him
so shaken, who is pilot of our ship.

[Enter Messenger from offstage.]

MESSENGER:

Could I learn from you, strangers, where lies
the house of King Oedipus? Or, indeed,
945　tell me where he himself is, if you know.

CHORUS:

This is his roof; he himself is within, stranger.
Here is his wife and mother of his children.

MESSENGER:

Then may there be happiness to you, now
and always, since you are his wedded wife.

JOCASTA:

950　And likewise to you also, stranger, which you earn
through your welcome words; but explain what
you have come needing and what you wish to tell him.

MESSENGER:

Good tidings for your house and your lord, my lady.

JOCASTA:

What tidings are these, and whence have you come?

MESSENGER:

955　From Corinth. The word I shall speak—at first you might
rejoice; how could you not? But you may also mourn.

JOCASTA:

What's this? What twofold power do you hold?

MESSENGER:

The people of the land of the Isthmus
make him their king, as it is announced there.

JOCASTA:

960　But why? Does old Polybus no longer rule there?

MESSENGER:

No, indeed, for death holds him in the tomb.

JOCASTA:

What did you say? Polybus is dead, old man?

MESSENGER:

    If I do not speak the truth, I should die here.

JOCASTA:

    Maid, won't you go inside as quick as you can,

965   and tell the master of these things? O prophecies

    of the gods, where are you? This man Oedipus

    has long feared and fled lest he kill him, and now

    this very man has died by chance and not by him.

    [Enter Oedipus from the palace.]

OEDIPUS:

    My dearest Jocasta, my wife, why did you

970   send for me to come here from the house?

JOCASTA:

    Listen to this man, and discover in his words

    where the august prophecies of God have come.

OEDIPUS:

    But who is he, and why would he speak to me?

JOCASTA:

    He is from Corinth, announcing that your father

975   Polybus is no more, but has perished.

OEDIPUS:

    What's this, stranger? You yourself tell me.

MESSENGER:

    If I must state this exactly to you first,

    know well that the man is gone, deceased.

OEDIPUS:

    By treachery, or meeting some disease?

MESSENGER:

980   A small turn of the scale lays old bodies to rest.

OEDIPUS:

    Destroyed by disease, it seems, the poor man.

MESSENGER:

    Yes, and by the long measuring of his years.

OEDIPUS:

    Well, well! Why, my wife, would anyone look

    to the prophesying hearth of Pytho or to

985   the shrieking birds above, under whose guidance

    I was to kill my own father? But, he died

    and sleeps below the earth; and I am here,

    without touching a spear—unless somehow he

    perished from longing for me, and thus died by me.

990   But still, Polybus has taken those prophecies

    as they are—worthless—with him and lies in Hades.

JOCASTA:

    Did I not predict it thus earlier?

OEDIPUS:

    You did, but I was led by my fear.

JOCASTA:

    Now, then, toss none of these matters in your heart.

OEDIPUS:

995   And how can I not dread my mother's bed?

JOCASTA:

    Why should a person fear when the ways of fortune
    are supreme, when there is no clear foresight?
    It's best to live at random, however one can.
    Do not worry you will wed your mother,
1000   for many mortals already have lain with
    their mothers in dreams. Rather, the one for whom
    these things are nothing bears life easiest.

OEDIPUS:

    All these matters you would explain well,
    if my mother were dead; but since she lives,
1005   I must fear, however prettily you speak.

JOCASTA:

    Surely your father's tomb is also a bright sign?

OEDIPUS:

    Bright, I agree, but my fear is of her who lives.

MESSENGER:

    And who is this woman who so frightens you?

OEDIPUS:

    Merope, old man, with whom Polybus lived.

MESSENGER:

1010   But what in her moves you to such fear?

OEDIPUS:

    A terrible prophecy sent by God, stranger.

MESSENGER:

    Tell me—or is it lawful that another know?

OEDIPUS:

    Certainly: Loxias once told me
    that I must sleep with my own mother and
1015   shed paternal blood with my own hands.
    Thus for a long time I have kept Corinth
    far from me—and prosperously, but still
    your parents' eyes are the sweetest thing to see.

MESSENGER:

    Dreading those things, then, you are exiled from that place?

OEDIPUS:

1020   And wishing not to murder my father, old man!

MESSENGER:

    Why, then, have I not freed you from this fear,
    my lord, since indeed I come in good will?

OEDIPUS:

    Indeed, you would take deserved grace from me.

MESSENGER:

    I came for this very purpose, so that when you
1025   returned home I would have done well by you!

OEDIPUS:

    But I will never go where my parents are!

MESSENGER:

    O child, you clearly do not know what you do.

OEDIPUS:

    How's that, old man? By the gods, teach me!

MESSENGER:

    If it is because of this you flee your home…

OEDIPUS:

1030   I dread that Phoebus accomplish these things for me.

MESSENGER:

    Or that you might take pollution from your parents?

OEDIPUS:

    This very thing, old sir, has ever been my fear.

MESSENGER:

    Don't you know you may justly fear nothing?

OEDIPUS:

    How so, if I am the child of those parents?

MESSENGER:

1035   Because Polybus is nothing to you by birth!

OEDIPUS:

    How can you say this? Did Polybus not sire me?

MESSENGER:

    You have nothing from him, no more than from me.

OEDIPUS:

    How can my father be equal to nothing?

MESSENGER:

    That man did not beget you, no more than I!

OEDIPUS:

1040   But then…why did he call me his child?

MESSENGER:

    Know that he took you as a gift from my own arms.

OEDIPUS:

    And still he loved me greatly, though not his own?

MESSENGER:

    His former childlessness persuaded him.

OEDIPUS:

    But you—had you purchased me or found me by chance?

MESSENGER:

1045   I found you in the woody glens of Cithaeron.

OEDIPUS:

    Why were you traveling in that place?

MESSENGER:

    At that time I had the care of mountain flocks.

OEDIPUS:

Why, you were a shepherd, a nomad for hire?

MESSENGER:

And also at that time, my child, your savior.

OEDIPUS:

1050   What misfortune was mine when you found me?

MESSENGER:

Your ankles should testify to that.

OEDIPUS:

Oh, why must you mention that old affliction?

MESSENGER:

I freed you when your feet were pierced at the ankles.

OEDIPUS:

Such terrible disgrace I took from my cradle.

MESSENGER:

1055   Such that you were named from this misfortune.

OEDIPUS:

Tell me, by god, from my mother or father?

MESSENGER:

I don't know; he who gave you to me would know this.

OEDIPUS:

You took me from someone, didn't find me yourself?

MESSENGER:

No, another shepherd gave you to me.

OEDIPUS:

1060   Who was he? Could you describe him clearly?

MESSENGER:

I believe he was called one of Laius' people.

OEDIPUS:

The former king of this very land?

MESSENGER:

Exactly—he was a herdsman of that man.

OEDIPUS:

And is this man still alive, so I could see him?

MESSENGER:

1065   You who live here would know that better than I.

OEDIPUS:

Does anyone standing here now know
the herdsman of whom he speaks? You might
have seen him in the fields or even here! Tell me,
for now it is time for this to be learned at last!

CHORUS:

1070   I know of none other than the one from the fields
whom you wanted to see earlier, but
Jocasta here could say these things best of all.

OEDIPUS:

Lady, do you know that man, whom just now
we summoned? Is he the one this man speaks of?

JOCASTA:

1075   What does it matter whom he means? Ignore it.
Don't think about it—it will all end in vain.

OEDIPUS:

It is impossible that when I have found
such signs, I will not discover my birth.

JOCASTA:

No, by the gods! If indeed you care for your
1080   own life, do not go after this! I grieve enough.

OEDIPUS:

Cheer up, for even if I am revealed a slave
three generations back, you will not be proved base.

JOCASTA:

All the same, obey me, I pray. Do not do this.

OEDIPUS:

I cannot be persuaded not to learn this clearly.

JOCASTA:

1085   Yet I understand it well—what I say is best.

OEDIPUS:

What you say is best has long annoyed me.

JOCASTA:

Unlucky man, may you never know who you are!

OEDIPUS:

Will someone go and bring the shepherd to me?
Let this one rejoice in her own rich birth.

JOCASTA:

1090   Alas, alas—unhappy man! This alone can
I say to you, and nothing else ever after.

[Exit Jocasta into the palace.]

CHORUS:

Why ever did your wife go away,
Oedipus, stirred by wild grief? I fear that
something evil will burst out from that silence.

OEDIPUS:

1095   Let it all burst out, if it must! As for me,
though it be small, I wish to know my stock.
But she, since a woman is proud of such things,
she is troubled by this low birth of mine.
But I deem myself the child of Chance,
1100   who gives good things, and I will not be dishonored.
She is my mother, and my brothers,
the Months, have seen me both small and great.
Being born what I am, I could never be
another, so I should seek out my descent.

CHORUS:

1105   *Str.* If I am a prophet
    and wise with intelligence,
    by heaven, o Cithaeron, you will surely know
    at tomorrow's full moon
    that you are the fellow countryman of Oedipus
1110   and, as nurse and mother, made him grow.
    We will sing and dance for you, for you
    have served our kings!
    Hail, Phoebus, to you also
    may these things be pleasing.
1115   *Ant.* Who bore you, child,
    which of the long-lived maids
    was the mountain-ranging bride of Pan?
    for to him all the beast-pasturing highlands are dear.
    Perhaps the lord of Cyllene
1120   or the Bacchic god
    who dwells on mountain tops,
    will accept you, foundling,
    from one of the glancing-eyed nymphs,
    with whom he plays most of all.

OEDIPUS:

1125   If I must surmise the identity of one
    I've never met, aged sirs, I think I see
    the shepherd we have long been seeking. For measured
    by his great old age he could be this man,
    and moreover those leading him I know as
1130   my own servants; but you should have surer
    knowledge than I, as you've seen the man before.
    [Enter Shepherd.]

CHORUS:

    Yes, I recognize him. Know it clearly, for if
    any man were Laius' trusted shepherd, it's him.

OEDIPUS:

    First I will ask you, the Corinthian stranger,
1135   is this the man you meant?

MESSENGER:

    That very man you see.

OEDIPUS:

    You there, old man, look at me and say
    whatever I ask you: Were you once Laius' man?

SHEPHERD:

    Yes, his slave, not purchased, but born to his house.

OEDIPUS:

1140   What work and what livelihood was your care?

SHEPHERD:

For most of my life I have followed flocks.

OEDIPUS:

In what regions did you live most of the time?

SHEPHERD:

Sometimes Cithaeron, sometimes places near it.

OEDIPUS:

Did you see this man at some point and know him?

SHEPHERD:

1145   See him doing what? Who are you talking about?

OEDIPUS:

This one who's here! Have you ever met him?

SHEPHERD:

Not such that my memory quickly answers yes.

MESSENGER:

This, at least, is nothing strange, master, but I
clearly remember him; and I know well that
1150   he remembers when that same spot on Cithaeron
he grazed with two flocks and I with one.
I was his neighbor there three whole times,
six months apiece, from spring to autumn.
Then in winter I drove my flocks to the
1155   fold and he to the stables of Laius.
Didn't it happen just like I said?

SHEPHERD:

You speak the truth, although a long time has passed.

MESSENGER:

Then say now, do you remember giving me then
a child to raise for myself as my foster-son?

SHEPHERD:

1160   What does it matter? Why do you ask this question?

MESSENGER:

Here is that man, my friend, who was so little then!

SHEPHERD:

Go to hell! Will you not be silent?

OEDIPUS:

Ah! Do not reproach him, old man, when
your words deserve more reproach than him.

SHEPHERD:

1165   But what, o best of masters, have I done wrong?

OEDIPUS:

You do not discuss the child whom he researches.

SHEPHERD:

Because he speaks without knowing, but acts in vain.

OEDIPUS:

If you'll not speak for my favor, you'll speak in pain!

SHEPHERD:
 By the gods, surely you will not hurt an old man!
OEDIPUS:
1170 Quickly—someone twist back this man's arms!
SHEPHERD:
 Unhappy me! Why? What do you desire to learn?
OEDIPUS:
 Did you give him the child he mentioned?
SHEPHERD:
 I did, but I should have died that day!
OEDIPUS:
 If you don't talk, you'll come to that today!
SHEPHERD:
1175 I will be destroyed even more if I do talk.
OEDIPUS:
 This man, it seems, is trying to stall.
SHEPHERD:
 No, no! I said long ago that I did give it.
OEDIPUS:
 Where did you get it? From your house or another's?
SHEPHERD:
 It was not mine, but I took it from another.
OEDIPUS:
1180 From one of the citizens here, and from what house?
SHEPHERD:
 By the gods, master, do not inquire further!
OEDIPUS:
 You are dead if I have to ask it again!
SHEPHERD:
 Then…he was from the house of Laius.
OEDIPUS:
 A slave, or one born to his family?
SHEPHERD:
1185 Oh, I am about to say something terrible.
OEDIPUS:
 And I to hear it, but still it must be heard!
SHEPHERD:
 He was said to be the child of that man himself,
 but your wife could explain the situation best.
OEDIPUS:
 Because she gave it to you?
SHEPHERD:
1190 Yes, my lord.
OEDIPUS:
 To what end?
SHEPHERD:
 So that I would kill it.

OEDIPUS:

Its mother dared this?

SHEPHERD:

Fearing evil prophecies.

OEDIPUS:

1195   What were they?

SHEPHERD:

That he would kill his parents.

OEDIPUS:

Why, then, did you entrust him to this old man?

SHEPHERD:

Out of pity, master. It seemed he would bear him

away to another land, his home. But he

1200   rescued him into the greatest evils. For if

you are who he says, know that you were born cursed.

OEDIPUS:

Alas, alas. It's all come out so clearly.

Light, let me see the last of you now,

surrounded by those I ought to avoid—

1205   born from them, living with them, killing them.

[Exit Oedipus into the palace.]

CHORUS:

Str.1 Oh, the generations of man—

while you live, I count you

as worthless, equal to nothing.

For who, what man

1210   wins more happiness than

just its shape

and the ruin when that shape collapses?

With your example, your fate, your self,

suffering Oedipus,

1215   I call nothing of mortals blessed.

Ant. 1 He shot with unsurpassed aim

and gained every kind of

happiness, o Zeus; destroying

the riddle-singer,

1220   the maiden with twisted talons,

like a tower

he stood and defended my land from death.

Since that time he has been called my king

and beyond all men

1225   was honored, ruling in glorious Thebes.

Str. 2 But now, who could be called

more wretched, more bound to toil and wild madness,

more the paradigm of life's reversals?

Oh, famous Oedipus,

1230 you alone sufficed to lie
as son, father, and bridegroom;
how was it, how, poor man,
could your paternal furrows
bear you in such long silence?

1235 *Ant. 2* All-seeing time discovered you unwilling,
it judged long ago your marriage that is no marriage,
you, both the siring and sired.
Alas, o child of Laius,
if only, if only we had never
1240 set eyes on you!
My grief is like a libation poured from my mouth.
But to speak the truth, because of you I could breath again
and because of you I sink my eyes into sleep.

[Enter Servant from the palace.]

SERVANT:
Gentlemen, of this land always the most honored,
1245 what deeds you shall hear, what deeds you shall see, and what
grief you will take upon yourselves, if you still care
as kin for the house of the Labdacids.
For I think that neither the Danube nor Volga
could wash through this house to purify all
1250 it conceals, but soon will come into the light
evils both willing and unwilling, but even
the self-chosen of these pains will grieve you greatly.

CHORUS:
What we knew before did not fail to be
grievous, but what will you say in addition?

SERVANT:
1255 It is the fastest of words both to say and
to learn: Our divine queen, Jocasta, is dead.

CHORUS:
O poor woman! By whatever cause?

SERVANT:
By herself! But, of what has been done the worst pain
you will avoid, for you cannot see it.
1260 Still, as much as I can remember
of that poor woman's woes you shall learn.
After she had gone into her chamber, frenzied,
she threw herself onto her bridal couch,
snatching at her hair with both hands. Bolting the doors
1265 from the inside, she called on Laius, so long
a corpse, remembering that ancient creation,
by which he himself died and left her, as mother,
to his offspring for their own evil brood.
She groaned over her bed, where twice doomed she had

1270   born husband from husband, children from her child.
When she died, I do not know; for Oedipus
burst in shouting, and so we did not note her doom,
but were looking at him, ranging about.
He paced back and forth, asking us to bring a sword,
1275   asking where she had gone, his wife who was no wife,
but a doubly-ploughed field, mother of him
and his children. Some god led him on,
for it was none of us men who were nearby;
shouting terribly, as if led there by some guide,
1280   he was driven to the doors, and from their sockets
he forced the groaning bolts and fell into the room.
Then inside we saw the woman hanging,
all twisted up in a twisted noose.
When he saw her, the wretch shouted awfully
1285   and cut her down from the noose. When she lay
on the ground, poor thing, it was terrible to see.
For he removed from her garment the golden
brooches which she was wearing; he lifted them
and struck the sockets of his own eyes,
1290   shouting that they would not see either the evils
he had suffered or the evils he had done,
now only in darkness could they see those whom
they must not see, in darkness could they mistake
those whom they wanted to recognize.
1295   Repeating these things, many times and not once
only he raised his hands and struck his eyes. At once
his bloody eyeballs moistened his cheeks.
In torrent together flowed the drops of blood;
all at once a dark storm of blood like hail rained down.
1300   From two, not one alone, these evils burst forth,
evils wedded together for husband and wife.
Their old happiness that was before was justly
called happiness, but now on this one day
mourning, madness, death, disgrace, every way
1305   to name all evils—none have been absent.
CHORUS:
Does the poor wretch now have some rest from evil?
SERVANT:
He shouts at us to open the doors and reveal
to all the people of Cadmus the parricide,
and his mother's…what he said I will not repeat.
1310   He wants to cast himself from the land and not
stay at home accursed with his own curses.
He lacks, however, strength and a guide,
for the pain is greater than he can bear.

But he will show you also, for the doors
1315   are opening. Soon you will see a sight
that even his enemy would pity.
[Enter Oedipus from the palace with attendants.]
CHORUS:
O suffering terrible for men to see,
o most terrible of all I have
encountered! What mania, poor wretch,
1320   stood by you? What spirit
leapt from beyond the highest places
onto your unhappy fate?
Alas, alas, unfortunate man,
I cannot look at you,
1325   though I wish to ask many things,
to learn and ponder them;
how you make me shudder and fear!
OEDIPUS:
Ah! Ah! How miserable is my life!
Where does my pain take me?
1330   How does my voice rush about me?
O doom, how you've pounced!
CHORUS:
Onto horror that can neither be heard nor viewed.
Str. 1
OEDIPUS:
Oh, darkness!
This cloud of mine, abominable, approaching ineffable,
1335   unconquered, driven on by a fatally favorable wind.
Sorrow!
And still more sorrow—Upon me fall together
so many stinging goads and the memory of evils.
CHORUS:
And it is no wonder that in such woes
1340   you suffer doubly and doubly cry aloud.
Ant. 1
OEDIPUS:
Oh, my friend!
You are still my only companion, for
still you remain by me, tending the blind man.
Sorrow!
1345   For I have not missed your presence, but, although
in darkness, I recognize your voice clearly.
CHORUS:
O agent of terrors, how could you dare to
put out your eyes like that? What god set you to it?
Str. 2

OEDIPUS:

    Apollo, my friends—these things are Apollo,

1350   who brought to pass these evil, evil sufferings of mine.
    But no man struck me with his hand,
    but I myself dared it.
    For why must I see,
    I for whom no sight is sweet?

CHORUS:

1355   Indeed, it is as you say.

OEDIPUS:

    What, then, could be worth seeing to me,
    or lovable, what word addressed to me
    could I hear gladly, friends?
    Lead me into exile quickly,

1360   lead me away, friends, completely destroyed,
    the most accursed, and to the gods
    the most hated of men!

CHORUS:

    Equally wretched in your mind and your
    misfortune, how I wish I had never known you.
    Ant. 2

OEDIPUS:

1365   Let him die who took off the fierce fetters,
    feeding off my feet, and rescued and saved
    me from my death, no good deed for me!
    For if I had died then,
    I would not have brought

1370   so much pain to my friends or me!

CHORUS:

    It is my wish, too, that it have been thus.

OEDIPUS:

    I'd not then be my father's slayer,
    nor called the groom of her whence I was born.
    Abandoned by the gods, child of sacrilege,

1375   sharing the source of those I myself sired.
    Were some evil greater still than evil,
    this, too, would be Oedipus' lot.

CHORUS:

    for you are better not living than living blind.

OEDIPUS:

    Do not tell me that these things were not

1380   done well, nor offer me further counsel.
    For I don't know with what eyes I could look
    and see my father when I go down to Hell,
    nor again my poor mother; to those two
    my deeds are beyond what hanging could punish.

1385   Or is the sight of my children desirable
for me to see, sprouting as they sprouted?
Surely never to those eyes of mine!
Nor the city nor citadel, nor the holy
shrines of the gods, from which I, the worst of men,

1390   removed myself, myself decreeing
that all expel the impious one, revealed
unholy by the gods and, now, of Laius' race.
Exposing such defilement as this,
did I intend to see them with my own eyes?

1395   Not at all. Rather if I could somehow block
my hearing from the ears, I would not hold back
from fully shutting off this wretched frame of mine,
so that I'd be blind and hear nothing, for to live
outside comprehension of these woes would be sweet.

1400   Oh, Cithaeron! Why did you accept me? Why did
you not kill me at once, so that I would never
reveal to men my origins? O Polybus
and Corinth and my old ancestral home—
so-called—in what a pretty festering

1405   of evils you brought me up! For now I
find myself evil and born from evil people.
O three paths and hidden groves and the
narrow oak coppice at the triple crossroads,
which drank my own blood from my father

1410   from my own hands, do you still remember me?
What deeds I performed in your presence,
what deeds I was still to do! O marriage, marriage,
you brought me forth, and afterwards again
you harvested that same seed and revealed

1415   father-brothers, children of kin blood,
brides who were wives and mothers, and all else
counted the most shameful acts by men.
But, since these matters are as foully said as done,
by the gods, quickly hide me from the sight of men

1420   somehow, or kill me or cast me into the sea,
where you will never see me again.
Go, deem it worthy to touch a poor man!
Yield, do not fear; for my evils are
such that no one of men can bear but me.

CHORUS:

1425   No, Creon is here, the right one to decide
whether to act or advise on what you ask; since
he alone remains to guard our land in your stead.
[Enter Creon from offstage.]

OEDIPUS:

Alas! What can I say to this man?

What real faith can he have in me? For in all
1430   that went before I am found false to him.
    CREON:
       I have not come to mock you, Oedipus,
       nor to scold you for some previous wrong.
       [He addresses the attendants.]
       But you, if you feel no shame before the races
       of men, then revere at least the nourishing
1435   light of lord Helios, and do not thus
       show this blight unconcealed, which neither
       earth nor holy rain nor light accept.
       Take him into the house as quick as you can,
       for it is right for only blood relatives
1440   to see and hear familial evils.
    OEDIPUS:
       By the gods, since you've cheated my expectations
       and come as the best of men to me, the worst,
       grant me this; I ask for you and not for me.
    CREON:
       What is this thing you need so greatly?
    OEDIPUS:
1445   Cast me immediately from this land,
       somewhere I can avoid all mortal speech.
    CREON:
       Know well that I would do this, but first I
       must learn from the god what must be done.
    OEDIPUS:
       But his entire prophecy was made clear;
1450   destroy the patricide, the accursed, me!
    CREON:
       It was said thus, but still, where we stand
       it is better to learn what must be done.
    OEDIPUS:
       You would ask on behalf of one so wretched?
    CREON:
       Yes, for now even you should bear faith to the god.
    OEDIPUS:
1455   Then I enjoin you and make this request:
       to her…who is inside…bury her as you will,
       rightly will you act on behalf of your own—
       but as for me, may this, my native city,
       suffer me to dwell here while I live,
1460   but let me to dwell in the mountains, with my own
       famous Cithaeron, which my mother and
       father while they lived appointed as my tomb,
       so that I may die as those two wished.
       Although this much at least I know: No disease

1465 nor anything else can kill me, for I would not
have been saved from death, but for some dire fate.
This destiny of mine, let it go where it may,
but for my children, Creon—don't worry
over my sons; they are men, so that
1470 they will never lack a livelihood, wherever
they may be. But, for my poor little girls,
they've not so much as eaten a meal
apart from me; but whatever I touched,
those two always had a share in all of it.
1475 Worry over them, and most of all I beg you,
let me touch them with my hands and mourn our woes.
Please, my lord!
Please, o truly noble man, could my hands touch them,
I'd think I held them as I did when I could see.
[Servants lead onstage the two girls.]
1480 What's this now?
By the gods, do I somehow hear my two dear girls
crying? Has Creon pitied me and
sent to me the dearest of my offspring?
Is it true?

CREON:

1485 You are, for I am the one who prepared these things,
knowing the joy they have long brought you.

OEDIPUS:

Then may you be blessed, and for this meeting
may fate guard you better than it did me!
My children, where are you? Come here, come
1490 to these hands of mine that are siblings to yours,
hands that brought to this sad state the once
bright eyes of your begetting father,
who, children, neither seeing nor knowing was
proved your father from the same place he himself sprang.
1495 And I weep for you, although I cannot see you;
contemplating the bitterness of your lives,
the sort of life men will force you to live.
What sort of company will you keep in town?
What festivals will you attend that will not
1500 send you home in tears, instead of joy?
When you come to the age ripe for marriage,
who will he be who will run the risk, children,
to take for himself the reproaches that will
be banes for my parents and offspring alike?
1505 What evil is absent? Your father
slew his father; he ploughed his mother,
where he himself was sown, and he sired

you in the same fount where he himself was sired.
Such taunts you will hear, and then who will marry you?
1510 There is no one, my children, but surely
you must die untilled and unmarried.
Son of Menoeceus, since you alone are left
as father to them, for we who created them
have both been destroyed, do not allow them,
1515 your kin, to die unwed and beggars,
nor make them party to my evils;
but pity them, seeing how young they are
and bereft of everything, except for you.
Consent, noble one, and touch me with your hand.
1520 Oh, children, if you could understand, I would
give you so much advice; as it is, just pray
with me that you obtain a better life
than did the father who sired you.

CREON:
You have gone far enough in weeping; go inside.

OEDIPUS:
1525 I will, though sadly.

CREON:
All things are fair in time.

OEDIPUS:
Do you know my conditions?

CREON:
Speak; I shall learn them.

OEDIPUS:
Send me from this land.

CREON:
1530 You ask me what is God's to give.

OEDIPUS:
The gods hate me.

CREON:
Then they will grant your wish.

OEDIPUS:
Then you will do it?

CREON:
I'll say only what I think.

OEDIPUS:
1535 Then lead me away.

CREON:
Come, let go of the children.

OEDIPUS:
Do not take them from me!

CREON:
It is not your place to decide;

the power you had has not remained with you.

[Exeunt Creon and Oedipus with the attendants and children into the palace.]

CHORUS:

1540   People of our country Thebes, behold this Oedipus,
      who knew the famous riddle and was a most powerful man,
      whose fortunes all the citizens watched with emulation,
      how deep the sea of dire misfortune that has taken him!
      Therefore, it is necessary to call no man blessed
1545   as we await the final day, until he has reached
      the limit of life and suffered nothing grievous.

Questions for Discussion:

1. What did you learn from this tragedy about human nature and humanity?
2. Throughout the play, what morals are represented by the characters and their actions? Which are upheld? What morals are condemned?
3. From this play, psychoanalyst Sigmund Freud developed the term "Oedipal Complex." Spoiler alert: he uses this term to suggest than men have an unconscious desire to kill their father and wed their mother. Do you agree or disagree with this term? Do you think the play agrees or disagree with this term?
4. How do you think the meaning of the play would change is the sexes of the characters were reversed? Do you think Queen Oedipus would make the same decisions as King Oedipus? Explain and defend your answer.

Literary Elements:

1. What is Oedipus Rex's hamartia?
2. Which characters have hubris? Why?
3. Who does the Chorus represent in the play? What do you think they feel about the events of the play?
4. What catharsis is felt by the audience at the conclusion of the play?

Trifles

Susan Glaspell

Author Biography: Once called "American drama's best kept secret," Susan Glaspell was born in Davenport, Iowa in 1876, where she accomplished many things thought of as unorthodox for a woman of her time: she enrolled in college, competed in state debate tournaments, and, directly after graduation, began working as a journalist covering politics and murders. She soon turned, though, to writing fiction—composing plays, short stories, and novels. Wanting to escape small town Iowa, she eventually moved to New York City, where she became involved in the cutting-edge theater industry. She was a prolific and esteemed writer through the entirety of her life.

Context: *Trifles* is Glaspell's first play, based on a murder trial she covered while a reporter in Davenport, Iowa. The work showcases many of Glaspell's unconventional takes on justice and morality, for the time. It is also considered an early work of feminist thought and literature.

Literary Terms:
Spectacle: How do the staging and props add to our understanding of the play?
Theme: What major themes are developed in the work?
Plot: What is the climax of the play? How do several literary elements come together to heighten this moment?
Character/Dialogue: Miss Minnie Wright might arguably be the most interesting character in the play, but she never appears. How is her character developed through dialogue among her peers?

Scene: *The kitchen in the now abandoned farmhouse of John Wright, a gloomy kitchen, and left without having been put in order—unwashed pans under the sink, a loaf of bread outside the breadbox, a dish towel on the table—other signs of incompleted work. At the rear the outer door opens, and the Sheriff comes in, followed by the County Attorney and Hale: The Sheriff and Hale are men in middle life, the County Attorney is a young man; all are much bundled up and go at once to the stove. They are followed by the two women—the Sheriff's Wife first; she is a slight wiry woman, a thin nervous face. Mrs. Hale is larger and would ordinarily be called more comfortable looking, but she is disturbed now and looks fearfully about as she enters. The women have come in slowly and stand close together near the door.*

County Attorney *(rubbing his hands):* This feels good. Come up to the fire, ladies.
Mrs. Peters *(after taking a step forward)*: I'm not—cold.
Sheriff *(unbuttoning his overcoat and stepping away from the stove as if to the beginning of official business)*: Now, Mr. Hale, before we move things about, you explain to Mr. Henderson just what you saw when you came here yesterday morning.

County Attorney: By the way, has anything been moved? Are things just as you left them yesterday?

Sheriff (*looking about*): It's just the same. When it dropped below zero last night, I thought I'd better send Frank out this morning to make a fire for us—no use getting pneumonia with a big case on; but I told him not to touch anything except the stove—and you know Frank.

County Attorney: Somebody should have been left here yesterday.

Sheriff: Oh—yesterday. When I had to send Frank to Morris Center for that man who went crazy—I want you to know I had my hands full yesterday. I knew you could get back from Omaha by today, and as long as I went over everything here myself—

County Attorney: Well, Mr. Hale, tell just what happened when you came here yesterday morning.

Hale: Harry and I had started to town with a load of potatoes. We came along the road from my place; and as I got here, I said, "I'm going to see if I can't get John Wright to go in with me on a party telephone." I spoke to Wright about it once before, and he put me off, saying folks talked too much anyway, and all he asked was peace and quiet I guess you know about how much he talked himself; but I thought maybe if I went to the house and talked about it before his wife, though I said to Harry that I didn't know as what his wife wanted made much difference to John—

County Attorney: Let's talk about that later, Mr. Hale: I do want to talk about that, but tell now just what happened when you got to the house.

Hale: I didn't hear or see anything; I knocked at the door, and still it was all quiet inside. I knew they must be up, it was past eight o'clock. so I knocked again, and I thought I heard somebody say, "Come in." I wasn't sure, I'm not sure yet, but I opened the door—this door (*indicating the door by which the two women are still standing*), and there in that rocker—(*pointing to it*) sat Mrs. Wright. (*They all look at the rocker.*)

County Attorney: What—was she doing?

Hale: She was rockin' back and forth. She had her apron in her hand and was kind of pleating it.

County Attorney: And how did she—look?

Hale: Well, she looked queer.

County Attorney: How do you mean—queer?

Hale: Well, as if she didn't know what she was going to do next. And kind of done up.

County Attorney: How did she seem to feel about your coming?

Hale: Why, I don't think she minded—one way or other. She didn't pay much attention. I said, "How do, Mrs. Wright, it's cold, ain't it?" And she said, "Is it?"—and went on kind of pleating at her apron. Well, I was surprised; she didn't ask me to come up to the stove, or to set down, but just sat there, not even looking at me, so I said, "I want to see John." And then she—laughed. I guess you would call it a laugh. I thought of Harry and the team outside, so I said a little sharp:" Can't I see John?" "No," she says, kind o' dull like. "Ain't he home?" says I. "Yes," says she, "he's home." "Then why can't I see him?" I asked her, out of patience. "'Cause he's dead," says she. "*Dead?*" says I. She just nodded her head, not getting a bit excited, but rockin' back and forth. "Why—where is he?" says I, not knowing what to say. She just pointed upstairs—like that (*himself pointing to the room above*): I got up, with the idea of going up there. I talked from there to here—then I says, "Why, what did he die of?" "He died of a rope around his neck," says she, and just went on pleatin' at her apron. Well, I went out and called Harry. I thought I might—need help. We went upstairs, and there he was lyin'—

County Attorney: I think I'd rather have you go into that upstairs, where you can point it all out. Just go on now with the rest of the story.

Hale: Well, my first thought was to get that rope off. I looked . . . (*Stops, his face twitches*) . . . but Harry, he went up to him, and he said, "No, he's dead all right, and we'd better not touch anything." So we went back downstairs. She was still sitting that same way. "Has anybody been notified?" I asked." "No," says she, unconcerned. "Who did this, Mrs. Wright?" said Harry. He said it businesslike—and she stopped pleatin' of her apron. "I don't know," she says. "You don't know?" says Harry. "No," says she, "Weren't you sleepin' in the bed with him?" says Harry. "Yes," says she, "but I was on the inside." "Somebody slipped a rope round his neck and strangled him, and you didn't wake up?" says Harry. "I didn't wake up," she said after him. We must 'a looked as if we didn't see how that could be, for after a minute she said, "I sleep sound." Harry was going to ask her more questions, but I said maybe we ought to let her tell her story first to the coroner, or the Sheriff, so Harry went fast as he could to Rivers' place, where there's a telephone.

County Attorney: And what did Mrs. Wright do when she knew that you had gone for the coroner.

Hale: She moved from that chair to this over here . . . (*pointing to a small chair in the corner*) . . . and just sat there with her hands held together and looking down. I got a feeling that I ought to make some conversation, so I said I had come in to see if John wanted to put in a telephone, and at that she started to laugh, and then she stopped and looked at me—scared. (*The County Attorney, who has had his notebook out, makes a note.*) I dunno, maybe it wasn't scared. I wouldn't like to say it was. Soon Harry got back, and then Dr. Lloyd came, and you, Mr. Peters, and so I guess that's all I know that you don't.

County Attorney (*looking around*): I guess we'll go upstairs first—and then out to the barn and around there. (*To the Sheriff*) You're convinced that there was nothing important here—nothing that would point to any motive?

Sheriff: Nothing here but kitchen things.

(*The County Attorney, after again looking around the kitchen, opens the door of a cupboard closet. He gets up on a chair and looks on a shelf. Pulls his hand away, sticky.*)

County Attorney: Here's a nice mess. (*The women draw nearer.*)

Mrs. Peters (*to the other woman*): Oh, her fruit; it did freeze. (*To the County Attorney*) She worried about that when it turned so cold. She said the fire'd go out and her jars would break.

Sheriff: Well, can you beat the women! Held for murder and worryin' about her preserves.

County Attorney: I guess before we're through she may have something more serious than preserves to worry about.

Hale: Well, women are used to worrying over trifles. (*The two women move a little closer together.*)

County Attorney (*with the gallantry of a young politician*): And yet, for all their worries, what would we do without the ladies? (*The women do not unbend. He goes to the sink, takes dipperful of water from the pail and, pouring it into a basin, washes his hands. Starts to wipe them on the roller towel, turns it for a cleaner place.*) Dirty towels! (*Kicks his foot against the pans under the sink.*) Not much of a housekeeper, would you say, ladies?

Mrs. Hale (*stiffly*): There's a great deal of work to be done on a farm.

County Attorney: To be sure. And yet . . . (*With a little bow to her.*) . . . I know there are some Dickson county farmhouses which do not have such roller towels. (*He gives it a pull to expose its full length again.*)

Mrs. Hale: Those towels get dirty awful quick. Men's hands aren't always as clean as they might be.

County Attorney: Ah, loyal to your sex, I see. But you and Mrs. Wright were neighbors. I suppose you were friends, too.

Mrs. Hale (*shaking her head*): I've not seen much of her of late years. I've not been in this house—it's more than a year.

County Attorney: And why was that? You didn't like her?

Mrs. Hale: I liked her all well enough. Farmers' wives have their hands full, Mr. Henderson. And then—

County Attorney: Yes—?

Mrs. Hale (*looking about*): It never seemed a very cheerful place.

County Attorney: No—it's not cheerful. I shouldn't say she had the homemaking instinct.

Mrs. Hale: Well, I don't know as Wright had, either.

County Attorney: You mean that they didn't get on very well?

Mrs. Hale: No, I don't mean anything. But I don't think a place'd be any cheerfuller for John Wright's being in it.

County Attorney: I'd like to talk more of that a little later. I want to get the lay of things upstairs now. (He goes to the left, where three steps lead to a stair door.)

Sheriff: I suppose anything Mrs. Peters does'll be all right. She was to take in some clothes for her, you know, and a few little things. We left in such a hurry yesterday.

County Attorney: Yes, but I would like to see what you take, Mrs. Peters, and keep an eye out for anything that might be of use to us.

Mrs. Peters: Yes, Mr. Henderson. (*The women listen to the men's steps on the stairs, then look about the kitchen.*)

Mrs. Hale: I'd hate to have men coming into my kitchen, snooping around and criticizing. (*She arranges the pans under sink which the Lawyer had shoved out of place.*)

Mrs. Peters: Of course it's no more than their duty.

Mrs. Hale: Duty's all right, but I guess that deputy Sheriff that came out to make the fire might have got a little of this on. (*Gives the roller towel a pull.*) Wish I'd thought of that sooner. Seems mean to talk about her for not having things slicked up when she had to come away in such a hurry. Mrs. Peters (*who has gone to a small table in the left rear corner of the room, and lifted one end of a towel that covers a pan*): She had bread set. (*Stands still.*) Mrs. Hale (*eyes fixed on a loaf of bread beside the* breadbox, *which is on a low shelf at the other side of the room; moves slowly toward it.*): She was going to put this in there. (*Picks up loaf, then abruptly drops it. In a manner of returning to familiar things.*) It's a shame about her fruit. I wonder if it's all gone. (*Gets up on the chair and looks.*) I think there's some here that's all right, Mrs. Peters: Yes—here; (*holding it toward the window.*) This is cherries, too. (*Looking again.*) I declare I believe that's the only one. (*Gets down, bottle in her hand. Goes to the sink and wipes it off on the outside.*) She'll feel awful bad after all her hard work in the hot weather. I remember the afternoon I put up my cherries last summer

(*She puts the bottle on the big kitchen table, center of the room, front table. With a sigh, is about to sit down in the rocking chair. Before she is seated realizes what chair it is; with a slow look at it, steps back. The chair, which she has touched, rocks back and forth.*)

Mrs. Peters: Well, I must get those things from the front room closet. (*She goes to the door at the right, but after looking into the other room, steps back.*) You coming with me, Mrs. Hale? You could help me carry them. (*They go into the other room; reappear, Mrs. Peters carrying a dress and skirt, Mrs. Hale following with a pair of shoes.*)

Mrs. Peters: My, it's cold in there. (*She puts the clothes on the big table, and hurries to the stove.*)

Mrs. Hale (*examining the skirt*): Wright was close. I think maybe that's why she kept so much to herself. She didn't even belong to the Ladies' Aid. I suppose she felt she couldn't do her part, and then you don't enjoy things when you feel shabby. She used to wear pretty clothes and be lively, when she was Minnie Foster, one of the town girls singing in the choir. But that—oh, that was thirty years ago. This all you was to take in?

Mrs. Peters: She said she wanted an apron. Funny thing to want, for there isn't much to get you dirty in jail, goodness knows. But I suppose just to make her feel more natural. She said they was in the top drawer in this cupboard. Yes, here. And then her little shawl that always hung behind the door. (*Opens stair door and looks.*) Yes, here it is.(*Quickly shuts door leading upstairs.*)

Mrs. Hale (*abruptly moving toward her*): Mrs. Peters?

Mrs. Peters: Yes, Mrs. Hale?

Mrs. Hale: Do you think she did it?

Mrs. Peters (*in a frightened voice*): Oh, I don't know.

Mrs. Hale: Well, I don't think she did. Asking for an apron and her little shawl. Worrying about her fruit.

Mrs. Peters (*starts to speak, glances up, where footsteps are heard in the room above. In a low voice.*): Mr. Peters says it looks bad for her. Mr. Henderson is awful sarcastic in speech and he'll make fun of her say in' she didn't wake up.

Mrs. Hale: Well, I guess John Wright didn't wake when they was slipping that rope under his neck.

Mrs. Peters: No, it's strange. It must have been done awful crafty and still. They say it was such a—funny way to kill a man, rigging it all up like that.

Mrs. Hale: That's just what Mr. Hale said. There was a gun in the house. He says that's what he can't understand.

Mrs. Peters: Mr. Henderson said coming out that what was needed for the case was a motive; something to show anger or—sudden feeling.

Mrs. Hale (*who is standing by the table*): Well, I don't see any signs of anger around here. (*She puts her hand on the dish towel which lies on the table, stands looking down at the table, one half of which is clean, the other half messy.*) It's wiped here. (*Makes a move as if to finish work, then turns and looks at loaf of bread outside the breadbox. Drops towel. In that voice of coming back to familiar things.*) Wonder how they are finding things upstairs? I hope she had a little more red-up there. You know, it seems kind of *sneaking*. Locking her up in town and then coming out here and trying to get her own house to turn against her!

Mrs. Peters: But, Mrs. Hale, the law is the law.

Mrs. Hale: I s'pose 'tis. (*Unbuttoning her coat*) Better loosen up your things, Mrs. Peters. You won't feel them when you go out. (*Mrs. Peters takes off her fur tippet, goes to hang it on hook at the back of room, stands looking at the under part of the small corner table.*)

Mrs. Peters: She was piecing a quilt. (*She brings the large sewing basket, and they look at the bright pieces.*)

Mrs. Hale: It's log cabin pattern. Pretty, isn't it? I wonder if she was goin' to quilt or just knot it? (*Footsteps have been heard coming down the stairs. The Sheriff enters, followed by Hale and the County Attorney.*)

Sheriff: They wonder if she was going to quilt it or just knot it. (*The men laugh; the women look abashed.*)

County Attorney (*rubbing his hands over the stove*): Frank's fire didn't do much up there, did it? Well, let's go out to the barn and get that cleared up. (*The men go outside.*)

Mrs. Hale (*resentfully*): I don't know as there's anything so strange, our takin' up our time with little things while we're waiting for them to get the evidence. (*She sits down at the big table, smoothing out a block with decision.*) I don't see as it's anything to laugh about.

Mrs. Peters (*apologetically*): Of course they've got awful important things on their minds. (*Pulls up a chair and joins Mrs. Hale at the table.*)

Mrs. Hale (*examining another block*): Mrs. Peters, look at this one. Here, this is the one she was working on, and look at the sewing! All the rest of it has been so nice and even. And look at this! It's all over the place! Why, it looks as if she didn't know what she was about!

(*After she has said this, they look at each other, then start to glance back at the door. After an instant Mrs. Hale has pulled at a knot and ripped the sewing.*)

Mrs. Peters: Oh, what are you doing, Mrs. Hale?

Mrs. Hale (*mildly*): Just pulling out a stitch or two that's not sewed very good. (*Threading a needle*) Bad sewing always made me fidgety.

Mrs. Peters (*nervously*): I don't think we ought to touch things.

Mrs. Hale: I'll just finish up this end. (*Suddenly stopping and leaning forward.*) Mrs. Peters?

Mrs. Peters: Yes, Mrs. Hale?

Mrs. Hale: What do you suppose she was so nervous about?

Mrs. Peters: Oh—I don't know. I don't know as she was nervous. I sometimes sew awful queer when I'm just tired. (*Mrs. Hale starts to say something looks at Mrs. Peters, then goes on sewing.*) Well, I must get these things wrapped up. They may be through sooner than we think. (*Putting apron and other things together.*) I wonder where I can find a piece of paper, and string.

Mrs. Hale: In that cupboard, maybe.

Mrs. Peters (*looking in cupboard*): Why, here's a birdcage. (*Holds it up.*) Did she have a bird, Mrs. Hale?

Mrs. Hale: Why, I don't know whether she did or not—I've not been here for so long. There was a man around last year selling canaries cheap, but I don't know as she took one;maybe she did. She used to sing real pretty herself.

Mrs. Peters (*glancing around*): Seems funny to think of a bird here. But she must have had one, or why should she have a cage? I wonder what happened to it?

Mrs. Hale: I s'pose maybe the cat got it.

Mrs. Peters: No, she didn't have a cat. She's got that feeling some people have about cats being afraid of them. My cat got in her room and she was real upset and asked me to take it out.

Mrs. Hale: My sister Bessie was like that. Queer, ain't it?

Mrs. Peters (*examining the cage*): Why, look at this door. It's broke. One hinge is pulled apart.

Mrs. Hale (*looking, too*): Looks as if someone must have been rough with it.

Mrs. Peters: Why, yes. (*She brings the cage forward and puts it on the table.*)

Mrs. Hale: I wish if they're going to find any evidence they'd be about it. I don't like this place.

Mrs. Peters: But I'm awful glad you came with me, Mrs. Hale: It would be lonesome of me sitting here alone.

Mrs. Hale: It would, wouldn't it? (*Dropping her sewing*): But I tell you what I do wish, Mrs. Peters: I wish I had come over sometimes *she* was here. I—(*Looking around the room.*)—wish I had.

Mrs. Peters: But of course you were awful busy, Mrs. Hale—your house and your children.

Mrs. Hale: I could've come. I stayed away because it weren't cheerful—and that's why I ought to have come. I—I've never liked this place. Maybe because it's down in a hollow and you don't see the road. I dunno what it is, but it's a lonesome place and always was. I wish I had come over to see Minnie Foster sometimes. I can see now—(shakes her head).

Mrs. Peters: Well, you mustn't reproach yourself, Mrs. Hale. Somehow we just don't see how it is with other folks until—something comes up.

Mrs. Hale: Not having children makes less work—but it makes a quiet house, and Wright out to work all day, and no company when he did come in. Did you know John Wright, Mrs. Peters?

Mrs. Peters: Not to know him; I've seen him in town. They say he was a good man.

Mrs. Hale: Yes—good; he didn't drink, and kept his word as well as most, I guess, and paid his debts. But he was a hard man, Mrs. Peters: Just to pass the time of day with him(*shivers*). Like a raw wind that gets to the bone. (*Pauses, her eye falling on the cage*) I should think she would 'a wanted a bird. But what do you suppose went with it?

Mrs. Peters: I don't know, unless it got sick and died. (*She reaches over and swings the broken door, swings it again; both women watch it.*)

Mrs. Hale: You weren't raised round here, were you? (*Mrs. Peters shakes her head.*) You didn't know—her?

Mrs. Peters: Not till they brought her yesterday.

Mrs. Hale: She—come to think of it, she was kind of like a bird herself—real sweet and pretty, but kind of timid and—fluttery. How—she—did—change. (*Silence; then as if struck by a happy thought and relieved to get back to everyday things.*) Tell you what, Mrs. Peters, why don't you take the quilt in with you? It might take up her mind.

Mrs. Peters: Why, I think that's a real nice idea, Mrs. Hale. There couldn't possibly be any objection to it, could there? Now, just what would I take? I wonder if her patches are in here—and her things. (*They look in the sewing basket.*)

Mrs. Hale: Here's some red. I expect this has got sewing things in it (*Brings out a fancy box.*) What a pretty box. Looks like something somebody would give you. Maybe her scissors are in here. (*Opens box. Suddenly puts her hand to her nose.*) Why—(*Mrs. Peters bends nearer, then turns her face away.*) There's something wrapped up in this piece of silk.

Mrs. Peters: Why, this isn't her scissors.

Mrs. Hale (*lifting the silk.*) Oh, Mrs. Peters—it's—(*Mrs. Peters bends closer.*)

Mrs. Peters: It's the bird.

Mrs. Hale (*jumping up*): But, Mrs. Peters—look at it. Its neck! Look at its neck! It's all—other side to.

Mrs. Peters: Somebody—wrung—its neck.

(*Their eyes meet. A look of growing comprehension of horror. Steps are heard outside. Mrs. Hale slips box under quilt pieces, and sinks into her chair. Enter Sheriff and County Attorney. Mrs. Peters rises.*)

County Attorney (*as one turning from serious thing to little pleasantries*): Well, ladies, have you decided whether she was going to quilt it or knot it?

Mrs. Peters: We think she was going to—knot it.

County Attorney: Well, that's interesting, I'm sure. (*Seeing the birdcage.*) Has the bird flown?

Mrs. Hale (*putting more quilt pieces over the box*): We think the—cat got it.

County Attorney (*preoccupied*): Is there a cat? (*Mrs. Hale glances in a quick covert way at Mrs. Peters.*)

Mrs. Peters: Well, not now. They're superstitious, you know. They leave.

County Attorney (*to Sheriff Peters, continuing an interrupted conversation*): No sign at all of anyone having come from the outside. Their own rope. Now let's go up again and goover it piece by piece. (*They start upstairs.*) It would have to have been someone who knew just the—

(*Mrs. Peters sits down. The two women sit there not looking at one another, but as if peering into something and at the same time holding back. When they talk now, it is the manner of feeling their way over strange ground, as if afraid of what they are saying, but as if they cannot help saying it.*)

Mrs. Hale: She liked the bird. She was going to bury it in that pretty box.

Mrs. Peters (*in a whisper*): When I was a girl—my kitten—there was a boy took a hatchet,and before my eyes—and before I could get there—(*covers her face an instant.*) If they hadn't held me back, I would have—(*catches herself, looks upstairs, where steps are heard, falters weakly*)—hurt him.

Mrs. Hale (*with a slow look around her*): I wonder how it would seem never to have had any children around (*Pause*). No, Wright wouldn't like the bird—a thing that sang. She used to sing. He killed that, too.

Mrs. Peters (*moving uneasily*): We don't know who killed the bird.

Mrs. Hale: I knew John Wright.

Mrs. Peters: It was an awful thing was done in this house that night, Mrs. Hale. Killing a man while he slept, slipping a rope around his neck that choked the life out of him.

Mrs. Hale: His neck, Choked the life out of him. (*Her hand goes out and rests on the birdcage.*)

Mrs. Peters (*with a rising voice*): We don't know who killed him. We don't know it.

Mrs. Hale (*her own feeling not interrupted*): If there'd been years and years of nothing, then a bird to sing to you, it would be awful—still, after the bird was still.

Mrs. Peters (*something within her speaking*): I know what stillness is. When we home-steaded in Dakota, and my first baby died—after he was two years old, and me with no other then—

Mrs. Hale (*moving*): How soon do you suppose they'll be through, looking for the evidence?

Mrs. Peters: I know what stillness is. (*Pulling herself back*). The law has got to punish crime, Mrs. Hale.

Mrs. Hale (*not as if answering that*): I wish you'd seen Minnie Foster when she wore a white dress with blue ribbons and stood up there in the choir and sang. (*She looks around the room.*) Oh, I wish I'd come over here once in a while! That was a crime! That was a crime! Who's going to punish that?

Mrs. Peters (*looking upstairs*): We mustn't—take on.

Mrs. Hale: I might have known she needed help! I know how things can be—for women. I tell you, it's queer, Mrs. Peters: We live close together and we live far apart. We all go through the same things—it's all just a different kind of the same thing. (*Brushes her eyes; noticing the bottle of fruit, reaches out for it.*) If I was you, I wouldn't tell her her fruit was gone. Tell her it ain't. Tell her it's all right. Take this in to prove it to her. She—she may never know whether it was broke or not.

Mrs. Peters (*takes the bottle, looks about for something to wrap it in; takes petticoat from the clothes brought from the other room, very nervously begins winding this around the bottle. In a false voice*): My, it's a good thing the men couldn't hear us. Wouldn't they just laugh! Getting all stirred up over a little thing like a—dead canary. As if that could have anything to do with—with—wouldn't they laugh! (*The men are heard coming downstairs.*)

Mrs. Hale (*under her breath*): Maybe they would—maybe they wouldn't.

County Attorney: No, Peters, it's all perfectly clear except a reason for doing it. But you know juries when it comes to women. If there was some definite thing. Something to show—something to make a story about—a thing that would connect up with this strange way of doing it. (*The women's eyes meet for an instant. Enter Hale from outer door.*)

Hale: Well, I've got the team around. Pretty cold out there.

County Attorney: I'm going to stay here awhile by myself (*To the Sheriff*): You can send Frank out for me, can't you? I want to go over everything. I'm not satisfied that we can't do better.

Sheriff: Do you want to see what Mrs. Peters is going to take in? (*The County Attorney goes to the table, picks up the apron, laughs.*)

County Attorney: Oh I guess they're not very dangerous things the ladies have picked out. (*Moves a few things about, disturbing the quilt pieces which cover the box. Steps back.*) No, Mrs. Peters doesn't need supervising. For that matter, a Sheriff's wife is married to the law. Ever think of it that way, Mrs. Peters?

Mrs. Peters: Not—just that way.

Sheriff (*chuckling*): Married to the law. (*Moves toward the other room.*) I just want you to come in here a minute, George. We ought to take a look at these windows.

County Attorney (*scoffingly*): Oh, windows!

Sheriff: We'll be right out, Mr. Hale.

(*Hale goes outside. The Sheriff follows the County Attorney into the other room. Then Mrs. Hale rises, hands tight together, looking intensely at Mrs. Peters, whose eyes take a slow turn, finally meeting Mrs. Hale's. A moment Mrs. Hale holds her, then her own eyes point the way to where the box is concealed. Suddenly Mrs. Peters throws back quilt pieces and tries to put the box in the bag she is wearing. It is too big. She opens box, starts to take the bird out, cannot touch it, goes to pieces, stands there helpless. Sound of a knob turning in the other room. Mrs. Hale snatches the box and puts it in the pocket of her big coat. Enter County Attorney and Sheriff.*)

County Attorney (*facetiously*): Well, Henry, at least we found out that she was not going to quilt it. She was going to—what is it you call it, ladies!

Mrs. Hale (*her hand against her pocket*): We call it—knot it, Mr. Henderson.

Questions for Discussion:

1. What are the "trifles" that the men ignore and the two women notice? Why do the men dismiss them, and why do the women see them as significant clues? What is the thematic importance of the "trifles"?

2. If a 21st-century playwright were to write an updated version of *Trifles*, what details of plot, character, and setting would be different from those in Glaspell's play? What would be the same? What are some possible "trifles" that might serve the same dramatic functions as those in Glaspell's play? the these "trifles"?

3. Consider Glaspell's title "A Jury of Her Peers" for the short story version of this same series of events. What does this title add to your thematic understanding of the play? What is gained or lost by translating the short story to a play?

5. Is Mrs. Minnie Wright a villain or her own hero?

Fiction is a form of literature written in prose that tells imaginary stories about imaginary people. Fiction allows the reader to enter a world of fantasy in which seemingly real and unreal characters can interact in ways that are purely a product of the author's imagination. While fiction can, sometimes, be based on real events, by nature, fictional elements are a part of every story. The short story is one of the most common and compelling forms of fictional writing.

The actual length of the short story varies to some extent. There are short stories as brief as a few paragraphs, and others as long as multiple chapters or sections. Regardless, the great strength of the short story actually lies in its length. The novel has hundreds of pages to allow its setting to unfold, to reveal the plot points of its story, and to develop its characters. Often a short story must do all of this in just a few pages. The ability of a short story author to reveal a great deal about a particular character in a few short lines, sometimes even in just a brief physical description, is one of the hallmarks of the genre.

While a novel might have various subplots, a short story will typically focus on a plot that is less complex. It might consider one incident or one plot point. It will usually focus on a shorter period of time than a novel might. When reading a short story, one should pay particular attention to its atmosphere, or general tone/mood, its setting, and its character development.

"The Yellow Wallpaper"

Charlotte Perkins Gilman

Author Biography: Charlotte Perkins Gilman was an author, lecturer, activist for social reform, and is credited with being an early feminist. Born in 1860 in Hartford, Connecticut, Gilman showed a proclivity for the arts, enrolling at the Rhode Island School of Design and becoming a tutor and painter. Gilman separated from and subsequently divorced her husband, something rarely heard of at the time. She moved to Pasadena California, where she became involved in a number of progressive social movements, including several for the benefit of women.

Context: After the birth of her first daughter, Gilman suffered serious post-partum depression. At the time, women who experienced such symptoms were diagnosed as "hysterical" and thought to have diseases of the nerves such as "neurasthenia." One so-called cure of the time to treat such feminine illness was the "rest cure," popularized by an American physician named Silas Weir Mitchell and in which women were confined to bed for long periods of time to sooth their nerves. Gilman's short story fictionalizes these conditions.

Literary Terms: theme, imagery, symbolism, characterization

It is very seldom that mere ordinary people like John and myself secure ancestral halls for the summer.

A colonial mansion, a hereditary estate, I would say a haunted house, and reach the height of romantic felicity,—but that would be asking too much of fate!

Still I will proudly declare that there is something queer about it.

Else, why should it be let so cheaply? And why have stood so long untenanted?

John laughs at me, of course, but one expects that in marriage.

John is practical in the extreme. He has no patience with faith, an intense horror of superstition, and he scoffs openly at any talk of things not to be felt and seen and put down in figures.

John is a physician, and *perhaps*—(I would not say it to a living soul, of course, but this is dead paper and a great relief to my mind)—*perhaps* that is one reason I do not get well faster.

You see, he does not believe I am sick!

And what can one do?

If a physician of high standing, and one's own husband, assures friends and relatives that there is really nothing the matter with one but temporary nervous depression,—a slight hysterical tendency,—what is one to do?

My brother is also a physician, and also of high standing, and he says the same thing.

So I take phosphates or phosphites,—whichever it is,—and tonics, and journeys, and air, and exercise, and am absolutely forbidden to "work" until I am well again.

Personally I disagree with their ideas.

Personally I believe that congenial work, with excitement and change, would do me good.

But what is one to do?

I did write for a while in spite of them; but it *does* exhaust me a good deal—having to be so sly about it, or else meet with heavy opposition.

I sometimes fancy that in my condition if I had less opposition and more society and stimulus—but John says the very worst thing I can do is to think about my condition, and I confess it always makes me feel bad.

So I will let it alone and talk about the house.

The most beautiful place! It is quite alone, standing well back from the road, quite three miles from the village. It makes me think of English places that you read about, for there are hedges and walls and gates that lock, and lots of separate little houses for the gardeners and people.

There is a *delicious* garden! I never saw such a garden—large and shady, full of box-bordered paths, and lined with long grape-covered arbors with seats under them.

There were greenhouses, too, but they are all broken now.

There was some legal trouble, I believe, something about the heirs and co-heirs; anyhow, the place has been empty for years.

That spoils my ghostliness, I am afraid; but I don't care—there is something strange about the house—I can feel it.

I even said so to John one moonlight evening, but he said what I felt was a *draught*, and shut the window.

I get unreasonably angry with John sometimes. I'm sure I never used to be so sensitive. I think it is due to this nervous condition.

But John says if I feel so I shall neglect proper self-control; so I take pains to control myself,—before him, at least,—and that makes me very tired.

I don't like our room a bit. I wanted one downstairs that opened on the piazza and had roses all over the window, and such pretty, old-fashioned chintz hangings! But John would not hear of it.

He said there was only one window and not room for two beds, and no near room for him if he took another.

He is very careful and loving, and hardly lets me stir without special direction.

I have a schedule prescription for each hour in the day; he takes all care from me, and so I feel basely ungrateful not to value it more.

He said we came here solely on my account, that I was to have perfect rest and all the air I could get. "Your exercise depends on your strength, my dear," said he, "and your food somewhat on your appetite; but air you can absorb all the time." So we took the nursery, at the top of the house.

It is a big, airy room, the whole floor nearly, with windows that look all ways, and air and sunshine galore. It was nursery first and then playground and gymnasium, I should judge; for the windows are barred for little children, and there are rings and things in the walls.

The paint and paper look as if a boys' school had used it. It is stripped off—the paper—in great patches all around the head of my bed, about as far as I can reach, and in a great place on the other side of the room low down. I never saw a worse paper in my life.

One of those sprawling flamboyant patterns committing every artistic sin.

It is dull enough to confuse the eye in following, pronounced enough to constantly irritate, and provoke study, and when you follow the lame, uncertain curves for a little distance they suddenly commit suicide—plunge off at outrageous angles, destroy themselves in unheard-of contradictions.

The color is repellant, almost revolting; a smouldering, unclean yellow, strangely faded by the slow-turning sunlight.

It is a dull yet lurid orange in some places, a sickly sulphur tint in others.

No wonder the children hated it! I should hate it myself if I had to live in this room long.

There comes John, and I must put this away,—he hates to have me write a word.

We have been here two weeks, and I haven't felt like writing before, since that first day.

I am sitting by the window now, up in this atrocious nursery, and there is nothing to hinder my writing as much as I please, save lack of strength.

John is away all day, and even some nights when his cases are serious.

I am glad my case is not serious!

But these nervous troubles are dreadfully depressing.

John does not know how much I really suffer. He knows there is no *reason* to suffer, and that satisfies him.

Of course it is only nervousness. It does weigh on me so not to do my duty in any way!

I meant to be such a help to John, such a real rest and comfort, and here I am a comparative burden already!

Nobody would believe what an effort it is to do what little I am able—to dress and entertain, and order things.

It is fortunate Mary is so good with the baby. Such a dear baby!

And yet I *cannot* be with him, it makes me so nervous.

I suppose John never was nervous in his life. He laughs at me so about this wall paper!

At first he meant to repaper the room, but afterwards he said that I was letting it get the better of me, and that nothing was worse for a nervous patient than to give way to such fancies.

He said that after the wall paper was changed it would be the heavy bedstead, and then the barred windows, and then that gate at the head of the stairs, and so on.

"You know the place is doing you good," he said, "and really, dear, I don't care to renovate the house just for a three months' rental."

"Then do let us go downstairs," I said, "there are such pretty rooms there."

Then he took me in his arms and called me a blessed little goose, and said he would go down cellar if I wished, and have it whitewashed into the bargain.

But he is right enough about the beds and windows and things.

It is as airy and comfortable a room as any one need wish, and, of course, I would not be so silly as to make him uncomfortable just for a whim.

I'm really getting quite fond of the big room, all but that horrid paper.

Out of one window I can see the garden, those mysterious deep-shaded arbors, the riotous old-fashioned flowers, and bushes and gnarly trees.

Out of another I get a lovely view of the bay and a little private wharf belonging to the estate. There is a beautiful shaded lane that runs down there from the house. I always fancy I see people walking in these numerous paths and arbors, but John has cautioned me not to give way to fancy in the least. He says that with my imaginative power and habit of story-making a nervous weakness like mine is sure to lead to all manner of excited fancies, and that I ought to use my will and good sense to check the tendency. So I try.

I think sometimes that if I were only well enough to write a little it would relieve the press of ideas and rest me.

But I find I get pretty tired when I try.

It is so discouraging not to have any advice and companionship about my work. When I get really well John says we will ask Cousin Henry and Julia down for a long visit; but he says he would as soon put fire-works in my pillow-case as to let me have those stimulating people about now.

I wish I could get well faster.

But I must not think about that. This paper looks to me as if it *knew* what a vicious influence it had!

There is a recurrent spot where the pattern lolls like a broken neck and two bulbous eyes stare at you upside-down.

I got positively angry with the impertinence of it and the everlastingness. Up and down and sideways they crawl, and those absurd, unblinking eyes are everywhere. There is one place where two breadths didn't match, and the eyes go all up and down the line, one a little higher than the other.

I never saw so much expression in an inanimate thing before, and we all know how much expression they have! I used to lie awake as a child and get more entertainment and terror out of blank walls and plain furniture than most children could find in a toy-store.

I remember what a kindly wink the knobs of our big old bureau used to have, and there was one chair that always seemed like a strong friend.

I used to feel that if any of the other things looked too fierce I could always hop into that chair and be safe.

The furniture in this room is no worse than inharmonious, however, for we had to bring it all from downstairs. I suppose when this was used as a playroom they had to take the nursery things out, and no wonder! I never saw such ravages as the children have made here.

The wall paper, as I said before, is torn off in spots, and it sticketh closer than a brother—they must have had perseverance as well as hatred.

Then the floor is scratched and gouged and splintered, the plaster itself is dug out here and there, and this great heavy bed, which is all we found in the room, looks as if it had been through the wars.

But I don't mind it a bit—only the paper.

There comes John's sister. Such a dear girl as she is, and so careful of me! I must not let her find me writing.

She is a perfect, an enthusiastic housekeeper, and hopes for no better profession. I verily believe she thinks it is the writing which made me sick!

But I can write when she is out, and see her a long way off from these windows.

There is one that commands the road, a lovely, shaded, winding road, and one that just looks off over the country. A lovely country, too, full of great elms and velvet meadows.

This wall paper has a kind of sub-pattern in a different shade, a particularly irritating one, for you can only see it in certain lights, and not clearly then.

But in the places where it isn't faded, and where the sun is just so, I can see a strange, provoking, formless sort of figure, that seems to sulk about behind that silly and conspicuous front design.

There's sister on the stairs!

Well, the Fourth of July is over! The people are all gone and I am tired out. John thought it might do me good to see a little company, so we just had mother and Nellie and the children down for a week.

Of course I didn't do a thing. Jennie sees to everything now.

But it tired me all the same.

John says if I don't pick up faster he shall send me to Weir Mitchell in the fall.

But I don't want to go there at all. I had a friend who was in his hands once, and she says he is just like John and my brother, only more so!

Besides, it is such an undertaking to go so far.

I don't feel as if it was worthwhile to turn my hand over for anything, and I'm getting dreadfully fretful and querulous.

I cry at nothing, and cry most of the time.

Of course I don't when John is here, or anybody else, but when I am alone.

And I am alone a good deal just now. John is kept in town very often by serious cases, and Jennie is good and lets me alone when I want her to.

So I walk a little in the garden or down that lovely lane, sit on the porch under the roses, and lie down up here a good deal.

I'm getting really fond of the room in spite of the wall paper. Perhaps *because* of the wall paper.

It dwells in my mind so!

I lie here on this great immovable bed—it is nailed down, I believe—and follow that pattern about by the hour. It is as good as gymnastics, I assure you. I start, we'll say, at the bottom, down in the corner over there where it has not been touched, and I determine for the thousandth time that I *will* follow that pointless pattern to some sort of a conclusion.

I know a little of the principles of design, and I know this thing was not arranged on any laws of radiation, or alternation, or repetition, or symmetry, or anything else that I ever heard of.

It is repeated, of course, by the breadths, but not otherwise.

Looked at in one way, each breadth stands alone, the bloated curves and flourishes—a kind of "debased Romanesque" with *delirium tremens*—go waddling up and down in isolated columns of fatuity.

But, on the other hand, they connect diagonally, and the sprawling outlines run off in great slanting waves of optic horror, like a lot of wallowing seaweeds in full chase.

The whole thing goes horizontally, too, at least it seems so, and I exhaust myself in trying to distinguish the order of its going in that direction.

They have used a horizontal breadth for a frieze, and that adds wonderfully to the confusion.

There is one end of the room where it is almost intact, and there, when the cross-lights fade and the low sun shines directly upon it, I can almost fancy radiation, after all,—the interminable grotesques seem to form around a common centre and rush off in headlong plunges of equal distraction.

It makes me tired to follow it. I will take a nap, I guess.

I don't know why I should write this.

I don't want to.

I don't feel able.

And I know John would think it absurd. But I *must* say what I feel and think in some way—it is such a relief!

But the effort is getting to be greater than the relief.

Half the time now I am awfully lazy, and lie down ever so much.

John says I mustn't lose my strength, and has me take cod-liver oil and lots of tonics and things, to say nothing of ale and wine and rare meat.

Dear John! He loves me very dearly, and hates to have me sick. I tried to have a real earnest reasonable talk with him the other day, and tell him how I wished he would let me go and make a visit to Cousin Henry and Julia.

But he said I wasn't able to go, nor able to stand it after I got there; and I did not make out a very good case for myself, for I was crying before I had finished.

It is getting to be a great effort for me to think straight. Just this nervous weakness, I suppose.

And dear John gathered me up in his arms, and just carried me upstairs and laid me on the bed, and sat by me and read to me till he tired my head.

He said I was his darling and his comfort and all he had, and that I must take care of myself for his sake, and keep well.

He says no one but myself can help me out of it, that I must use my will and self-control and not let my silly fancies run away with me.

There's one comfort, the baby is well and happy, and does not have to occupy this nursery with the horrid wall paper.

If we had not used it that blessed child would have! What a fortunate escape! Why, I wouldn't have a child of mine, an impressionable little thing, live in such a room for worlds.

I never thought of it before, but it is lucky that John kept me here, after all. I can stand it so much easier than a baby, you see.

Of course I never mention it to them anymore,—I am too wise,—but I keep watch of it all the same.

There are things in that paper that nobody knows but me, or ever will.

Behind that outside pattern the dim shapes get clearer every day.

It is always the same shape, only very numerous.

And it is like a woman stooping down and creeping about behind that pattern. I don't like it a bit. I wonder—I begin to think—I wish John would take me away from here!

It is so hard to talk with John about my case, because he is so wise, and because he loves me so.

But I tried it last night.

It was moonlight. The moon shines in all around, just as the sun does.

I hate to see it sometimes, it creeps so slowly, and always comes in by one window or another.

John was asleep and I hated to waken him, so I kept still and watched the moonlight on that undulating wall paper till I felt creepy.

The faint figure behind seemed to shake the pattern, just as if she wanted to get out.

I got up softly and went to feel and see if the paper *did* move, and when I came back John was awake.

"What is it, little girl?" he said. "Don't go walking about like that—you'll get cold."

I thought it was a good time to talk, so I told him that I really was not gaining here, and that I wished he would take me away.

"Why, darling!" said he, "our lease will be up in three weeks, and I can't see how to leave before.

"The repairs are not done at home, and I cannot possibly leave town just now. Of course if you were in any danger I could and would, but you really are better, dear, whether you can see it or not. I am a doctor, dear, and I know. You are gaining flesh and color, your appetite is better. I feel really much easier about you."

"I don't weigh a bit more," said I, "nor as much; and my appetite may be better in the evening, when you are here, but it is worse in the morning, when you are away."

"Bless her little heart!" said he with a big hug; "she shall be as sick as she pleases. But now let's improve the shining hours by going to sleep, and talk about it in the morning."

"And you won't go away?" I asked gloomily.

"Why, how can I, dear? It is only three weeks more and then we will take a nice little trip of a few days while Jennie is getting the house ready. Really, dear, you are better!"

"Better in body, perhaps"—I began, and stopped short, for he sat up straight and looked at me with such a stern, reproachful look that I could not say another word.

"My darling," said he, "I beg of you, for my sake and for our child's sake, as well as for your own, that you will never for one instant let that idea enter your mind! There is nothing so dangerous, so fascinating, to a temperament like yours. It is a false and foolish fancy. Can you not trust me as a physician when I tell you so?"

So of course I said no more on that score, and we went to sleep before long. He thought I was asleep first, but I wasn't,—I lay there for hours trying to decide whether that front pattern and the back pattern really did move together or separately.

On a pattern like this, by daylight, there is a lack of sequence, a defiance of law, that is a constant irritant to a normal mind.

The color is hideous enough, and unreliable enough, and infuriating enough, but the pattern is torturing.

You think you have mastered it, but just as you get well under way in following, it turns a back somersault, and there you are. It slaps you in the face, knocks you down, and tramples upon you. It is like a bad dream.

The outside pattern is a florid arabesque, reminding one of a fungus. If you can imagine a toadstool in joints, an interminable string of toadstools, budding and sprouting in endless convolutions,—why, that is something like it.

That is, sometimes!

There is one marked peculiarity about this paper, a thing nobody seems to notice but myself, and that is that it changes as the light changes.

When the sun shoots in through the east window—I always watch for that first long, straight ray—it changes so quickly that I never can quite believe it.

That is why I watch it always.

By moonlight—the moon shines in all night when there is a moon—I wouldn't know it was the same paper.

At night in any kind of light, in twilight, candlelight, lamplight, and worst of all by moonlight, it becomes bars! The outside pattern, I mean, and the woman behind it is as plain as can be.

I didn't realize for a long time what the thing was that showed behind,—that dim sub-pattern,—but now I am quite sure it is a woman.

By daylight she is subdued, quiet. I fancy it is the pattern that keeps her so still. It is so puzzling. It keeps me quiet by the hour.

I lie down ever so much now. John says it is good for me, and to sleep all I can.

Indeed, he started the habit by making me lie down for an hour after each meal.

It is a very bad habit, I am convinced, for, you see, I don't sleep.

And that cultivates deceit, for I don't tell them I'm awake,—oh, no!

The fact is, I am getting a little afraid of John.

He seems very queer sometimes, and even Jennie has an inexplicable look.

It strikes me occasionally, just as a scientific hypothesis, that perhaps it is the paper!

I have watched John when he did not know I was looking, and come into the room suddenly on the most innocent excuses, and I've caught him several times *looking at the paper!* And Jennie too. I caught Jennie with her hand on it once.

She didn't know I was in the room, and when I asked her in a quiet, a very quiet voice, with the most restrained manner possible, what she was doing with the paper she turned around as if she had been caught stealing, and looked quite angry—asked me why I should frighten her so!

Then she said that the paper stained everything it touched, that she had found yellow smooches on all my clothes and John's, and she wished we would be more careful!

Did not that sound innocent? But I know she was studying that pattern, and I am determined that nobody shall find it out but myself!

Life is very much more exciting now than it used to be. You see I have something more to expect, to look forward to, to watch. I really do eat better, and am more quiet than I was.

John is so pleased to see me improve! He laughed a little the other day, and said I seemed to be flourishing in spite of my wall paper.

I turned it off with a laugh. I had no intention of telling him it was *because* of the wall paper—he would make fun of me. He might even want to take me away.

I don't want to leave now until I have found it out. There is a week more, and I think that will be enough.

I'm feeling ever so much better! I don't sleep much at night, for it is so interesting to watch developments; but I sleep a good deal in the daytime.

In the daytime it is tiresome and perplexing.

There are always new shoots on the fungus, and new shades of yellow all over it. I cannot keep count of them, though I have tried conscientiously.

It is the strangest yellow, that wall paper! It makes me think of all the yellow things I ever saw—not beautiful ones like buttercups, but old foul, bad yellow things.

But there is something else about that paper—the smell! I noticed it the moment we came into the room, but with so much air and sun it was not bad. Now we have had a week of fog and rain, and whether the windows are open or not the smell is here.

It creeps all over the house.

I find it hovering in the dining-room, skulking in the parlor, hiding in the hall, lying in wait for me on the stairs.

It gets into my hair.

Even when I go to ride, if I turn my head suddenly and surprise it—there is that smell!

Such a peculiar odor, too! I have spent hours in trying to analyze it, to find what it smelled like.

It is not bad—at first, and very gentle, but quite the subtlest, most enduring odor I ever met.

In this damp weather it is awful. I wake up in the night and find it hanging over me.

It used to disturb me at first. I thought seriously of burning the house—to reach the smell.

But now I am used to it. The only thing I can think of that it is like is the *color* of the paper—a yellow smell!

There is a very funny mark on this wall, low down, near the mopboard. A streak that runs around the room. It goes behind every piece of furniture, except the bed, a long, straight, even *smooch*, as if it had been rubbed over and over.

I wonder how it was done and who did it, and what they did it for. Round and round and round—round and round and round—it makes me dizzy!

I really have discovered something at last.

Through watching so much at night, when it changes so, I have finally found out.

The front pattern *does* move—and no wonder! The woman behind shakes it!

Sometimes I think there are a great many women behind, and sometimes only one, and she crawls around fast, and her crawling shakes it all over.

Then in the very bright spots she keeps still, and in the very shady spots she just takes hold of the bars and shakes them hard.

And she is all the time trying to climb through. But nobody could climb through that pattern—it strangles so; I think that is why it has so many heads.

They get through, and then the pattern strangles them off and turns them upside-down, and makes their eyes white!

If those heads were covered or taken off it would not be half so bad.

I think that woman gets out in the daytime!

And I'll tell you why—privately—I've seen her!

I can see her out of every one of my windows!

It is the same woman, I know, for she is always creeping, and most women do not creep by daylight.

I see her in that long shaded lane, creeping up and down. I see her in those dark grape arbors, creeping all around the garden.

I see her on that long road under the trees, creeping along, and when a carriage comes she hides under the blackberry vines.

I don't blame her a bit. It must be very humiliating to be caught creeping by daylight!

I always lock the door when I creep by daylight. I can't do it at night, for I know John would suspect something at once.

And John is so queer, now, that I don't want to irritate him. I wish he would take another room! Besides, I don't want anybody to get that woman out at night but myself.

I often wonder if I could see her out of all the windows at once.

But, turn as fast as I can, I can only see out of one at one time.

And though I always see her she *may* be able to creep faster than I can turn!

I have watched her sometimes away off in the open country, creeping as fast as a cloud shadow in a high wind.

If only that top pattern could be gotten off from the under one! I mean to try it, little by little.

I have found out another funny thing, but I shan't tell it this time! It does not do to trust people too much.

There are only two more days to get this paper off, and I believe John is beginning to notice. I don't like the look in his eyes.

And I heard him ask Jennie a lot of professional questions about me. She had a very good report to give.

She said I slept a good deal in the daytime.

John knows I don't sleep very well at night, for all I'm so quiet!

He asked me all sorts of questions, too, and pretended to be very loving and kind.

As if I couldn't see through him!

Still, I don't wonder he acts so, sleeping under this paper for three months.

It only interests me, but I feel sure John and Jennie are secretly affected by it.

Hurrah! This is the last day, but it is enough. John is to stay in town overnight, and won't be out until this evening.

Jennie wanted to sleep with me—the sly thing! But I told her I should undoubtedly rest better for a night all alone.

That was clever, for really I wasn't alone a bit! As soon as it was moonlight, and that poor thing began to crawl and shake the pattern, I got up and ran to help her.

I pulled and she shook, I shook and she pulled, and before morning we had peeled off yards of that paper.

A strip about as high as my head and half around the room.

And then when the sun came and that awful pattern began to laugh at me I declared I would finish it today!

We go away to-morrow, and they are moving all my furniture down again to leave things as they were before.

Jennie looked at the wall in amazement, but I told her merrily that I did it out of pure spite at the vicious thing.

She laughed and said she wouldn't mind doing it herself, but I must not get tired.

How she betrayed herself that time!

But I am here, and no person touches this paper but me—not *alive!*

She tried to get me out of the room—it was too patent! But I said it was so quiet and empty and clean now that I believed I would lie down again and sleep all I could; and not to wake me even for dinner—I would call when I woke.

So now she is gone, and the servants are gone, and the things are gone, and there is nothing left but that great bed-stead nailed down, with the canvas mattress we found on it.

We shall sleep downstairs to-night, and take the boat home to-morrow.

I quite enjoy the room, now it is bare again.

How those children did tear about here!

This bedstead is fairly gnawed!

But I must get to work.

I have locked the door and thrown the key down into the front path.

I don't want to go out, and I don't want to have anybody come in, till John comes.

I want to astonish him.

I've got a rope up here that even Jennie did not find. If that woman does get out, and tries to get away, I can tie her!

But I forgot I could not reach far without anything to stand on!

This bed will *not* move!

I tried to lift and push it until I was lame, and then I got so angry I bit off a little piece at one corner—but it hurt my teeth.

Then I peeled off all the paper I could reach standing on the floor. It sticks horribly and the pattern just enjoys it! All those strangled heads and bulbous eyes and waddling fungus growths just shriek with derision!

I am getting angry enough to do something desperate. To jump out of the window would be admirable exercise, but the bars are too strong even to try.

Besides, I wouldn't do it. Of course not. I know well enough that a step like that is improper and might be misconstrued.

I don't like to *look* out of the windows even—there are so many of those creeping women, and they creep so fast.

I wonder if they all come out of that wall paper, as I did?

But I am securely fastened now by my well-hidden rope—you don't get *me* out in the road there!

I suppose I shall have to get back behind the pattern when it comes night, and that is hard!

It is so pleasant to be out in this great room and creep around as I please!

I don't want to go outside. I won't, even if Jennie asks me to.

For outside you have to creep on the ground, and everything is green instead of yellow.

But here I can creep smoothly on the floor, and my shoulder just fits in that long smooch around the wall, so I cannot lose my way.

Why, there's John at the door!

It is no use, young man, you can't open it!

How he does call and pound!

Now he's crying for an axe.

It would be a shame to break down that beautiful door!

"John, dear!" said I in the gentlest voice, "the key is down by the front steps, under a plantain leaf!"

That silenced him for a few moments.

Then he said—very quietly indeed, "Open the door, my darling!"

"I can't," said I. "The key is down by the front door, under a plantain leaf!"

And then I said it again, several times, very gently and slowly, and said it so often that he had to go and see, and he got it, of course, and came in. He stopped short by the door.

"What is the matter?" he cried. "For God's sake, what are you doing?"

I kept on creeping just the same, but I looked at him over my shoulder.

"I've got out at last," said I, "in spite of you and Jane! And I've pulled off most of the paper, so you can't put me back!"

Now why should that man have fainted? But he did, and right across my path by the wall, so that I had to creep over him every time!

Questions for Discussion:

1. Why have the narrator and her husband, John, rented the "colonial mansion"? What is its history, and what is the reaction of the heroine to this estate? Does she feel comfortable living in the house?

2. Give a description of John. Why does the heroine say that his profession is "*perhaps...* one reason I do not get well faster"? How does the narrator view her husband? Does she agree with John's diagnosis and treatment?

3. Who does the narrator see in the wallpaper? How have her perceptions of John and Jennie changed from the beginning of the story?

4. Abruptly, the narrator switches mood from boredom and frustration to excitement. To what does she attribute this change? How does John react to this? What new aspects of the wallpaper does she discuss?

"The Lottery"

Shirley Jackson

Author Biography: Shirley Jackson was born in San Francisco in 1916, though she moved to the East Coast, where she would live the rest of her life, when she was in high school. She then attended Syracuse University, where she met Stanley Edgar Hyman, her future husband and literary partner. Jackson and her husband were prolific writers throughout their lives, publishing in numerous major literary journals and magazines.

Context for These Works: A number of Jackson's works explore the "underside" of communities and cultures that seem ordinary or even attractive on their face, and her work verges into mystery and horror frequently. Written shortly after the end of World War II, "The Lottery" delves into themes of human evil and how it can be perpetrated.

Primary Literary Elements: theme, symbolism, setting, foreshadowing, irony

The morning of June 27th was clear and sunny, with the fresh warmth of a full-summer day; the flowers were blossoming profusely and the grass was richly green. The people of the village began to gather in the square, between the post office and the bank, around ten o'clock; in some towns there were so many people that the lottery took two days and had to be started on June 26th, but in this village, where there were only about three hundred people, the whole lottery took less than two hours, so it could begin at ten o'clock in the morning and still be through in time to allow the villagers to get home for noon dinner. The children assembled first, of course. School was recently over for the summer, and the feeling of liberty sat uneasily on most of them; they tended to gather together quietly for a while before they broke into boisterous play, and their talk was still of the classroom and the teacher, of books and reprimands. Bobby Martin had already stuffed his pockets full of stones, and the other boys soon followed his example, selecting the smoothest and roundest stones; Bobby and Harry Jones and Dickie Delacroix—the villagers pronounced this name "Dellacroy"—eventually made a great pile of stones in one corner of the square and guarded it against the raids of the other boys. The girls stood aside, talking among themselves, looking over their shoulders at the boys, and the very small children rolled in the dust or clung to the hands of their older brothers or sisters.

Soon the men began to gather, surveying their own children, speaking of planting and rain, tractors and taxes. They stood together, away from the pile of stones in the corner, and their jokes were quiet and they smiled rather than laughed. The women, wearing faded house dresses and sweaters, came shortly after their menfolk. They greeted one another and exchanged bits of gossip as they went to join their husbands.

Soon the women, standing by their husbands, began to call to their children, and the children came reluctantly, having to be called four or five times. Bobby Martin ducked under his mother's grasping hand and ran, laughing, back to the pile of stones. His father spoke up sharply, and Bobby came quickly and took his place between his father and his oldest brother.

The lottery was conducted—as were the square dances, the teenage club, the Halloween program—by Mr. Summers, who had time and energy to devote to civic activities. He was a roundfaced, jovial man and he ran the coal business, and people were sorry for him, because he had no children and his wife was a scold. When he arrived in the square, carrying the black wooden box, there was a murmur of conversation among the villagers and he waved and called, "Little late today, folks." The postmaster, Mr. Graves, followed him, carrying a three-legged stool, and the stool was put in the center of the square and Mr. Summers set the black box down on it. The villagers kept their distance, leaving a space between themselves and the stool and when Mr. Summers said, "Some of you fellows want to give me a hand?" there was a hesitation before two men, Mr. Martin and his oldest son, Baxter, came forward to hold the box steady on the stool while Mr. Summers stirred up the papers inside it.

The original paraphernalia for the lottery had been lost long ago, and the black box now resting on the stool had been put into use even before Old Man Warner, the oldest man in town, was born. Mr. Summers spoke frequently to the villagers about making a new box, but no one liked to upset even as much tradition as was represented by the black box. There was a story that the present box had been made with some pieces of the box that had preceded it, the one that had been constructed when the first people settled down to make a village here. Every year, after the lottery, Mr. Summers began talking again about a new box, but every year the subject was allowed to fade off without anything's being done. The black box grew shabbier each year; by now it was no longer completely black but splintered badly along one side to show the original wood color, and in some places faded or stained.

Mr. Martin and his oldest son, Baxter, held the black box securely on the stool until Mr. Summers had stirred the papers thoroughly with his hand. Because so much of the ritual had been forgotten or discarded, Mr. Summers had been successful in having slips of paper substituted for the chips of wood that had been used for generations. Chips of wood, Mr. Summers had argued, had been all very well when the village was tiny, but now that the population was more than three hundred and likely to keep on growing it was necessary to use something that would fit more easily into the black box. The night before the lottery, Mr. Summers and Mr. Graves made up the slips of paper and put them in the box, and it was then taken to the safe of Mr. Summers's coal company and locked up until Mr. Summers was ready to take it to the square next morning. The rest of the year, the box was put away, sometimes one place, sometimes another; it had spent one year in Mr. Graves's barn and another year underfoot in the post office, and sometimes it was set on a shelf in the Martin grocery and left there.

There was a great deal of fussing to be done before Mr. Summers declared the lottery open. There were lists to make up—of heads of families, heads of households in each family, members of each household in each family. There was the proper swearing-in of Mr. Summers by the postmaster, as the official of the lottery; at one time, some people remembered, there had been a recital of some sort, performed by the official of the lottery, a perfunctory, tuneless chant that had been rattled offduly each year; some people believed that the official of the lottery used to stand just so when he said or sang it, others believed that he was supposed to walk among the people, but years and years ago this part of the ritual had been allowed to lapse. There had been, also, a ritual salute, which the official of the lottery had had to use in addressing each person who came up to draw from the box, but this also had changed with time, until now it was felt necessary only for the official to speak to each person approaching. Mr. Summers was very good at all this; in his clean white shirt and blue jeans, with one hand resting carelessly on the black box, he seemed very proper and important as he talked interminably to Mr. Graves and the Martins.

Just as Mr. Summers finally left off talking and turned to the assembled villagers, Mrs. Hutchinson came hurriedly along the path to the square, her sweater thrown over her shoulders, and slid into place in the back of the crowd. "Clean forgot what day it was," she said to Mrs. Delacroix, who stood next to her, and they both laughed softly. "Thought my old man was out back stacking wood," Mrs. Hutchinson went on, "and then I looked out the window and the kids were gone, and then I remembered it was the twenty-seventh and came a-running." She dried her hands on her apron, and Mrs. Delacroix said, "You're in time, though. They're still talking away up there."

Mrs. Hutchinson craned her neck to see through the crowd and found her husband and children standing near the front. She tapped Mrs. Delacroix on the arm as a farewell and began to make her way through the crowd. The people separated good-humoredly to let her through; two or three people said, in voices just loud enough to be heard across the crowd, "Here comes your Missus, Hutchinson," and "Bill, she made it after all." Mrs. Hutchinson reached her husband, and Mr. Summers, who had been waiting, said cheerfully, "Thought we were going to have to get on without you, Tessie." Mrs. Hutchinson said, grinning, "Wouldn't have me leave m'dishes in the sink, now would you, Joe?" and soft laughter ran through the crowd as the people stirred back into position after Mrs. Hutchinson's arrival.

"Well, now," Mr. Summers said soberly, "guess we better get started, get this over with, so's we can go back to work. Anybody ain't here?"

"Dunbar," several people said. "Dunbar, Dunbar."

Mr. Summers consulted his list. "Clyde Dunbar," he said. "That's right. He's broke his leg, hasn't he? Who's drawing for him?"

"Me, I guess," a woman said, and Mr. Summers turned to look at her.

"Wife draws for her husband," Mr. Summers said. "Don't you have a grown boy to do it for you, Janey?" Although Mr. Summers and everyone else in the village knew the answer perfectly well, it was the business of the official of the lottery to ask such questions formally. Mr. Summers waited with an expression of polite interest while Mrs. Dunbar answered.

"Horace's not but sixteen yet," Mrs. Dunbar said regretfully. "Guess I gotta fill in for the old man this year."

"Right," Mr. Summers said. He made a note on the list he was holding. Then he asked, "Watson boy drawing this year?"

A tall boy in the crowd raised his hand. "Here," he said. "I'm drawing for m'mother and me." He blinked his eyes nervously and ducked his head as several voices in the crowd said things like "Good fellow, Jack," and "Glad to see your mother's got a man to do it."

"Well," Mr. Summers said, "guess that's everyone. Old Man Warner make it?"

"Here," a voice said, and Mr. Summers nodded.

A sudden hush fell on the crowd as Mr. Summers cleared his throat and looked at the list. "All ready?" he called. "Now, I'll read the names—heads of families first—and the men come up and take a paper out of the box. Keep the paper folded in your hand without looking at it until everyone has had a turn. Everything clear?"

The people had done it so many times that they only half listened to the directions; most of them were quiet, wetting their lips, not looking around. Then Mr. Summers raised one hand high and said, "Adams." A man disengaged himself from the crowd and came forward. "Hi, Steve," Mr. Summers said, and Mr. Adams said, "Hi, Joe." They grinned at one another humorlessly and nervously.

Then Mr. Adams reached into the black box and took out a folded paper. He held it firmly by one corner as he turned and went hastily back to his place in the crowd, where he stood a little apart from his family, not looking down at this hand.

"Allen," Mr. Summers said. "Anderson . . . Bentham."

"Seems like there's no time at all between lotteries any more," Mrs. Delacroix said to Mrs. Graves in the back row. "Seems like we got through with the last one only last week."

"Time sure goes fast," Mrs. Graves said.

"Clark . . . Delacroix."

"There goes my old man," Mrs. Delacroix said. She held her breath while her husband went forward.

"Dunbar," Mr. Summers said, and Mrs. Dunbar went steadily to the box while one of the women said, "Go on, Janey," and another said, "There she goes."

"We're next," Mrs. Graves said. She watched while Mr. Graves came around from the side of the box, greeted Mr. Summers gravely, and selected a slip of paper from the box. By now, all through the crowd there were men holding the small folded papers in their large hands, turning them over and over nervously. Mrs. Dunbar and her two sons stood together, Mrs. Dunbar holding the slip of paper.

"Harburt . . . Hutchinson."

"Get up there, Bill," Mrs. Hutchinson said, and the people near her laughed.

"Jones."

"They do say," Mr. Adams said to Old Man Warner, who stood next to him, "that over in the north village they're talking of giving up the lottery."

Old Man Warner snorted. "Pack of crazy fools," he said. "Listening to the young folks, nothing's good enough for *them*. Next thing you know, they'll be wanting to go back to living in caves, nobody work any more, live *that* way for a while. Used to be a saying about 'Lottery in June, corn be heavy soon.' First thing you know, we'd all be eating stewed chickweed and acorns. There's *always* been a lottery," he added petulantly. "Bad enough to see young Joe Summers up there joking with everybody."

"Some places have already quit lotteries," Mrs. Adams said.

"Nothing but trouble in *that*," Old Man Warner said stoutly. "Pack of young fools."

"Martin." And Bobby Martin watched his father go forward. "Overdyke . . .Percy."

"I wish they'd hurry," Mrs. Dunbar said to her older son. "I wish they'd hurry."

"They're almost through," her son said.

"You get ready to run tell Dad," Mrs. Dunbar said.

Mr. Summers called his own name and then stepped forward precisely and selected a slip from the box. Then he called, "Warner."

"Seventy-seventh year I been in the lottery," Old Man Warner said as he went through the crowd. "Seventy-seventh time."

"Watson." The tall boy came awkwardly through the crowd. Someone said, "Don't be nervous, Jack," and Mr. Summers said, "Take your time, son."

"Zanini."

After that, there was a long pause, a breathless pause, until Mr. Summers, holding his slip of paper in the air, said, "All right, fellows." For a minute, no one moved, and then all the slips of paper were opened. Suddenly, all women began to speak at once, saying, "Who is it?" "Who's got it?" "Is it the Dunbars?" "Is it the Watsons?" Then the voices began to say, "It's Hutchinson. It's Bill." "Bill Hutchinson's got it."

"Go tell your father," Mrs. Dunbar said to her older son.

People began to look around to see the Hutchinsons. Bill Hutchinson was standing quiet, staring down at the paper in his hand. Suddenly, Tessie Hutchinson shouted to Mr. Summers, "You didn't give him time enough to take any paper he wanted. I saw you. It wasn't fair!"

"Be a good sport, Tessie," Mrs. Delacroix called, and Mrs. Graves said, "All of us took the same chance."

"Shut up, Tessie," Bill Hutchinson said.

"Well, everyone," Mr. Summers said, "that was done pretty fast, and now we've got to be hurrying a little more to get done in time." He consulted his next list. "Bill," he said, "you draw for the Hutchinson family. You got any other households in the Hutchinsons?"

"There's Don and Eva," Mrs. Hutchinson yelled. "Make them take their chance!"

"Daughters draw with their husbands' families, Tessie," Mr. Summers said gently. "You know that as well as anyone else."

"It wasn't fair," Tessie said.

"I guess not, Joe," Bill Hutchinson said regretfully. "My daughter draws with her husband's family, that's only fair. And I've got no other family except the kids."

"Then, as far as drawing for families is concerned, it's you," Mr. Summers said in explanation, "and as far as drawing for households is concerned, that's you, too. Right?"

"Right," Bill Hutchinson said.

"How many kids, Bill?" Mr. Summers asked formally.

"Three," Bill Hutchinson said. "There's Bill, Jr., and Nancy, and little Dave. And Tessie and me."

"All right, then," Mr. Summers said. "Harry, you got their tickets back?" Mr. Graves nodded and held up the slips of paper. "Put them in the box, then," Mr. Summers directed. "Take Bill's and put it in."

"I think we ought to start over," Mrs. Hutchinson said, as quietly as she could. "I tell you it wasn't fair. You didn't give him time enough to choose. Everybody saw that."

Mr. Graves had selected the five slips and put them in the box, and he dropped all the papers but those onto the ground, where the breeze caught them and lifted them off.

"Listen, everybody," Mrs. Hutchinson was saying to the people around her.

"Ready, Bill?" Mr. Summers asked, and Bill Hutchinson, with one quick glance around at his wife and children, nodded.

"Remember," Mr. Summers said, "take the slips and keep them folded until each person has taken one. Harry, you help little Dave." Mr. Graves took the hand of the little boy, who came willingly with him up to the box.

"Take a paper out of the box, Davy," Mr. Summers said. Davy put his hand into the box and laughed. "Take just one paper," Mr. Summers said. "Harry, you hold it for him." Mr. Graves took the child's hand and removed the folded paper from the tight fist and held it while little Dave stood next to him and looked up at him wonderingly.

"Nancy next," Mr. Summers said. Nancy was twelve, and her school friends breathed heavily as she went forward, switching her skirt, and took a slip daintily from the box. "Bill, Jr.," Mr. Summers said, and Billy, his face red and his feet over-large, nearly knocked the box over as he got a paper out. "Tessie," Mr. Summers said. She hesitated for a minute, looking around defiantly, and then set her lips and went up to the box. She snatched a paper out and held it behind her.

"Bill," Mr. Summers said, and Bill Hutchinson reached into the box and felt around, bringing his hand out at last with the slip of paper in it.

The crowd was quiet. A girl whispered, "I hope it's not Nancy," and the sound of the whisper reached the edges of the crowd.

"It's not the way it used to be," Old Man Warner said clearly. "People ain't the way they used to be."

"All right," Mr. Summers said. "Open the papers. Harry, you open little Dave's."

Mr. Graves opened the slip of paper and there was a general sigh through the crowd as he held it up and everyone could see that it was blank. Nancy and Bill, Jr., opened theirs at the same time, and both beamed and laughed, turning around to the crowd and holding their slips of paper above their heads.

"Tessie," Mr. Summers said. There was a pause, and then Mr. Summers looked at Bill Hutchinson, and Bill unfolded his paper and showed it. It was blank.

"It's Tessie," Mr. Summers said, and his voice was hushed. "Show us her paper, Bill."

Bill Hutchinson went over to his wife and forced the slip of paper out of her hand. It had a black spot on it, the black spot Mr. Summers had made the night before with the heavy pencil in the coal-company office. Bill Hutchinson held it up, and there was a stir in the crowd.

"All right, folks," Mr. Summers said, "let's finish quickly."

Although the villagers had forgotten the ritual and lost the original black box, they still remembered to use stones. The pile of stones the boys had made earlier was ready; there were stones on the ground with the blowing scraps of paper that had come out of the box. Mrs. Delacroix selected a stone so large she had to pick it up with both hands and turned to Mrs. Dunbar. "Come on," she said. "Hurry up."

Mrs. Dunbar had small stones in both hands, and she said, gasping for breath, "I can't run at all. You'll have to go ahead, and I'll catch up with you."

The children had stones already, and someone gave little Davy Hutchinson a few pebbles.

Tessie Hutchinson was in the center of a cleared space by now, and she held her hands out desperately as the villagers moved in on her. "It isn't fair," she said. A stone hit her on the side of the head.

Old Man Warner was saying, "Come on, come on, everyone." Steve Adams was in the front of the crowd of villagers, with Mrs. Graves beside him.

"It isn't fair, it isn't right," Mrs. Hutchinson screamed, and then they were upon her.

Questions for Discussion:

1. What seems to have been the original purpose of the lottery? What do people believe about it?
2. Is it important that the original paraphernalia for the lottery had been lost? What do you suppose the original ceremony was like? Why have some of the villages given up this practice? Why hasn't this one?
3. Is the lottery a collective act of murder? Is it morally justified? Is tradition sufficient justification for such actions? How would you respond to cultures that are different from ours that perform "strange" rituals?

"Young Goodman Brown"

Nathaniel Hawthorne

Author Biography: Nathaniel Hawthorne was born in Salem, Massachusetts in 1804. Reluctantly pursuing college, he graduated from Bowdoin College and a scant three years later began to publish fiction. Hawthorne was a prolific writer throughout his life, publishing both novels and short stories, many based on his experiences and the culture in New England where he lived. Hawthorne spent a short time in Liverpool, England as a consul of the U.S. Government before returning to the U.S., where he died in 1864.

Context for This Work: Like his contemporaries Emerson and Thoreau, Hawthorne belonged to the American Romantic movement. Unlike his fellow writers, though, Hawthorne had a tendency towards darker themes, and often ruminated in his works on themes of sin, evil, and guilt. This is perhaps not surprising given that Hawthorne's ancestor was the one judge from the Salem Witch Trials never to recant that his actions in that spectacle were right and just.

Primary Literary Elements: theme, symbolism, irony, characterization

Young Goodman Brown came forth at sunset into the street at Salem village; but put his head back, after crossing the threshold, to exchange a parting kiss with his young wife. And Faith, as the wife was aptly named, thrust her own pretty head into the street, letting the wind play with the pink ribbons of her cap while she called to Goodman Brown.

"Dearest heart," whispered she, softly and rather sadly, when her lips were close to his ear, "prithee put off your journey until sunrise and sleep in your own bed tonight. A lone woman is troubled with such dreams and such thoughts that she's afeard of herself sometimes. Pray tarry with me this night, dear husband, of all nights in the year."

"My love and my Faith," replied young Goodman Brown, "of all nights in the year, this one night must I tarry away from thee. My journey, as thou callest it, forth and back again, must needs be done 'twixt now and sunrise. What, my sweet, pretty wife, dost thou doubt me already, and we but three months married?"

"Then God bless you!" said Faith, with the pink ribbons; "and may you find all well when you come back."

"Amen!" cried Goodman Brown. "Say thy prayers, dear Faith, and go to bed at dusk, and no harm will come to thee."

So they parted; and the young man pursued his way until, being about to turn the corner by the meeting-house, he looked back and saw the head of Faith still peeping after him with a melancholy air, in spite of her pink ribbons.

"Poor little Faith!" thought he, for his heart smote him. "What a wretch am I to leave her on such an errand! She talks of dreams, too. Methought as she spoke there was trouble in her face, as if a dream had warned her what work is to be done tonight. But no, no't would kill her to think it. Well, she's a blessed angel on earth; and after this one night I'll cling to her skirts and follow her to heaven."

With this excellent resolve for the future, Goodman Brown felt himself justified in making more haste on his present evil purpose. He had taken a dreary road, darkened by all the gloomiest trees of the forest, which barely stood aside to let the narrow path creep through, and closed immediately behind. It was all as lonely as could be; and there is this peculiarity in such a solitude, that the traveller knows not who may be concealed by the innumerable trunks and the thick boughs overhead; so that with lonely footsteps he may yet be passing through an unseen multitude.

"There may be a devilish Indian behind every tree," said Goodman Brown to himself; and he glanced fearfully behind him as he added, "What if the devil himself should be at my very elbow!"

His head being turned back, he passed a crook of the road, and, looking forward again, beheld the figure of a man, in grave and decent attire, seated at the foot of an old tree. He arose at Goodman Brown's approach and walked onward side by side with him.

"You are late, Goodman Brown," said he. "The clock of the Old South was striking as I came through Boston, and that is full fifteen minutes agone."

"Faith kept me back a while," replied the young man, with a tremor in his voice, caused by the sudden appearance of his companion, though not wholly unexpected.

It was now deep dusk in the forest, and deepest in that part of it where these two were journeying. As nearly as could be discerned, the second traveller was about fifty years old, apparently in the same rank of life as Goodman Brown, and bearing a considerable resemblance to him, though perhaps more in expression than features. Still they might have been taken for father and son. And yet, though the elder person was as simply clad as the younger, and as simple in manner too, he had an indescribable air of one who knew the world, and who would not have felt abashed at the governor's dinner table or in King William's court, were it possible that his affairs should call him thither. But the only thing about him that could be fixed upon as remarkable was his staff, which bore the likeness of a great black snake, so curiously wrought that it might almost be seen to twist and wriggle itself like a living serpent. This, of course, must have been an ocular deception, assisted by the uncertain light.

"Come, Goodman Brown," cried his fellow-traveller, "this is a dull pace for the beginning of a journey. Take my staff, if you are so soon weary."

"Friend," said the other, exchanging his slow pace for a full stop, "having kept covenant by meeting thee here, it is my purpose now to return whence I came. I have scruples touching the matter thou wot'st of."

"Sayest thou so?" replied he of the serpent, smiling apart. "Let us walk on, nevertheless, reasoning as we go; and if I convince thee not thou shalt turn back. We are but a little way in the forest yet."

"Too far! Too far!" exclaimed the goodman, unconsciously resuming his walk. "My father never went into the woods on such an errand, nor his father before him. We have been a race of honest men and good Christians since the days of the martyrs; and shall I be the first of the name of Brown that ever took this path and kept"

"Such company, thou wouldst say," observed the elder person, interpreting his pause. "Well said, Goodman Brown! I have been as well acquainted with your family as with ever a one among the Puritans; and that's no trifle to say. I helped your grandfather, the constable, when he lashed the Quaker woman so smartly through the streets of Salem; and it was I that brought your father a pitch-pine knot, kindled at my own hearth, to set fire to an Indian village, in King Philip's war. They were my good friends, both; and many a pleasant walk have we had along this path, and returned merrily after midnight. I would fain be friends with you for their sake."

"If it be as thou sayest," replied Goodman Brown, "I marvel they never spoke of these matters; or, verily, I marvel not, seeing that the least rumor of the sort would have driven them from New England. We are a people of prayer, and good works to boot, and abide no such wickedness."

"Wickedness or not," said the traveller with the twisted staff, "I have a very general acquaintance here in New England. The deacons of many a church have drunk the communion wine with me; the selectmen of divers towns make me their chairman; and a majority of the Great and General Court are firm supporters of my interest. The governor and I, too—But these are state secrets."

"Can this be so?" cried Goodman Brown, with a stare of amazement at his undisturbed companion. "Howbeit, I have nothing to do with the governor and council; they have their own ways, and are no rule for a simple husbandman like me. But, were I to go on with thee, how should I meet the eye of that good old man, our minister, at Salem village? Oh, his voice would make me tremble both Sabbath day and lecture day."

Thus far the elder traveller had listened with due gravity; but now burst into a fit of irrepressible mirth, shaking himself so violently that his snake-like staff actually seemed to wriggle in sympathy.

"Ha! ha! ha!" shouted he again and again; then composing himself, "Well, go on, Goodman Brown, go on; but, prithee, don't kill me with laughing."

"Well, then, to end the matter at once," said Goodman Brown, considerably nettled, "there is my wife, Faith. It would break her dear little heart; and I'd rather break my own."

"Nay, if that be the case," answered the other, "e'en go thy ways, Goodman Brown. I would not for twenty old women like the one hobbling before us that Faith should come to any harm."

As he spoke he pointed his staff at a female figure on the path, in whom Goodman Brown recognized a very pious and exemplary dame, who had taught him his catechism in youth, and was still his moral and spiritual adviser, jointly with the minister and Deacon Gookin.

"A marvel, truly, that Goody Cloyse should be so far in the wilderness at nightfall," said he. "But with your leave, friend, I shall take a cut through the woods until we have left this Christian woman behind. Being a stranger to you, she might ask whom I was consorting with and whither I was going."

"Be it so," said his fellow-traveller. "Betake you to the woods, and let me keep the path." Accordingly the young man turned aside, but took care to watch his companion, who advanced softly along the road until he had come within a staff's length of the old dame. She, meanwhile, was making the best of her way, with singular speed for so aged a woman, and mumbling some indistinct words—a prayer, doubtless—as she went.

The traveller put forth his staff and touched her withered neck with what seemed the serpent's tail.

"The devil!" screamed the pious old lady.

"Then Goody Cloyse knows her old friend?" observed the traveller, confronting her and leaning on his writhing stick.

"Ah, forsooth, and is it your worship indeed?" cried the good dame. "Yea, truly is it, and in the very image of my old gossip, Goodman Brown, the grandfather of the silly fellow that now is. But—would your worship believe it?—my broomstick hath strangely disappeared, stolen, as I suspect, by that unhanged witch, Goody Cory, and that, too, when I was all anointed with the juice of smallage, and cinquefoil, and wolf's bane"

"Mingled with fine wheat and the fat of a newborn babe," said the shape of old Goodman Brown.

"Ah, your worship knows the recipe," cried the old lady, cackling aloud. "So, as I was saying, being all ready for the meeting, and no horse to ride on, I made up my mind to foot it; for they tell me there is a nice young man to be taken into communion tonight. But now your good worship will lend me your arm, and we shall be there in a twinkling."

"That can hardly be," answered her friend. "I may not spare you my arm, Goody Cloyse; but here is my staff, if you will."

So saying, he threw it down at her feet, where, perhaps, it assumed life, being one of the rods which its owner had formerly lent to the Egyptian magi. Of this fact, however, Goodman Brown could not take cognizance. He had cast up his eyes in astonishment, and, looking down again, beheld neither Goody Cloyse nor the serpentine staff, but his fellow-traveller alone, who waited for him as calmly as if nothing had happened.

"That old woman taught me my catechism," said the young man; and there was a world of meaning in this simple comment.

They continued to walk onward, while the elder traveller exhorted his companion to make good speed and persevere in the path, discoursing so aptly that his arguments seemed rather to spring up in the bosom of his auditor than to be suggested by himself. As they went, he plucked a branch of maple to serve for a walking stick, and began to strip it of the twigs and little boughs, which were wet with evening dew. The moment his fingers touched them they became strangely withered and dried up as with a week's sunshine. Thus the pair proceeded, at a good free pace, until suddenly, in a gloomy hollow of the road, Goodman Brown sat himself down on the stump of a tree and refused to go any farther.

"Friend," said he, stubbornly, "my mind is made up. Not another step will I budge on this errand. What if a wretched old woman do choose to go to the devil when I thought she was going to heaven: is that any reason why I should quit my dear Faith and go after her?"

"You will think better of this by and by," said his acquaintance, composedly. "Sit here and rest yourself a while; and when you feel like moving again, there is my staff to help you along."

Without more words, he threw his companion the maple stick, and was as speedily out of sight as if he had vanished into the deepening gloom. The young man sat a few moments by the roadside, applauding himself greatly, and thinking with how clear a conscience he should meet the minister in his morning walk, nor shrink from the eye of good old Deacon Gookin. And what calm sleep would be his that very night, which was to have been spent so wickedly, but so purely and sweetly now, in the arms of Faith! Amidst these pleasant and praiseworthy meditations, Goodman Brown heard the tramp of horses along the road, and deemed it advisable to conceal himself within the verge of the forest, conscious of the guilty purpose that had brought him thither, though now so happily turned from it.

On came the hoof tramps and the voices of the riders, two grave old voices, conversing soberly as they drew near. These mingled sounds appeared to pass along the road, within a few yards of the young man's hiding-place; but, owing doubtless to the depth of the gloom at that particular spot, neither the travellers nor their steeds were visible. Though their figures brushed the small boughs by the wayside, it could not be seen that they intercepted, even for a moment, the faint gleam from the strip of bright sky athwart which they must have passed. Goodman Brown alternately crouched and stood on tiptoe, pulling aside the branches and thrusting forth his head as far as he durst without discerning so much as a shadow. It vexed him the more, because he could have sworn, were such a thing possible, that he recognized the voices of the minister and Deacon Gookin, jogging along quietly, as they were wont to do, when bound to some ordination or ecclesiastical council. While yet within hearing, one of the riders stopped to pluck a switch.

"Of the two, reverend sir," said the voice like the deacon's, "I had rather miss an ordination dinner than tonight's meeting. They tell me that some of our community are to be here from Falmouth and beyond, and others from Connecticut and Rhode Island, besides several of the Indian powwows, who, after their fashion, know almost as much deviltry as the best of us. Moreover, there is a goodly young woman to be taken into communion."

"Mighty well, Deacon Gookin!" replied the solemn old tones of the minister. "Spur up, or we shall be late. Nothing can be done, you know, until I get on the ground."

The hoofs clattered again; and the voices, talking so strangely in the empty air, passed on through the forest, where no church had ever been gathered or solitary Christian prayed. Whither, then, could these holy men be journeying so deep into the heathen wilderness? Young Goodman Brown caught hold of a tree for support, being ready to sink down on the ground, faint and overburdened with the heavy sickness of his heart. He looked up to the sky, doubting whether there really was a heaven above him. Yet there was the blue arch, and the stars brightening in it.

"With heaven above and Faith below, I will yet stand firm against the devil!" cried Goodman Brown.

While he still gazed upward into the deep arch of the firmament and had lifted his hands to pray, a cloud, though no wind was stirring, hurried across the zenith and hid the brightening stars. The blue sky was still visible, except directly overhead, where this black mass of cloud was sweeping swiftly northward. Aloft in the air, as if from the depths of the cloud, came a confused and doubtful sound of voices. Once the listener fancied that he could distinguish the accents of towns-people of his own, men and women, both pious and ungodly, many of whom he had met at the communion table, and had seen others rioting at the tavern. The next moment, so indistinct were the sounds, he doubted whether he had heard aught but the murmur of the old forest, whispering without a wind. Then came a stronger swell of those familiar tones, heard daily in the sunshine at Salem village, but never until now from a cloud of night There was one voice of a young woman, uttering lamentations, yet with an uncertain sorrow, and entreating for some favor, which, perhaps, it would grieve her to obtain; and all the unseen multitude, both saints and sinners, seemed to encourage her onward.

"Faith!" shouted Goodman Brown, in a voice of agony and desperation; and the echoes of the forest mocked him, crying, "Faith! Faith!" as if bewildered wretches were seeking her all through the wilderness.

The cry of grief, rage, and terror was yet piercing the night, when the unhappy husband held his breath for a response. There was a scream, drowned immediately in a louder murmur of voices, fading into far-off laughter, as the dark cloud swept away, leaving the clear and silent sky above Goodman Brown. But something fluttered lightly down through the air and caught on the branch of a tree. The young man seized it, and beheld a pink ribbon.

"My Faith is gone!" cried he, after one stupefied moment. "There is no good on earth; and sin is but a name. Come, devil; for to thee is this world given."

And, maddened with despair, so that he laughed loud and long, did Goodman Brown grasp his staff and set forth again, at such a rate that he seemed to fly along the forest path rather than to walk or run. The road grew wilder and drearier and more faintly traced, and vanished at length, leaving him in the heart of the dark wilderness, still rushing onward with the instinct that guides mortal man to evil. The whole forest was peopled with frightful sounds—the creaking of the trees, the howling of wild beasts, and the yell of Indians; while sometimes the wind tolled like a distant church bell, and sometimes gave a broad roar around the traveller, as if all Nature were laughing him to scorn. But he was himself the chief horror of the scene, and shrank not from its other horrors.

"Ha! ha! ha!" roared Goodman Brown when the wind laughed at him.

"Let us hear which will laugh loudest. Think not to frighten me with your deviltry. Come witch, come wizard, come Indian powwow, come devil himself, and here comes Goodman Brown. You may as well fear him as he fear you."

In truth, all through the haunted forest there could be nothing more frightful than the figure of Goodman Brown. On he flew among the black pines, brandishing his staff with frenzied gestures, now giving vent to an inspiration of horrid blasphemy, and now shouting forth such laughter as set all the echoes of the forest laughing like demons around him. The fiend in his own shape is less hideous than when he rages in the breast of man. Thus sped the demoniac on his course, until, quivering among the trees, he saw a red light before him, as when the felled trunks and branches of a clearing have been set on fire, and throw up their lurid blaze against the sky, at the hour of midnight. He paused, in a lull of the tempest that had driven him onward, and heard the swell of what seemed a hymn, rolling solemnly from a distance with the weight of many voices. He knew the tune; it was a familiar one in the choir of the village meeting-house. The verse died heavily away, and was lengthened by a chorus, not of human voices, but of all the sounds of the benighted wilderness pealing in awful harmony together. Goodman Brown cried out, and his cry was lost to his own ear by its unison with the cry of the desert.

In the interval of silence he stole forward until the light glared full upon his eyes. At one extremity of an open space, hemmed in by the dark wall of the forest, arose a rock, bearing some rude, natural resemblance either to an alter or a pulpit, and surrounded by four blazing pines, their tops aflame, their stems untouched, like candles at an evening meeting. The mass of foliage that had overgrown the summit of the rock was all on fire, blazing high into the night and fitfully illuminating the whole field. Each pendent twig and leafy festoon was in a blaze. As the red light arose and fell, a numerous congregation alternately shone forth, then disappeared in shadow, and again grew, as it were, out of the darkness, peopling the heart of the solitary woods at once.

"A grave and dark-clad company," quoth Goodman Brown.

In truth they were such. Among them, quivering to and fro between gloom and splendor, appeared faces that would be seen next day at the council board of the province, and others which, Sabbath after Sabbath, looked devoutly heavenward, and benignantly over the crowded pews, from the holiest pulpits in the land. Some affirm that the lady of the governor was there. At least there were high dames well known to her, and wives of honored husbands, and widows, a great multitude, and ancient maidens, all of excellent repute, and fair young girls, who trembled lest their mothers should espy them. Either the sudden gleams of light flashing over the obscure field bedazzled Goodman Brown, or he recognized a score of the church members of Salem village famous for their especial sanctity. Good old Deacon Gookin had arrived, and waited at the skirts of that venerable saint, his revered pastor. But, irreverently consorting with these grave, reputable, and pious people, these elders of the church, these chaste dames and dewy virgins, there were men of dissolute lives and women of spotted fame, wretches given over to all mean and filthy vice, and suspected even of horrid crimes. It was strange to see that the good shrank not from the wicked, nor were the sinners abashed by the saints. Scattered also among their pale-faced enemies were the Indian priests, or powwows, who had often scared their native forest with more hideous incantations than any known to English witchcraft.

"But where is Faith?" thought Goodman Brown; and, as hope came into his heart, he trembled. Another verse of the hymn arose, a slow and mournful strain, such as the pious love, but joined to words which expressed all that our nature can conceive of sin, and darkly hinted at far more.

Unfathomable to mere mortals is the lore of fiends. Verse after verse was sung; and still the chorus of the desert swelled between like the deepest tone of a mighty organ; and with the final peal of that dreadful anthem there came a sound, as if the roaring wind, the rushing streams, the howling beasts, and every other voice of the unconcerted wilderness were mingling and according with the voice of guilty man in homage to the prince of all. The four blazing pines threw up a loftier flame, and obscurely discovered shapes and visages of horror on the smoke wreaths above the impious assembly. At the same moment the fire on the rock shot redly forth and formed a glowing arch above its base, where now appeared a figure. With reverence be it spoken, the figure bore no slight similitude, both in garb and manner, to some grave divine of the New England churches.

"Bring forth the converts!" cried a voice that echoed through the field and rolled into the forest.

At the word, Goodman Brown stepped forth from the shadow of the trees and approached the congregation, with whom he felt a loathful brotherhood by the sympathy of all that was wicked in his heart. He could have well-nigh sworn that the shape of his own dead father beckoned him to advance, looking downward from a smoke wreath, while a woman, with dim features of despair, threw out her hand to warn him back. Was it his mother? But he had no power to retreat one step, nor to resist, even in thought, when the minister and good old Deacon Gookin seized his arms and led him to the blazing rock. Thither came also the slender form of a veiled female, led between Goody Cloyse, that pious teacher of the catechism, and Martha Carrier, who had received the devil's promise to be queen of hell. A rampant hag was she. And there stood the proselytes beneath the canopy of fire.

"Welcome, my children," said the dark figure, "to the communion of your race. Ye have found thus young your nature and your destiny. My children, look behind you!"

They turned; and flashing forth, as it were, in a sheet of flame, the fiend worshippers were seen; the smile of welcome gleamed darkly on every visage.

"There," resumed the sable form, "are all whom ye have reverenced from youth. Ye deemed them holier than yourselves, and shrank from your own sin, contrasting it with their lives of righteousness and prayerful aspirations heavenward. Yet here are they all in my worshipping assembly. This night it shall be granted you to know their secret deeds: how hoary-bearded elders of the church have whispered wanton words to the young maids of their households; how many a woman, eager for widows' weeds, has given her husband a drink at bedtime and let him sleep his last sleep in her bosom; how beardless youths have made haste to inherit their fathers' wealth; and how fair damsels—blush not, sweet ones—have dug little graves in the garden, and bidden me, the sole guest to an infant's funeral. By the sympathy of your human hearts for sin ye shall scent out all the places—whether in church, bedchamber, street, field, or forest—where crime has been committed, and shall exult to behold the whole earth one stain of guilt, one mighty blood spot. Far more than this. It shall be yours to penetrate, in every bosom, the deep mystery of sin, the fountain of all wicked arts, and which inexhaustibly supplies more evil impulses than human power—than my power at its utmost—can make manifest in deeds. And now, my children, look upon each other."

They did so; and, by the blaze of the hell-kindled torches, the wretched man beheld his Faith, and the wife her husband, trembling before that unhallowed altar.

"Lo, there ye stand, my children," said the figure, in a deep and solemn tone, almost sad with its despairing awfulness, as if his once angelic nature could yet mourn for our miserable race. "Depending upon one another's hearts, ye had still hoped that virtue were not all a dream. Now are ye undeceived. Evil is the nature of mankind. Evil must be your only happiness. Welcome again, my children, to the communion of your race."

"Welcome," repeated the fiend worshippers, in one cry of despair and triumph.

And there they stood, the only pair, as it seemed, who were yet hesitating on the verge of wickedness in this dark world. A basin was hollowed, naturally, in the rock. Did it contain water, reddened by the lurid light? or was it blood? or, perchance, a liquid flame? Herein did the shape of evil dip his hand and prepare to lay the mark of baptism upon their foreheads, that they might be partakers of the mystery of sin, more conscious of the secret guilt of others, both in deed and thought, than they could now be of their own. The husband cast one look at his pale wife, and Faith at him. What polluted wretches would the next glance show them to each other, shuddering alike at what they disclosed and what they saw!

"Faith! Faith!" cried the husband, "look up to heaven, and resist the wicked one."

Whether Faith obeyed he knew not. Hardly had he spoken when he found himself amid calm night and solitude, listening to a roar of the wind which died heavily away through the forest. He staggered against the rock, and felt it chill and damp; while a hanging twig, that had been all on fire, besprinkled his cheek with the coldest dew.

The next morning young Goodman Brown came slowly into the street of Salem village, staring around him like a bewildered man. The good old minister was taking a walk along the graveyard to get an appetite for breakfast and meditate his sermon, and bestowed a blessing, as he passed, on Goodman Brown. He shrank from the venerable saint as if to avoid an anathema. Old Deacon Gookin was at domestic worship, and the holy words of his prayer were heard through the open window. "What God doth the wizard pray to?" quoth Goodman Brown. Goody Cloyse, that excellent old Christian, stood in the early sunshine at her own lattice, catechizing a little girl who had brought her a pint of morning's milk. Goodman Brown snatched away the child as from the grasp of the fiend himself. Turning the corner by the meeting-house, he spied the head of Faith, with the pink ribbons, gazing anxiously forth, and bursting into such joy at sight of him that she skipped along the street and almost kissed her husband before the whole village. But Goodman Brown looked sternly and sadly into her face, and passed on without a greeting.

Had Goodman Brown fallen asleep in the forest and only dreamed a wild dream of a witch-meeting?

Be it so if you will; but, alas! it was a dream of evil omen for young Goodman Brown. A stern, a sad, a darkly meditative, a distrustful, if not a desperate man did he become from the night of that fearful dream. On the Sabbath day, when the congregation were singing a holy psalm, he could not listen because an anthem of sin rushed loudly upon his ear and drowned all the blessed strain. When the minister spoke from the pulpit with power and fervid eloquence, and, with his hand on the open Bible, of the sacred truths of our religion, and of saint-like lives and triumphant deaths, and of future bliss or misery unutterable, then did Goodman Brown turn pale, dreading lest the roof should thunder down upon the gray blasphemer and his hearers. Often, waking suddenly at midnight, he shrank from the bosom of Faith; and at morning or eventide, when the family knelt down at prayer, he scowled and muttered to himself, and gazed sternly at his wife, and turned away. And when he had lived long, and was borne to his grave a hoary corpse, followed by Faith, an aged woman, and children and grandchildren, a goodly procession, besides neighbors not a few, they carved no hopeful verse upon his tombstone, for his dying hour was gloom.

Questions for Discussion:

1 Faith tells her husband not to travel "this night, dear husband, of all nights of the year?" What do you think she means by "this night?" Why do you think Goodman Brown feels like he has to take this journey?

2 Not long after entering the woods, Brown comes across "the figure of a man, in grave and decent attire." Who do you think this man is?

3 Do you think Brown really experienced what he did in the woods? Or could it have been a dream? What evidence in the text can you point to that supports your idea?

"A Worn Path"

Eudora Welty

Author Biography: Eudora Welty was born in Jackson, Mississippi in 1909, earning a degree in English literature from the University of Wisconsin. Trained in advertising and promotion, she worked for the Works Progress Administration (after doing some work in radio and journalism) and published her first piece of fiction shortly after. Welty won the Pulitzer Prize in 1973 for her novel *The Optimist's Daughter*, the Presidential Medal of Freedom in 1980, and the National Book Award in 1983, among other honors.

Context: Welty began her writing career with pieces about Jackson society, and her interest in the South was a pervasive theme throughout much of her work. Such is the case in "A Worn Path," which focuses on the journey of an elderly African-American woman to get medicine for her grandson. Her name, Phoenix, gives us a hint to a theme of overcoming obstacles for important goals.

Literary Terms: theme, characterization, point of view, symbolism

It was December—a bright frozen day in the early morning. Far out in the country there was an old Negro woman with her head tied red rag, coming along a path through the pinewoods. Her name was Phoenix Jackson. She was very old and small and she walked slowly in the dark pine shadows, moving a little from side to side in her steps, with the balanced heaviness and lightness of a pendulum in a grand-father clock. She carried a thin, small cane made from an umbrella, and with this she kept tapping the frozen earth in front of her. This made a grave and persistent noise in the still air, that seemed meditative like the chirping of a solitary little bird.

She wore a dark striped dress reaching down to her shoe tops, and an equally long apron of bleached sugar sacks, with a full pocket: all neat and tidy, but every time she took a step she might have fallen over her shoelaces, which dragged from her unlaced shoes. She looked straight ahead. Her eyes were blue with age. Her skin had a pattern all its own of numberless branching wrinkles and as though a whole little tree stood in the middle of her forehead, but a golden color ran underneath, and the two knobs of her cheeks were illumined by a yellow burning under the dark. Under the red rag her hair came down on her neck in the frailest of ringlets, still black, and with an odor like copper.

Now and then there was a quivering in the thicket. Old Phoenix said, "Out of my way, all you foxes, owls, beetles, jack rabbits, coons and wild animals!... Keep out from under these feet, little bob-whites.... Keep the big wild hogs out of my path. Don't let none of those come running my direction. I got a long way." Under her small black-freckled hand her cane, limber as a buggy whip, would switch at the brush as if to rouse up any hiding things.

On she went. The woods were deep and still. The sun made the pine needles almost too bright to look at, up where the wind rocked. The cones dropped as light as feathers. Down in the hollow was the mourning dove—it was not too late for him.

The path ran up a hill. "Seem like there is chains about my feet, time I get this far," she said, in the voice of argument old people keep to use with themselves. "Something always take a hold of me on this hill— pleads I should stay."

After she got to the top she turned and gave a full, severe look behind her where she had come. "Up through pines," she said at length. "Now down through oaks."

Her eyes opened their widest, and she started down gently. But before she got to the bottom of the hill a bush caught her dress.

Her fingers were busy and intent, but her skirts were full and long, so that before she could pull them free in one place they were caught in another. It was not possible to allow the dress to tear. "I in the thorny bush," she said. "Thorns, you doing your appointed work. Never want to let folks pass, no sir. Old eyes thought you was a pretty little green bush."

Finally, trembling all over, she stood free, and after a moment dared to stoop for her cane.

"Sun so high!" she cried, leaning back and looking, while the thick tears went over her eyes. "The time getting all gone here."

At the foot of this hill was a place where a log was laid across the creek.

"Now comes the trial," said Phoenix.

Putting her right foot out, she mounted the log and shut her eyes. Lifting her skirt, leveling her cane fiercely before her, like a festival figure in some parade, she began to march across. Then she opened her eyes and she was safe on the other side.

"I wasn't as old as I thought," she said.

But she sat down to rest. She spread her skirts on the bank around her and folded her hands over her knees. Up above her was a tree in a pearly cloud of mistletoe. She did not dare to close her eyes, and when a little boy brought her a plate with a slice of marble-cake on it she spoke to him. "That would be acceptable," she said. But when she went to take it there was just her own hand in the air.

So she left that tree, and had to go through a barbed-wire fence. There she had to creep and crawl, spreading her knees and stretching her fingers like a baby trying to climb the steps. But she talked loudly to herself: she could not let her dress be torn now, so late in the day, and she could not pay for having her arm or her leg sawed off if she got caught fast where she was.

At last she was safe through the fence and risen up out in the clearing. Big dead trees, like black men with one arm, were standing in the purple stalks of the withered cotton field. There sat a buzzard.

"Who you watching?"

In the furrow she made her way along.

"Glad this not the season for bulls," she said, looking sideways, "and the good Lord made his snakes to curl up and sleep in the winter. A pleasure I don't see no two-headed snake coming around that tree, where it come once. It took a while to get by him, back in the summer."

She passed through the old cotton and went into a field of dead corn. It whispered and shook and was taller than her head. "Through the maze now," she said, for there was no path.

Then there was something tall, black, and skinny there, moving before her.

At first she took it for a man. It could have been a man dancing in the field. But she stood still and listened, and it did not make a sound. It was as silent as a ghost.

"Ghost," she said sharply, "who be you the ghost of? For I have heard of nary death close by."

But there was no answer—only the ragged dancing in the wind.

She shut her eyes, reached out her hand, and touched a sleeve. She found a coat and inside that an emptiness, cold as ice.

"You scarecrow," she said. Her face lighted. "I ought to be shut up for good," she said with laughter. "My senses is gone. I too old. I the oldest people I ever know. Dance, old scarecrow," she said, "while I dancing with you."

She kicked her foot over the furrow, and with mouth drawn down, shook her head once or twice in a little strutting way. Some husks blew down and whirled in streamers about her skirts.

Then she went on, parting her way from side to side with the cane, through the whispering field. At last she came to the end, to a wagon track where the silver grass blew between the red ruts. The quail were walking around like pullets, seeming all dainty and unseen.

"Walk pretty," she said. "This the easy place. This the easy going."

She followed the track, swaying through the quiet bare fields, through the little strings of trees silver in their dead leaves, past cabins silver from weather, with the doors and windows boarded shut, all like old women under a spell sitting there. "I walking in their sleep," she said, nodding her head vigorously.

In a ravine she went where a spring was silently flowing through a hollow log. Old Phoenix bent and drank. "Sweet-gum makes the water sweet," she said, and drank more. "Nobody know who made this well, for it was here when I was born."

The track crossed a swampy part where the moss hung as white as lace from every limb. "Sleep on, alligators, and blow your bubbles." Then the track went into the road.

Deep, deep the road went down between the high green-colored banks. Overhead the live-oaks met, and it was as dark as a cave.

A black dog with a lolling tongue came up out of the weeds by the ditch. She was meditating, and not ready, and when he came at her she only hit him a little with her cane. Over she went in the ditch, like a little puff of milkweed.

Down there, her senses drifted away. A dream visited her, and she reached her hand up, but nothing reached down and gave her a pull. So she lay there and presently went to talking. "Old woman," she said to herself, "that black dog come up out of the weeds to stall you off, and now there he sitting on his fine tail, smiling at you."

A white man finally came along and found her—a hunter, a young man, with his dog on a chain.

"Well, Granny!" he laughed. "What are you doing there?"

"Lying on my back like a June-bug waiting to be turned over, mister," she said, reaching up her hand.

He lifted her up, gave her a swing in the air, and set her down. "Anything broken, Granny?"

"No sir, them old dead weeds is springy enough," said Phoenix, when she had got her breath. "I thank you for your trouble."

"Where do you live, Granny?" he asked, while the two dogs were growling at each other.

"Away back yonder, sir, behind the ridge. You can't even see it from here."

"On your way home?"

"No sir, I going to town."

"Why, that's too far! That's as far as I walk when I come out myself, and I get something for my trouble." He patted the stuffed bag he carried, and there hung down a little closed claw. It was one of the bob-whites, with its beak hooked bitterly to show it was dead. "Now you go on home, Granny!"

"I bound to go to town, mister," said Phoenix. "The time come around."

He gave another laugh, filling the whole landscape. "I know you old colored people! Wouldn't miss going to town to see Santa Claus!"

But something held old Phoenix very still. The deep lines in her face went into a fierce and different radiation. Without warning, she had seen with her own eyes a flashing nickel fall out of the man's pocket onto the ground.

"How old are you, Granny?" he was saying.

"There is no telling, mister," she said, "no telling."

Then she gave a little cry and clapped her hands and said, "Git on away from here, dog! Look! Look at that dog!" She laughed as if in admiration. "He ain't scared of nobody. He a big black dog." She whispered, "Sic him!"

"Watch me get rid of that cur," said the man. "Sic him, Pete! Sic him!"

Phoenix heard the dogs fighting, and heard the man running and throwing sticks. She even heard a gunshot. But she was slowly bending forward by that time, further and further forward, the lids stretched down over her eyes, as if she were doing this in her sleep. Her chin was lowered almost to her knees. The yellow palm of her hand came out from the fold of her apron. Her fingers slid down and along the ground under the piece of money with the grace and care they would have in lifting an egg from under a setting hen. Then she slowly straightened up, she stood erect, and the nickel was in her apron pocket. A bird flew by. Her lips moved. "God watching me the whole time. I come to stealing."

The man came back, and his own dog panted about them. "Well, I scared him off that time," he said, and then he laughed and lifted his gun and pointed it at Phoenix.

She stood straight and faced him.

"Doesn't the gun scare you?" he said, still pointing it.

"No, sir, I seen plenty go off closer by, in my day, and for less than what I done," she said, holding utterly still.

He smiled, and shouldered the gun. "Well, Granny," he said, "you must be a hundred years old, and scared of nothing. I'd give you a dime if I had any money with me. But you take my advice and stay home, and nothing will happen to you."

"I bound to go on my way, mister," said Phoenix. She inclined her head in the red rag. Then they went in different directions, but she could hear the gun shooting again and again over the hill.

She walked on. The shadows hung from the oak trees to the road like curtains. Then she smelled wood-smoke, and smelled the river, and she saw a steeple and the cabins on their steep steps. Dozens of little black children whirled around her. There ahead was Natchez shining. Bells were ringing. She walked on.

In the paved city it was Christmas time. There were red and green electric lights strung and crisscrossed everywhere, and all turned on in the daytime. Old Phoenix would have been lost if she had not distrusted her eyesight and depended on her feet to know where to take her.

She paused quietly on the sidewalk where people were passing by. A lady came along in the crowd, carrying an armful of red-, green- and silver-wrapped presents; she gave off perfume like the red roses in hot summer, and Phoenix stopped her.

"Please, missy, will you lace up my shoe?" She held up her foot.

"What do you want, Grandma?"

"See my shoe," said Phoenix. "Do all right for out in the country, but wouldn't look right to go in a big building." "Stand still then, Grandma," said the lady. She put her packages down on the sidewalk beside her and laced and tied both shoes tightly.

"Can't lace 'em with a cane," said Phoenix. "Thank you, missy. I doesn't mind asking a nice lady to tie up my shoe, when I gets out on the street."

Moving slowly and from side to side, she went into the big building, and into a tower of steps, where she walked up and around and around until her feet knew to stop.

She entered a door, and there she saw nailed up on the wall the document that had been stamped with the gold seal and framed in the gold frame, which matched the dream that was hung up in her head.

"Here I be," she said. There was a fixed and ceremonial stiffness over her body.

"A charity case, I suppose," said an attendant who sat at the desk before her.

But Phoenix only looked above her head. There was sweat on her face, the wrinkles in her skin shone like a bright net.

"Speak up, Grandma," the woman said. "What's your name? We must have your history, you know. Have you been here before? What seems to be the trouble with you?"

Old Phoenix only gave a twitch to her face as if a fly were bothering her.

"Are you deaf?" cried the attendant.

But then the nurse came in.

"Oh, that's just old Aunt Phoenix," she said. "She doesn't come for herself—she has a little grandson. She makes these trips just as regular as clockwork. She lives away back off the Old Natchez Trace." She bent down. "Well, Aunt Phoenix, why don't you just take a seat? We won't keep you standing after your long trip." She pointed.

The old woman sat down, bolt upright in the chair.

"Now, how is the boy?" asked the nurse.

Old Phoenix did not speak.

"I said, how is the boy?"

But Phoenix only waited and stared straight ahead, her face very solemn and withdrawn into rigidity.

"Is his throat any better?" asked the nurse. "Aunt Phoenix, don't you hear me? Is your grandson's throat any better since the last time you came for the medicine?"

With her hands on her knees, the old woman waited, silent, erect and motionless, just as if she were in armor.

"You mustn't take up our time this way, Aunt Phoenix," the nurse said. "Tell us quickly about your grandson, and get it over. He isn't dead, is he?'

At last there came a flicker and then a flame of comprehension across her face, and she spoke.

"My grandson. It was my memory had left me. There I sat and forgot why I made my long trip."

"Forgot?" The nurse frowned. "After you came so far?"

Then Phoenix was like an old woman begging a dignified forgiveness for waking up frightened in the night. "I never did go to school, I was too old at the Surrender," she said in a soft voice. "I'm an old woman without an education. It was my memory fail me. My little grandson, he is just the same, and I forgot it in the coming."

"Throat never heals, does it?" said the nurse, speaking in a loud, sure voice to old Phoenix. By now she had a card with something written on it, a little list. "Yes. Swallowed lye. When was it?—January—two, three years ago—"

Phoenix spoke unasked now. "No, missy, he not dead, he just the same. Every little while his throat begin to close up again, and he not able to swallow. He not get his breath. He not able to help himself. So the time come around, and I go on another trip for the soothing medicine."

"All right. The doctor said as long as you came to get it, you could have it," said the nurse. "But it's an obstinate case."

"My little grandson, he sit up there in the house all wrapped up, waiting by himself," Phoenix went on. "We is the only two left in the world. He suffer and it don't seem to put him back at all. He got a sweet look. He going to last. He wear a little patch quilt and peep out holding his mouth open like a little bird. I remembers so plain now. I not going to forget him again, no, the whole enduring time. I could tell him from all the others in creation."

"All right." The nurse was trying to hush her now. She brought her a bottle of medicine. "Charity," she said, making a check mark in a book.

Old Phoenix held the bottle close to her eyes, and then carefully put it into her pocket.

"I thank you," she said.

"It's Christmas time, Grandma," said the attendant. "Could I give you a few pennies out of my purse?"

"Five pennies is a nickel," said Phoenix stiffly.

"Here's a nickel," said the attendant.

Phoenix rose carefully and held out her hand. She received the nickel and then fished the other nickel out of her pocket and laid it beside the new one. She stared at her palm closely, with her head on one side.

Then she gave a tap with her cane on the floor.

"This is what come to me to do," she said. "I going to the store and buy my child a little windmill they sells, made out of paper. He going to find it hard to believe there such a thing in the world. I'll march myself back where he waiting, holding it straight up in this hand."

She lifted her free hand, gave a little nod, turned around, and walked out of the doctor's office. Then her slow step began on the stairs, going down

Questions for Discussion:

1. Why is Phoenix an appropriate name for the protagonist?
2. What was the purpose of Phoenix Jackson's trip to town? What obstacles did she face along the way?
3. Several of the characters Phoenix meets are conflicting in the way they treat her. Sometimes they're nice, sometimes they're impatient, and sometimes they're downright hostile. Why the range in how the characters treat Phoenix?

"The Masque of the Red Death"

Edgar Allan Poe

Author Biography: Edgar Allan Poe was born in Boston in 1809, a child of two actors. His mother died when he was young, however, and his father left; Poe was unofficially adopted by the Allan family in Richmond, Virginia. Poe had a short military career but later dropped out of West Point to pursue writing. Though he met some success during his life, he was constantly saddled with debt, and the untimely death of his young wife pushed Poe into alcoholism. He died in Baltimore in 1849 after being found delirious in the street.

Context: Poe is often regarded as an American Romanticist, but his work has strong elements of the gothic, bordering on horror and even science fiction. Poe is also considered one of the first creators of detective fiction, which was a new genre that burgeoned in the nineteenth century with the creation of police forces and the rise of science. One sees throughout much of his work the mysterious and the paranormal.

Literary Terms: theme, tone, symbolism, plot

The "Red Death" had long devastated the country. No pestilence had ever been so fatal, or so hideous. Blood was its Avatar and its seal—the redness and the horror of blood. There were sharp pains, and sudden dizziness, and then profuse bleeding at the pores, with dissolution. The scarlet stains upon the body and especially upon the face of the victim, were the pest ban which shut him out from the aid and from the sympathy of his fellow-men. And the whole seizure, progress and termination of the disease, were the incidents of half an hour.

But the Prince Prospero was happy and dauntless and sagacious. When his dominions were half depopulated, he summoned to his presence a thousand hale and light-hearted friends from among the knights and dames of his court, and with these retired to the deep seclusion of one of his castellated abbeys. This was an extensive and magnificent structure, the creation of the prince's own eccentric yet august taste. A strong and lofty wall girdled it in. This wall had gates of iron. The courtiers, having entered, brought furnaces and massy hammers and welded the bolts. They resolved to leave means neither of ingress or egress to the sudden impulses of despair or of frenzy from within. The abbey was amply provisioned. With such precautions the courtiers might bid defiance to contagion. The external world could take care of itself. In the meantime it was folly to grieve, or to think. The prince had provided all the appliances of pleasure. There were buffoons, there were improvisatori, there were ballet-dancers, there were musicians, there was Beauty, there was wine. All these and security were within. Without was the "Red Death."

It was toward the close of the fifth or sixth month of his seclusion, and while the pestilence raged most furiously abroad, that the Prince Prospero entertained his thousand friends at a masked ball of the most unusual magnificence.

It was a voluptuous scene, that masquerade. But first let me tell of the rooms in which it was held. There were seven—an imperial suite. In many palaces, however, such suites form a long and straight vista, while the folding doors slide back nearly to the walls on either hand, so that the view of the whole extent is scarcely impeded. Here the case was very different; as might have been expected from the duke's love of the bizarre. The apartments were so irregularly disposed that the vision embraced but little more than one at a time. There was a sharp turn at every twenty or thirty yards, and at each turn a novel effect. To the right and left, in the middle of each wall, a tall and narrow Gothic window looked out upon a closed corridor which pursued the windings of the suite. These windows were of stained glass whose color varied in accordance with the prevailing hue of the decorations of the chamber into which it opened. That at the eastern extremity was hung, for example, in blue—and vividly blue were its windows. The second chamber was purple in its ornaments and tapestries, and here the panes were purple. The third was green throughout, and so were the casements. The fourth was furnished and lighted with orange—the fifth with white—the sixth with violet. The seventh apartment was closely shrouded in black velvet tapestries that hung all over the ceiling and down the walls, falling in heavy folds upon a carpet of the same material and hue. But in this chamber only, the color of the windows failed to correspond with the decorations. The panes here were scarlet—a deep blood color. Now in no one of the seven apartments was there any lamp or candelabrum, amid the profusion of golden ornaments that lay scattered to and fro or depended from the roof. There was no light of any kind emanating from lamp or candle within the suite of chambers. But in the corridors that followed the suite, there stood, opposite to each window, a heavy tripod, bearing a brazier of fire that protected its rays through the tinted glass and so glaringly illumined the room. And thus were produced a multitude of gaudy and fantastic appearances. But in the western or black chamber the effect of the fire-light that streamed upon the dark hangings through the blood-tinted panes, was ghastly in the extreme, and produced so wild a look upon the countenances of those who entered, that there were few of the company bold enough to set foot within its precincts at all.

It was in this apartment, also, that there stood against the western wall, a gigantic clock of ebony. Its pendulum swung to and fro with a dull, heavy, monotonous clang; and when the minute-hand made the circuit of the face, and the hour was to be stricken, there came from the brazen lungs of the clock a sound which was clear and loud and deep and exceedingly musical, but of so peculiar a note and emphasis that, at each lapse of an hour, the musicians of the orchestra were constrained to pause, momentarily, in their performance, to hearken to the sound; and thus the waltzers perforce ceased their evolutions; and there was a brief disconcert of the whole gay company; and, while the chimes of the clock yet rang, it was observed that the giddiest grew pale, and the more aged and sedate passed their hands over their brows as if in confused reverie or meditation. But when the echoes had fully ceased, a light laughter at once pervaded the assembly; the musicians looked at each other and smiled as if at their own nervousness and folly, and made whispering vows, each to the other, that the next chiming of the clock should produce in them no similar emotion; and then, after the lapse of sixty minutes, (which embrace three thousand and six hundred seconds of the Time that flies,) there came yet another chiming of the clock, and then were the same disconcert and tremulousness and meditation as before.

But, in spite of these things, it was a gay and magnificent revel. The tastes of the duke were peculiar. He had a fine eye for colors and effects. He disregarded the decora of mere fashion. His plans were bold and fiery, and his conceptions glowed with barbaric lustre. There are some who would have thought him mad. His followers felt that he was not. It was necessary to hear and see and touch him to be sure that he was not.

He had directed, in great part, the moveable embellishments of the seven chambers, upon occasion of this great fete; and it was his own guiding taste which had given character to the masqueraders. Be sure they were grotesque. There were much glare and glitter and piquancy and phantasm—much of what has been since seen in "Hernani." There were arabesque figures with unsuited limbs and appointments. There were delirious fancies such as the madman fashions. There was much of the beautiful, much of the wanton, much of the bizarre, something of the terrible, and not a little of that which might have excited disgust. To and fro in the seven chambers there stalked, in fact, a multitude of dreams. And these—the dreams—writhed in and about, taking hue from the rooms, and causing the wild music of the orchestra to seem as the echo of their steps. And, anon, there strikes the ebony clock which stands in the hall of the velvet. And then, for a moment, all is still, and all is silent save the voice of the clock. The dreams are stiff-frozen as they stand. But the echoes of the chime die away—they have endured but an instant—and a light, half-subdued laughter floats after them as they depart. And now again the music swells, and the dreams live, and writhe to and fro more merrily than ever, taking hue from the many-tinted windows through which stream the rays from the tripods. But to the chamber which lies most westwardly of the seven, there are now none of the maskers who venture; for the night is waning away; and there flows a ruddier light through the blood-colored panes; and the blackness of the sable drapery appals; and to him whose foot falls upon the sable carpet, there comes from the near clock of ebony a muffled peal more solemnly emphatic than any which reaches their ears who indulge in the more remote gaieties of the other apartments.

But these other apartments were densely crowded, and in them beat feverishly the heart of life. And the revel went whirlingly on, until at length there commenced the sounding of midnight upon the clock. And then the music ceased, as I have told; and the evolutions of the waltzers were quieted; and there was an uneasy cessation of all things as before. But now there were twelve strokes to be sounded by the bell of the clock; and thus it happened, perhaps, that more of thought crept, with more of time, into the meditations of the thoughtful among those who revelled. And thus, too, it happened, perhaps, that before the last echoes of the last chime had utterly sunk into silence, there were many individuals in the crowd who had found leisure to become aware of the presence of a masked figure which had arrested the attention of no single individual before. And the rumor of this new presence having spread itself whisperingly around, there arose at length from the whole company a buzz, or murmur, expressive of disapprobation and surprise—then, finally, of terror, of horror, and of disgust.

In an assembly of phantasms such as I have painted, it may well be supposed that no ordinary appearance could have excited such sensation. In truth the masquerade license of the night was nearly unlimited; but the figure in question had out-Heroded

Herod, and gone beyond the bounds of even the prince's indefinite decorum. There are chords in the hearts of the most reckless which cannot be touched without emotion. Even with the utterly lost, to whom life and death are equally jests, there are matters of which no jest can be made. The whole company, indeed, seemed now deeply to feel that in the costume and bearing of the stranger neither wit nor propriety existed. The figure was tall and gaunt, and shrouded from head to foot in the habiliments of the grave. The mask which concealed the visage was made so nearly to resemble the countenance of a stiffened corpse that the closest scrutiny must have had difficulty in detecting the cheat. And yet all this might have been endured, if not approved, by the mad revellers around. But the mummer had gone so far as to assume the type of the Red Death. His vesture was dabbled in blood—and his broad brow, with all the features of the face, was besprinkled with the scarlet horror.

When the eyes of Prince Prospero fell upon this spectral image (which with a slow and solemn movement, as if more fully to sustain its role, stalked to and fro among the waltzers) he was seen to be convulsed, in the first moment with a strong shudder either of terror or distaste; but, in the next, his brow reddened with rage.

"Who dares?" he demanded hoarsely of the courtiers who stood near him—"who dares insult us with this blasphemous mockery? Seize him and unmask him—that we may know whom we have to hang at sunrise, from the battlements!"

It was in the eastern or blue chamber in which stood the Prince Prospero as he uttered these words. They rang throughout the seven rooms loudly and clearly—for the prince was a bold and robust man, and the music had become hushed at the waving of his hand.

It was in the blue room where stood the prince, with a group of pale courtiers by his side. At first, as he spoke, there was a slight rushing movement of this group in the direction of the intruder, who at the moment was also near at hand, and now, with deliberate and stately step, made closer approach to the speaker. But from a certain nameless awe with which the mad assumptions of the mummer had inspired the whole party, there were found none who put forth hand to seize him; so that, unimpeded, he passed within a yard of the prince's person; and, while the vast assembly, as if with one impulse, shrank from the centres of the rooms to the walls, he made his way uninter-ruptedly, but with the same solemn and measured step which had distinguished him from the first, through the blue chamber to the purple—through the purple to the green—through the green to the orange —through this again to the white—and even thence to the violet, ere a decided movement had been made to arrest him. It was then, however, that the Prince Prospero, maddening with rage and the shame of his own momentary cowardice, rushed hurriedly through the six chambers, while none followed him on account of a deadly terror that had seized upon all. He bore aloft a drawn dagger, and had approached, in rapid impetuosity, to within three or four feet of the retreating figure, when the latter, having attained the extremity of the velvet apartment, turned suddenly and confronted his pursuer. There was a sharp cry—and the dagger dropped gleaming upon the sable carpet, upon which, instantly afterwards, fell prostrate in death the Prince Prospero. Then, summoning the wild courage of despair, a throng of the revellers at once threw themselves into the black apartment, and, seizing the mummer, whose tall figure stood erect and motionless within the shadow of the ebony clock, gasped in unutterable horror at finding the grave-cerements and corpse-like mask which they handled with so violent a rudeness, untenanted by any tangible form.

And now was acknowledged the presence of the Red Death. He had come like a thief in the night. And one by one dropped the revellers in the blood-bedewed halls of their revel, and died each in the despairing posture of his fall. And the life of the ebony clock went out with that of the last of the gay. And the flames of the tripods expired. And Darkness and Decay and the Red Death held illimitable dominion over all.

Questions for Discussion:

1. What do you think is the significance of the colors of the chambers? Why is the final one black?
2. At the beginning of the story, Prince Prospero is described as "happy and dauntless and sagacious." By the end of the story, he is a changed man. What words would you use to describe him at the end of the story?
3. Time is often referenced in the story. How is this significant to the theme of the story?
4. Throughout the story, the Prince seems to control the events of the ball; however, when he spies the "spectral image" it is clear this is something he had not planned. In your opinion, who/what is this figure?

3. Death comes @ night, midnight is the turning of the day, so you won't see the next day. Stages of life are referenced through the rooms.

4. It is the desease + death itself. All the wealth + power can't control when you're supposed to die.

"Barn Burning"

William Faulkner

Author Biography: William Faulkner was born in Mississippi in 1897, where he lived most of his life in Oxford. Hoping to see action in World War I, Faulkner went to Canada where he joined the British Army, the U.S. Army having rejected him for his 5' 5" height. After the War, Faulkner attended the University of Mississippi but dropped out after three semesters. Working a number of jobs in his early life, Faulkner began writing around 1925 and continued throughout his life, writing short stories, plays, novels, and even pieces for Hollywood. He received the Nobel Prize in Literature in 1949, and is one of the foremost figures in American letters.

Context: Faulkner was born and raised in Mississippi and is one of the leading figures in literature about the American South. Much of his work takes place in fictional Yoknapatawpha County, in which many of his most memorable characters live, all based on his experiences in the South as well as stories he was told throughout his life. In his work, readers experience a raw and unvarnished picture of the old American South, a place that was changing rapidly in the nineteenth century and experienced all kinds of growing pains as a result.

Literary Terms: theme, structure, point of view, setting, characterization

The store in which the justice of the Peace's court was sitting smelled of cheese. The boy, crouched on his nail keg at the back of the crowded room, knew he smelled cheese, and more: from where he sat he could see the ranked shelves close-packed with the solid, squat, dynamic shapes of tin cans whose labels his stomach read, not from the lettering which meant nothing to his mind but from the scarlet devils and the silver curve of fish—this, the cheese which he knew he smelled and the hermetic meat which his intestines believed he smelled coming in intermittent gusts momentary and brief between the other constant one, the smell and sense just a little of fear because mostly of despair and grief, the old fierce pull of blood. He could not see the table where the Justice sat and before which his father and his father's enemy (our enemy he thought in that despair; ourn! mine and hisn both! He's my father!) stood, but he could hear them, the two of them that is, because his father had said no word yet:

"But what proof have you, Mr. Harris?"

"I told you. The hog got into my corn. I caught it up and sent it back to him. He had no fence that would hold it. I told him so, warned him. The next time I put the hog in my pen. When he came to get it I gave him enough wire to patch up his pen. The next time I put the hog up and kept it. I rode down to his house and saw the wire I gave him still rolled on to the spool in his yard. I told him he could have the hog when he paid me a dollar pound fee. That evening a nigger came with the dollar and got the hog. He was a strange nigger. He said, 'He say to tell you wood and hay kin burn.' I said, 'What?' 'That whut he say to tell you,' the nigger said. 'Wood and hay kin burn.' That night my barn burned. I got the stock out but I lost the barn."

"Where is the nigger? Have you got him?"

"He was a strange nigger, I tell you. I don't know what became of him."

"But that's not proof. Don't you see that's not proof?"

"Get that boy up here. He knows." For a moment the boy thought too that the man meant his older brother until Harris said, "Not him. The little one. The boy," and, crouching, small for his age, small and wiry like his father, in patched and faded jeans even too small for him, with straight, uncombed, brown hair and eyes gray and wild as storm scud, he saw the men between himself and the table part and become a lane of grim faces, at the end of which he saw the justice, a shabby, collarless, graying man in spectacles, beckoning him. He felt no floor under his bare feet; he seemed to walk beneath the palpable weight of the grim turning faces. His father, stiff in his black Sunday coat donned not for the trial but for the moving, did not even look at him. *He aims for me to lie,* he thought, again with that frantic grief and despair. *And I will have to do hit.*

"What's your name, boy?" the justice said.

"Colonel Sartoris Snopes," the boy whispered.

"Hey?" the Justice said. "Talk louder. Colonel Sartoris? I reckon anybody named for Colonel Sartoris in this country can't help but tell the truth, can they?" The boy said nothing. *Enemy! Enemy!* he thought; for a moment he could not even see, could not see that the justice's face was kindly nor discern that his voice was troubled when he spoke to the man named Harris: "Do you want me to question this boy?" But he could hear, and during those subsequent long seconds while there was absolutely no sound in the crowded little room save that of quiet and intent breathing it was as if he had swung outward at the end of a grape vine, over a ravine, and at the top of the swing had been caught in a prolonged instant of mesmerized gravity, weightless in time.

"No!" Harris said violently, explosively. "Damnation! Send him out of here!" Now time, the fluid world, rushed beneath him again, the voices coming to him again through the smell of cheese and sealed meat, the fear and despair and the old grief of blood:

"This case is closed. I can't find against you, Snopes, but I can give you advice. Leave this country and don't come back to it."

His father spoke for the first time, his voice cold and harsh, level, without emphasis: "I aim to. I don't figure to stay in a country among people who…" he said something unprintable and vile, addressed to no one.

"That'll do," the Justice said. "Take your wagon and get out of this country before dark. Case dismissed."

His father turned, and he followed the stiff black coat, the wiry figure walking a little stiffly from where a Confederate provost's man's musket ball had taken him in the heel on a stolen horse thirty years ago, followed the two backs now, since between the two lines of grim-faced men and out of the store and across the worn gallery and down the sagging steps and among the dogs and half-grown boys in the mild May dust, where as he passed a voice hissed:

"Barn burner!"

Again he could not see, whirling; there was a face in a red haze, moonlike, bigger than the full moon, the owner of it half again his size, he leaping in the red haze toward the face, feeling no blow, feeling no shock when his head struck the earth, scrabbling up and leaping again, feeling no blow this time either and tasting no blood, scrabbling up to see the other boy in full flight and himself already leaping into pursuit as his father's hand jerked him back, the harsh, cold voice speaking above him: "Go get in the wagon."

It stood in a grove of locusts and mulberries across the road. His two hulking sisters in their Sunday dresses and his mother and her sister in calico and sunbonnets were already in it, sitting on and among the sorry residue of the dozen and more movings which even the boy could remember the battered stove, the broken beds and chairs, the clock inlaid with mother-of-pearl, which would not run, stopped at some fourteen minutes past two o'clock of a dead and forgotten day and time, which had been his mother's dowry. She was crying, though when she saw him she drew her sleeve across her face and began to descend from the wagon. "Get back," the father said.

"He's hurt. I got to get some water and wash his…"

His older brother had appeared from somewhere in the crowd, no taller than the father but thicker, chewing tobacco steadily,

"Get back in the wagon," his father said. He got in too, over the tail-gate. His father mounted to the seat where the older brother already sat and struck the gaunt mules two savage blows with the peeled willow, but without heat. It was not even sadistic; it was exactly that same quality which in later years would cause his descendants to over-run the engine before putting a motor car into motion, striking and reining back in the same movement. The wagon went on, the store with its quiet crowd of grimly watching men dropped behind; a curve in the road hid it. Forever he thought. Maybe he's done satisfied now, now that he has … stopping himself, not to say it aloud even to himself. His mother's hand touched his shoulder.

"Does hit hurt?" she said.

"Naw," he said. "Hit don't hurt. Lemme be."

"Can't you wipe some of the blood off before hit dries?"

"I'll wash to-night," he said. "Lemme be, I tell you."

The wagon went on. He did not know where they were going. None of them ever did or ever asked, because it was always somewhere, always a house of sorts waiting for them a day or two days or even three days away. Likely his father had already arranged to make a crop on another farm before he . . .. Again he had to stop himself. He (the father) always did. There was something about his wolflike independence and even courage when the advantage was at least neutral which impressed strangers, as if they got from his latent ravening ferocity not so much a sense of dependability as a feeling that his ferocious conviction in the rightness of his own actions would be of advantage to all whose interest lay with his.

That night they camped in a grove of oaks and beeches where a spring ran. The nights were still cool and they had a fire against it, of a rail lifted from a nearby fence and cut into lengths—a small fire, neat, niggard almost, a shrewd fire; such fires were his father's habit and custom always, even in freezing weather. Older, the boy might have remarked this and wondered why not a big one; why should not a man who had not only seen the waste and extravagance of war, but who had in his blood an inherent voracious prodigality with material not his own, have burned everything in sight? Then he might have gone a step farther and thought that that was the reason: that niggard blaze was the living fruit of nights passed during those four years in the woods hiding from all men, blue or gray, with his strings of horses (captured horses, he called them). And older still, he might have divined the true reason: that the element of fire spoke to some deep mainspring of his father's being, as the element of steel or of powder spoke to other men, as the one weapon for the preservation of integrity, else breath were not worth the breathing, and hence to be regarded with respect and used with discretion.

But he did not think this now and he had seen those same niggard blazes all his life. He merely ate his supper beside it and was already half asleep over his iron plate when his father called him, and once more he followed the stiff back, the stiff and ruthless limp, up the slope and on to the starlit road where, turning, he could see his father against the stars but without face or depth-a shape black, flat, and bloodless as though cut from tin in the iron folds of the frockcoat which had not been made for him, the voice harsh like tin and without heat like tin:

"You were fixing to tell them. You would have told him." He didn't answer. His father struck him with the flat of his hand on the side of the head, hard but without heat, exactly as he had struck the two mules at the store, exactly as he would strike either of them with any stick in order to kill a horse fly, his voice still without heat or anger: "You're getting to be a man. You got to learn. You got to learn to stick to your own blood or you ain't going to have any blood to stick to you. Do you think either of them, any man there this morning would? Don't you know all they wanted was a chance to get at me because they knew I had them beat? Eh?" Later, twenty years later, he was to tell himself, "If I had said they wanted only truth, justice, he would have hit me again." But now he said nothing. He was not crying. He just stood there. "Answer me," his father said.

"Yes," he whispered. His father turned.

"Get on to bed. We'll be there to-morrow."

To-morrow they were there. In the early afternoon the wagon stopped before a paintless two-room house identical almost with the dozen others it had stopped before even in the boy's ten years, and again, as on the other dozen occasions, his mother and aunt got down and began to unload the wagon, although his two sisters and his father and brother had not moved.

"Likely hit ain't fitten for hawgs," one of the sisters said.

"Nevertheless, fit it will and you'll hog it and like it," his father said. "Get out of them chairs and help your Ma unload."

The two sisters got down, big, bovine, in a flutter of cheap ribbons; one of them drew from the jumbled wagon bed a battered lantern, the other a worn broom. His father handed the reins to the older son and began to climb stiffly over the wheel. "When they get unloaded, take the team to the barn and feed them." Then he said, and at first the boy thought he was still speaking to his brother: "Come with me."

"Me?" he said.

"Yes," his father said. "You."

"Abner," his mother said. His father paused and looked back—the harsh level stare beneath the shaggy, graying, irascible brows.

"I reckon I'll have a word with the man that aims to begin to-morrow owning me body and soul for the next eight months."

They went back up the road. A week ago—or before last night, that is—he would have asked where they were going, but not now. His father had struck him before last night but never before had he paused afterward to explain why; it was as if the blow and the following calm, outrageous voice still rang, repercussed, divulging nothing to him save the terrible handicap of being young, the light weight of his few years, just heavy enough to prevent his soaring free of the world as it seemed to be ordered but not heavy enough to keep him footed solid in it, to resist it and try to change the course of its events.

Presently he could see the grove of oaks and cedars and the other flowering trees and shrubs where the house would be, though not the house yet. They walked beside a fence massed with honeysuckle and Cherokee roses and came to a gate swinging open between two brick pillars, and now, beyond a sweep of drive, he saw the house for the first time and at that instant he forgot his father and the terror and despair both, and even when he remembered his father again (who had not stopped) the terror and despair did not return. Because, for all the twelve movings, they had sojourned until now in a poor country, a land of small farms and fields and houses, and he had never seen a house like this before. Hit's big as a courthouse he thought quietly, with a surge of peace and joy whose reason he could not have thought into words, being too young for that: They are safe from him. People whose lives are a part of this peace and dignity are beyond his touch, he no more to them than a buzzing wasp: capable of stinging for a little moment but that's all; the spell of this peace and dignity rendering even the barns and stable and cribs which belong to it impervious to the puny flames he might contrive ... this, the peace and joy, ebbing for an instant as he looked again at the stiff black back, the stiff and implacable limp of the figure which was not dwarfed by the house, for the reason that it had never looked big anywhere and which now, against the serene columned backdrop, had more than ever that impervious quality of something cut ruthlessly from tin, depthless, as though, sidewise to the sun, it would cast no shadow. Watching him, the boy remarked the absolutely undeviating course which his father held and saw the stiff foot come squarely down in a pile of fresh droppings where a horse had stood in the drive and which his father could have avoided by a simple change of stride. But it ebbed only for a moment, though he could not have thought this into words either, walking on in the spell of the house, which he could even want but without envy, without sorrow, certainly never with that ravening and jealous rage which unknown to him walked in the iron like black coat before him. Maybe he will feel it too. Maybe it will even change him now from what maybe he couldn't help but be.

They crossed the portico. Now he could hear his father's stiff foot as it came down on the boards with clocklike finality, a sound out of all proportion to the displacement of the body it bore and which was not dwarfed either by the white door before it, as though it had attained to a sort of vicious and ravening minimum not to be dwarfed by anything—the flat, wide, black hat, the formal coat of broadcloth which had once been black but which had now the friction-glazed greenish cast of the bodies of old house flies, the lifted sleeve which was too large, the lifted hand like a curled claw. The door opened so promptly that the boy knew the Negro must have been watching them all the time, an old man with neat grizzled hair, in a linen jacket, who stood barring the door with his body, saying, "Wipe yo foots, white man, fo you come in here. Major ain't home nohow."

"Get out of my way, nigger," his father said, without heat too, flinging the door back and the Negro also and entering, his hat still on his head. And now the boy saw the prints of the stiff foot on the doorjamb and saw them appear on the pale rug behind the machinelike deliberation of the foot which seemed to bear (or transmit) twice the weight which the body compassed. The Negro was shouting "Miss Lula! Miss Lula!" somewhere behind them, then the boy, deluged as though by a warm wave by a suave turn of carpeted stair and a pendant glitter of chandeliers and a mute gleam of gold frames, heard the swift feet and saw her too, a lady—perhaps he had never seen her like before either—in a gray, smooth gown with lace at the throat and an apron tied at the waist and the sleeves turned back, wiping cake or biscuit dough from her hands with a towel as she came up the hall, looking not at his father at all but at the tracks on the blond rug with an expression of incredulous amazement.

"I tried," the Negro cried. "I tole him to . . ."

"Will you please go away?" she said in a shaking voice. "Major de Spain is not at home. Will you please go away?"

His father had not spoken again. He did not speak again. He did not even look at her. He just stood stiff in the center of the rug, in his hat, the shaggy iron-gray brows twitching slightly above the pebble-colored eyes as he appeared to examine the house with brief deliberation. Then with the same deliberation he turned; the boy watched him pivot on the good leg and saw the stiff foot drag round the arc of the turning, leaving a final long and fading smear. His father never looked at it, he never once looked down at the rug. The Negro held the door. It closed behind them, upon the hysteric and indistinguishable woman-wail. His father stopped at the top of the steps and scraped his boot clean on the edge of it. At the gate he stopped again. He stood for a moment, planted stiffly on the stiff foot, looking back at the house. "Pretty and white, ain't it?" he said. "That's sweat. Nigger sweat. Maybe it ain't white enough yet to suit him. Maybe he wants to mix some white sweat with it."

Two hours later the boy was chopping wood behind the house within which his mother and aunt and the two sisters (the mother and aunt, not the two girls, he knew that; even at this distance and muffled by walls the flat loud voices of the two girls emanated an incorrigible idle inertia) were setting up the stove to prepare a meal, when he heard the hooves and saw the linen-clad man on a fine sorrel mare, whom he recognized even before he saw the rolled rug in front of the Negro youth following on a fat bay carriage horse—a suffused, angry face vanishing, still at full gallop, beyond the corner of the house where his father and brother were sitting in the two tilted chairs; and a moment later, almost before he could have put the axe down, he heard the hooves again and watched the sorrel mare go back out of the yard, already galloping again.

Then his father began to shout one of the sisters' names, who presently emerged backward from the kitchen door dragging the rolled rug along the ground by one end while the other sister walked behind it.

"If you ain't going to tote, go on and set up the wash pot," the first said.

"You, Sarty!" the second shouted, "Set up the wash pot!" His father appeared at the door, framed against that shabbiness, as he had been against that other bland perfection, impervious to either, the mother's anxious face at his shoulder.

"Go on," the father said. "Pick it up." The two sisters stooped, broad, lethargic; stooping, they presented an incredible expanse of pale cloth and a flutter of tawdry ribbons.

"If I thought enough of a rug to have to git hit all the way from France I wouldn't keep hit where folks coming in would have to tromp on hit," the first said. They raised the rug.

"Abner," the mother said. "Let me do it."

"You go back and git dinner," his father said. "I'll tend to this."

From the woodpile through the rest of the afternoon the boy watched them, the rug spread flat in the dust beside the bubbling wash-pot, the two sisters stooping over it with that profound and lethargic reluctance, while the father stood over them in turn, implacable and grim, driving them though never raising his voice again. He could smell the harsh homemade lye they were using; he saw his mother come to the door once and look toward them with an expression not anxious now but very like despair; he saw his father turn, and he fell to with the axe and saw from the corner of his eye his father raise from the ground a flattish fragment of field stone and examine it and return to the pot, and this time his mother actually spoke: "Abner. Abner. Please don't. Please, Abner."

Then he was done too. It was dusk; the whippoorwills had already begun. He could smell coffee from the room where they would presently eat the cold food remaining from the mid-afternoon meal, though when he entered the house he realized they were having coffee again probably because there was a fire on the hearth, before which the rug now lay spread over the backs of the two chairs. The tracks of his father's foot were gone. Where they had been were now long, water-cloudy scoriations resembling the sporadic course of a lilliputian mowing machine.

It still hung there while they ate the cold food and then went to bed, scattered without order or claim up and down the two rooms, his mother in one bed, where his father would later lie, the older brother in the other, himself, the aunt, and the two sisters on pallets on the floor. But his father was not in bed yet. The last thing the boy remembered was the depthless, harsh silhouette of the hat and coat bending over the rug and it seemed to him that he had not even closed his eyes when the silhouette was standing over him, the fire almost dead behind it, the stiff foot prodding him awake. "Catch up the mule," his father said.

When he returned with the mule his father was standing in the black door, the rolled rug over his shoulder. "Ain't you going to ride?" he said.

"No. Give me your foot."

He bent his knee into his father's hand, the wiry, surprising power flowed smoothly, rising, he rising with it, on to the mule's bare back (they had owned a saddle once; the boy could remember it though not when or where) and with the same effortlessness his father swung the rug up in front of him. Now in the starlight they retraced the afternoon's path, up the dusty road rife with honeysuckle, through the gate and up the black tunnel of the drive to the lightless house, where he sat on the mule and felt the rough warp of the rug drag across his thighs and vanish.

"Don't you want me to help?" he whispered. His father did not answer and now he heard again that stiff foot striking the hollow portico with that wooden and clocklike deliberation, that outrageous overstatement of the weight it carried. The rug, hunched, not flung (the boy could tell that even in the darkness) from his father's shoulder struck the angle of wall and floor with a sound unbelievably loud, thunderous, then the foot again, unhurried and enormous; a light came on in the house and the boy sat, tense, breathing steadily and quietly and just a little fast, though the foot itself did not increase its beat at all, descending the steps now; now the boy could see him.

"Don't you want to ride now?" he whispered. "We kin both ride now," the light within the house altering now, flaring up and sinking, He's coming down the stairs now, he thought. He had already ridden the mule up beside the horse block; presently his father was up behind him and he doubled the reins over and slashed the mule across the neck, but before the animal could begin to trot the hard, thin arm came round him, the hard, knotted hand jerking the mule back to a walk.

In the first red rays of the sun they were in the lot, putting plow gear on the mules. This time the sorrel mare was in the lot before he heard it at all, the rider collarless and even bareheaded, trembling, speaking in a shaking voice as the woman in the house had done, his father merely looking up once before stooping again to the hame he was buckling, so that the man on the mare spoke to his stooping back:

"You must realize you have ruined that rug. Wasn't there anybody here, any of your women…" he ceased, shaking, the boy watching him, the older brother leaning now in the stable door, chewing, blinking slowly and steadily at nothing apparently. "It cost a hundred dollars. But you never had a hundred dollars. You never will. So I'm going to charge you twenty bushels of corn against your crop. I'll add it in your contract and when you come to the commissary you can sign it. That won't keep Mrs. de Spain quiet but maybe it will teach you to wipe your feet off before you enter her house again."

Then he was gone. The boy looked at his father, who still had not spoken or even looked up again, who was now adjusting the logger-head in the hame.

"Pap," he said. His father looked at him—the inscrutable face, the shaggy brows beneath which the gray eyes glinted coldly. Suddenly the boy went toward him, fast, stopping as suddenly. "You done the best you could!" he cried. "If he wanted hit done different why didn't he wait and tell you how? He won't git no twenty bushels! He won't git none! We'll gether hit and hide hit! I kin watch…"

"Did you put the cutter back in that straight stock like I told you?"

"No sir," he said.

"Then go do it."

That was Wednesday. During the rest of that week he worked steadily, at what was within his scope and some which was beyond it, with an industry that did not need to be driven nor even commanded twice; he had this from his mother, with the difference that some at least of what he did he liked to do, such as splitting wood with the half-size axe which his mother and aunt had earned, or saved money somehow, to present him with at Christmas. In company with the two older women (and on one afternoon, even one of the sisters), he built pens for the shoat and the cow which were a part of his father's contract with the landlord, and one afternoon, his father being absent, gone somewhere on one of the mules, he went to the field,

They were running a middle buster now, his brother holding the plow straight while he handled the reins, and walking beside the straining mule, the rich black soil shearing cool and damp against his bare ankles, he thought Maybe this is the end of it. Maybe even that twenty bushels that seems hard to have to pay for just a rug will be a cheap price for him to stop forever and always from being what he used to be;

thinking, dreaming now, so that his brother had to speak sharply to him to mind the mule: Maybe he even won't collect the twenty bushels. Maybe it will all add up and balance and vanish—corn, rug, fire; the terror and grief, the being pulled two ways like between two teams of horses—gone, done with for ever and ever.

Then it was Saturday; he looked up from beneath the mule he was harnessing and saw his father in the black coat and hat. "Not that," his father said. "The wagon gear." And then, two hours later, sitting in the wagon bed behind his father and brother on the seat, the wagon accomplished a final curve, and he saw the weathered paintless store with its tattered tobacco and patent-medicine posters and the tethered wagons and saddle animals below the gallery. He mounted the gnawed steps behind his father and brother, and there again was the lane of quiet, watching faces for the three of them to walk through. He saw the man in spectacles sitting at the plank table and he did not need to be told this was a Justice of the Peace; he sent one glare of fierce, exultant, partisan defiance at the man in collar and cravat now, whom he had seen but twice before in his life, and that on a galloping horse, who now wore on his face an expression not of rage but of amazed unbelief which the boy could not have known was at the incredible circumstance of being sued by one of his own tenants, and came and stood against his father and cried at the justice: "He ain't done it! He ain't burnt..."

"Go back to the wagon," his father said.

"Burnt?" the Justice said. "Do I understand this rug was burned too?"

"Does anybody here claim it was?" his father said. "Go back to the wagon." But he did not, he merely retreated to the rear of the room, crowded as that other had been, but not to sit down this time, instead, to stand pressing among the motionless bodies, listening to the voices:

"And you claim twenty bushels of corn is too high for the damage you did to the rug?"

"He brought the rug to me and said he wanted the tracks washed out of it. I washed the tracks out and took the rug back to him."

"But you didn't carry the rug back to him in the same condition it was in before you made the tracks on it."

His father did not answer, and now for perhaps half a minute there was no sound at all save that of breathing, the faint, steady suspiration of complete and intent listening.

"You decline to answer that, Mr. Snopes?" Again his father did not answer. "I'm going to find against you, Mr. Snopes, I'm going to find that you were responsible for the injury to Major de Spain's rug and hold you liable for it. But twenty bushels of corn seems a little high for a man in your circumstances to have to pay. Major de Spain claims it cost a hundred dollars. October corn will be worth about fifty cents. I figure that if Major de Spain can stand a ninety-five dollar loss on something he paid cash for, you can stand a five-dollar loss you haven't earned yet. I hold you in damages to Major de Spain to the amount of ten bushels of corn over and above your contract with him, to be paid to him out of your crop at gathering time. Court adjourned."

It had taken no time hardly, the morning was but half begun. He thought they would return home and perhaps back to the field, since they were late, far behind all other farmers. But instead his father passed on behind the wagon, merely indicating with his hand for the older brother to follow with it, and he crossed the road toward the blacksmith shop opposite, pressing on after his father, overtaking him, speaking, whispering up at the harsh, calm face beneath the weathered hat: "He won't git no ten bushels neither. He won't git one. We'll…" until his father glanced for an instant down at him, the face absolutely calm, the grizzled eyebrows tangled above the cold eyes, the voice almost pleasant, almost gentle:

"You think so? Well, we'll wait till October anyway."

The matter of the wagon—the setting of a spoke or two and the tightening of the tires—did not take long either, the business of the tires accomplished by driving the wagon into the spring branch behind the shop and letting it stand there, the mules nuzzling into the water from time to time, and the boy on the seat with the idle reins, looking up the slope and through the sooty tunnel of the shed where the slow hammer rang and where his father sat on an upended cypress bolt, easily, either talking or listening, still sitting there when the boy brought the dripping wagon up out of the branch and halted it before the door.

"Take them on to the shade and hitch," his father said. He did so and returned. His father and the smith and a third man squatting on his heels inside the door were talking, about crops and animals; the boy, squatting too in the ammoniac dust and hoof-parings and scales of rust, heard his father tell a long and unhurried story out of the time before the birth of the older brother even when he had been a professional horse trader. And then his father came up beside him where he stood before a tattered last year's circus poster on the other side of the store, gazing rapt and quiet at the scarlet horses, the incredible poisings and convolutions of tulle and tights and the painted leer of comedians, and said, "It's time to eat."

But not at home. Squatting beside his brother against the front wall, he watched his father emerge from the store and produce from a paper sack a segment of cheese and divide it carefully and deliberately into three with his pocket knife and produce crackers from the same sack. They all three squatted on the gallery and ate, slowly, without talking; then in the store again, they drank from a tin dipper tepid water smelling of the cedar bucket and of living beech trees. And still they did not go home. It was a horse lot this time, a tall rail fence upon and along which men stood and sat and out of which one by one horses were led, to be walked and trotted and then cantered back and forth along the road while the slow swapping and buying went on and the sun began to slant westward, they—the three of them—watching and listening, the older brother with his muddy eyes and his steady, inevitable tobacco, the father commenting now and then on certain of the animals, to no one in particular.

It was after sundown when they reached home. They ate supper by lamplight, then, sitting on the doorstep, the boy watched the night fully accomplished, listening to the whippoorwills and the frogs, when he heard his mother's voice: "Abner! No! No! Oh, God. Oh, God. Abner!" and he rose, whirled, and saw the altered light through the door where a candle stub now burned in a bottle neck on the table and his father, still in the hat and coat, at once formal and burlesque as though dressed carefully for some shabby and ceremonial violence, emptying the reservoir of the lamp back into the five-gallon kerosene can from which it had been filled, while the mother tugged at his arm until he shifted the lamp to the other hand and flung her back, not savagely or viciously, just hard, into the wall, her hands flung out against the wall for balance, her mouth open and in her face the same quality of hopeless despair as had been in her voice. Then his father saw him standing in the door.

"Go to the barn and get that can of oil we were oiling the wagon with," he said. The boy did not move. Then he could speak.

"What…" he cried "What are you…"

"Go get that oil," his father said. "Go."

Then he was moving, running outside the house, toward the stable: this the old habit, the old blood which he had not been permitted to choose for himself, which had been bequeathed him willy nilly and which had run for so long (and who knew where, battening on what of outrage and savagery and lust) before it came to him. I could keep on, he thought. I could run on and on and never look back, never need to see his face again. Only I can't. I can't, the rusted can in his hand now, the liquid sploshing in it as he ran back to the house and into it, into the sound of his mother's weeping in the next room, and handed the can to his father.

"Ain't you going to even send a nigger?" he cried. "At least you sent a nigger before!"

This time his father didn't strike him. The hand came even faster than the blow had, the same hand which had set the can on the table with almost excruciating care flashing from the can toward him too quick for him to follow it, gripping him by the back of the shirt and on to tiptoe before he had seen it quit the can, the face stooping at him in breathless and frozen ferocity, the cold, dead voice speaking over him to the older brother who leaned against the table, chewing with that steady, curious, sidewise motion of cows:

"Empty the can into the big one and go on. I'll ketch up with you."

"Better tie him to the bedpost," the brother said.

"Do like I told you," the father said. Then the boy was moving, his bunched shirt and the hard, bony hand between his shoulder-blades, his toes just touching the floor, across the room and into the other one, past the sisters sitting with spread heavy thighs in the two chairs over the cold hearth, and to where his mother and aunt sat side by side on the bed, the aunt's arms about his mother's shoulders.

"Hold him," the father said. The aunt made a startled movement. "Not you," the father said. "Lennie. Take hold of him. I want to see you do it." His mother took him by the wrist. "You'll hold him better than that. If he gets loose don't you know what he is going to do? He will go up yonder." He jerked his head toward the road. "Maybe I'd better tie him."

"I'll hold him," his mother whispered.

"See you do then." Then his father was gone, the stiff foot heavy and measured upon the boards, ceasing at last.

Then he began to struggle. His mother caught him in both arms, he jerking and wrenching at them. He would be stronger in the end, he knew that. But he had no time to wait for it. "Lemme go!" he cried. "I don't want to have to hit you!"

"Let him go!" the aunt said. "If he don't go, before God, I am going up there myself!"

"Don't you see I can't?" his mother cried. "Sarty! Sarty! No! No! Help me, Lizzie!"

Then he was free. His aunt grasped at him but was too late. He whirled, running, his mother stumbled forward on to her knees behind him, crying to the nearer sister: "Catch him, Net! Catch him!" But that was too late too, the sister (the sisters were twins, born at the same time, yet either of them now gave the impression of being, encompassing as much living meat and volume and weight as any other two of the family) not yet having begun to rise from the chair, her head, face, alone merely turned, presenting to him in the flying instant an astonishing expanse of young female features untroubled by any surprise even, wearing only an expression of bovine interest. Then he was out of the room, out of the house, in the mild dust of the starlit road and the heavy rifeness of honeysuckle, the pale ribbon unspooling with terrific slowness under his running feet, reaching the gate at last and turning in, running, his heart and lungs drumming, on up the drive toward the lighted house, the lighted door. He did not knock, he burst in, sobbing for breath, incapable for the moment of speech; he saw the astonished face of the Negro in the linen jacket without knowing when the Negro had appeared.

"De Spain!" he cried, panted. "Where's…" then he saw the white man too emerging from a white door down the hall. "Barn!" he cried. "Barn!"

"What?" the white man said. "Barn?"

"Yes!" the boy cried. "Barn!"

"Catch him!" the white man shouted.

But it was too late this time too. The Negro grasped his shirt, but the entire sleeve, rotten with washing, carried away, and he was out that door too and in the drive again, and had actually never ceased to run even while he was screaming into the white man's face.

Behind him the white man was shouting, "My horse! Fetch my horse!" and he thought for an instant of cutting across the park and climbing the fence into the road, but he did not know the park nor how high the vine-massed fence might be and he dared not risk it. So he ran on down the drive, blood and breath roaring; presently he was in the road again though he could not see it. He could not hear either: the galloping mare was almost upon him before he heard her, and even then he held his course, as if the urgency of his wild grief and need must in a moment more find him wings, waiting until the ultimate instant to hurl himself aside and into the weed-choked roadside ditch as the horse thundered past and on, for an instant in furious silhouette against the stars, the tranquil early summer night sky which, even before the shape of the horse and rider vanished, strained abruptly and violently upward: a long, swirling roar incredible and soundless, blotting the stars, and he springing up and into the road again, running again, knowing it was too late yet still running even after he heard the shot and, an instant later, two shots, pausing now without knowing he had ceased to run, crying "Pap! Pap!," running again before he knew he had begun to run, stumbling, tripping over something and scrabbling up again without ceasing to run, looking backward over his shoulder at the glare as he got up, running on among the invisible trees, panting, sobbing, "Father! Father!"

At midnight he was sitting on the crest of a hill. He did not know it was midnight and he did not know how far he had come. But there was no glare behind him now and he sat now, his back toward what he had called home for four days anyhow, his face toward the dark woods which he would enter when breath was strong again, small, shaking steadily in the chill darkness, hugging himself into the remainder of his thin, rotten shirt, the grief and despair now no longer terror and fear but just grief and despair. Father. My father, he thought. "He was brave!" he cried suddenly, aloud but not loud, no more than a whisper: "He was! He was in the war! He was in Colonel Sartoris' cav'ry!" not knowing that his father had gone to that war a private in the fine old European sense, wearing no uniform, admitting the authority of and giving fidelity to no man or army or flag, going to war as Malbrouck himself did: for booty—it meant nothing and less than nothing to him if it were enemy booty or his own.

The slow constellations wheeled on. It would be dawn and then sun-up after a while and he would be hungry. But that would be to-morrow and now he was only cold, and walking would cure that. His breathing was easier now and he decided to get up and go on, and then he found that he had been asleep because he knew it was almost dawn, the night almost over. He could tell that from the whippoorwills. They were everywhere now among the dark trees below him, constant and inflectioned and ceaseless, so that, as the instant for giving over to the day birds drew nearer and nearer, there was no interval at all between them. He got up. He was a little stiff, but walking would cure that too as it would the cold, and soon there would be the sun. He went on down the hill, toward the dark woods within which the liquid silver voices of the birds called unceasing—the rapid and urgent beating of the urgent and quiring heart of the late spring night. He did not look back.

Questions for Discussion:

1. Discuss Sarty's interior monologues in the story. How do these function to help the reader understand his character and motivations?
2. What do you think are the major conflicts/tensions in this story?
3. Why do you think Sarty's father chooses fire as an outlet for his anger? Support your answer with examples from the text.
4. Discuss the stream-of-consciousness style technique used in "Barn Burning." How does this particular style of writing function to make the story more effective?

"The Veldt"

Ray Bradbury

Author Biography: Born in 1920 in Illinois, Ray Bradbury became one of the foremost American authors of the twentieth century. Writing primarily science fiction and horror, Bradbury's favorite themes were about the advancement of technology and concerns about dystopian futures.

Context: Bradbury was working during a time of great change in America. He saw the rise and fall of Hitler in Germany and the Civil Rights Movement of the 1960s. He also saw, and was deeply interested in, the rapid rise of technological advancement that led to the moon landing and the world's first computers. Much of his work is interested in the issues surrounding technology, which have only accelerated in our own time.

Literary Terms: theme, setting, (lack of) characterization, metaphor

"George, I wish you'd look at the nursery."

"What's wrong with it?"

"I don't know."

"Well, then."

"I just want you to look at it, is all, or call a psychologist in to look at it."

"What would a psychologist want with a nursery?"

"You know very well what he'd want." His wife paused in the middle of the kitchen and watched the stove busy humming to itself, making supper for four.

"It's just that the nursery is different now than it was."

"All right, let's have a look."

They walked down the hall of their soundproofed Happylife Home, which had cost them thirty thousand dollars installed, this house which clothed and fed and rocked them to sleep and played and sang and was good to them.

Their approach sensitized a switch somewhere and the nursery light flicked on when they came within ten feet of it. Similarly, behind them, in the halls, lights went on and off as they left them behind, with a soft automaticity.

"Well," said George Hadley.

They stood on the thatched floor of the nursery. It was forty feet across by forty feet long and thirty feet high; it had cost half again as much as the rest of the house. "But nothing's too good for our children," George had said.

The nursery was silent. It was empty as a jungle glade at hot high noon. The walls were blank and two dimensional. Now, as George and Lydia Hadley stood in the center of the room, the walls began to purr and recede into crystalline distance, it seemed, and presently an African veldt appeared, in three dimensions, on all sides, in color reproduced to the final pebble and bit of straw. The ceiling above them became a deep sky with a hot yellow sun.

George Hadley felt the perspiration start on his brow.

"Let's get out of this sun," he said. "This is a little too real. But I don't see anything wrong."

"Wait a moment, you'll see," said his wife.

Now the hidden odorophonics were beginning to blow a wind of odor at the two people in the middle of the baked veldtland. The hot straw smell of lion grass, the cool green smell of the hidden water hole, the great rusty smell of animals, the smell of dust like a red paprika in the hot air. And now the sounds: the thump of distant antelope feet on grassy sod, the papery rustling of vultures. A shadow passed through the sky. The shadow flickered on George Hadley's upturned, sweating face.

"Filthy creatures," he heard his wife say.

"The vultures."

"You see, there are the lions, far over, that way. Now they're on their way to the water hole. They've just been eating," said Lydia. "I don't know what."

"Some animal." George Hadley put his hand up to shield off the burning light from his squinted eyes. "A zebra or a baby giraffe, maybe."

"Are you sure?" His wife sounded peculiarly tense.

"No, it's a little late to be sure," be said, amused. "Nothing over there I can see but cleaned bone, and the vultures dropping for what's left."

"Did you hear that scream?" she asked.

'No."

"About a minute ago?"

"Sorry, no."

The lions were coming. And again George Hadley was filled with admiration for the mechanical genius who had conceived this room. A miracle of efficiency selling for an absurdly low price. Every home should have one. Oh, occasionally they frightened you with their clinical accuracy, they startled you, gave you a twinge, but most of the time what fun for everyone, not only your own son and daughter, but for yourself when you felt like a quick jaunt to a foreign land, a quick change of scenery. Well, here it was! And here were the lions now, fifteen feet away, so real, so feverishly and startlingly real that you could feel the prickling fur on your hand, and your mouth was stuffed with the dusty upholstery smell of their heated pelts, and the yellow of them was in your eyes like the yellow of an exquisite French tapestry, the yellows of lions and summer grass, and the sound of the matted lion lungs exhaling on the silent noontide, and the smell of meat from the panting, dripping mouths. The lions stood looking at George and Lydia Hadley with terrible green-yellow eyes.

"Watch out!" screamed Lydia.

The lions came running at them. Lydia bolted and ran. Instinctively, George sprang after her. Outside, in the hall, with the door slammed he was laughing and she was crying, and they both stood appalled at the other's reaction.

"George!"

"Lydia! Oh, my dear poor sweet Lydia!"

"They almost got us!"

"Walls, Lydia, remember; crystal walls, that's all they are. Oh, they look real, I must admit—Africa in your parlor—but it's all dimensional, superreactionary, supersensitive color film and mental tape film behind glass screens. It's all odorophonics and sonics, Lydia. Here's my handkerchief."

"I'm afraid." She came to him and put her body against him and cried steadily. "Did you see? Did you feel? It's too real."

"Now, Lydia . . ."

"You've got to tell Wendy and Peter not to read any more on Africa."

"Of course—of course." He patted her.

"Promise?"

"Sure."

"And lock the nursery for a few days until I get my nerves settled."

"You know how difficult Peter is about that. When I punished him a month ago by locking the nursery for even a few hours—the tantrum be threw! And Wendy too. They live for the nursery."

"It's got to be locked, that's all there is to it."

"All right." Reluctantly he locked the huge door. "You've been working too hard. You need a rest."

"I don't know—I don't know," she said, blowing her nose, sitting down in a chair that immediately began to rock and comfort her. "Maybe I don't have enough to do. Maybe I have time to think too much. Why don't we shut the whole house off for a few days and take a vacation?"

"You mean you want to fry my eggs for me?"

"Yes." She nodded.

"And darn my socks?"

"Yes." A frantic, watery-eyed nodding.

"And sweep the house?"

"Yes, yes—oh, yes!"

"But I thought that's why we bought this house, so we wouldn't have to do anything?"

"That's just it. I feel like I don't belong here. The house is wife and mother now, and nursemaid. Can I compete with an African veldt? Can I give a bath and scrub the children as efficiently or quickly as the automatic scrub bath can? I cannot. And it isn't just me. It's you. You've been awfully nervous lately."

"I suppose I have been smoking too much."

"You look as if you didn't know what to do with yourself in this house, either. You smoke a little more every morning and drink a little more every afternoon and need a little more sedative every night. You're beginning to feel unnecessary too."

"Am I?" He paused and tried to feel into himself to see what was really there.

"Oh, George!" She looked beyond him, at the nursery door. "Those lions can't get out of there, can they?"

He looked at the door and saw it tremble as if something had jumped against it from the other side.

"Of course not," he said.

At dinner they ate alone, for Wendy and Peter were at a special plastic carnival across town and had telephoned home to say they'd be late, to go ahead eating. So George Hadley, bemused, sat watching the dining-room table produce warm dishes of food from its mechanical interior.

"We forgot the ketchup," he said.

"Sorry," said a small voice within the table, and ketchup appeared.

As for the nursery, thought George Hadley, it won't hurt for the children to be locked out of it awhile. Too much of anything isn't good for anyone. And it was clearly indicated that the children had been spending a little too much time on Africa. That sun. He could feel it on his neck, still, like a hot paw. And the lions. And the smell of blood. Remarkable how the nursery caught the telepathic emanations of the children's minds and created life to fill their every desire. The children thought lions, and there were lions. The children thought zebras, and there were zebras. Sun—sun. Giraffes—giraffes. Death and death.

That last. He chewed tastelessly on the meat that the table had cut for him. Death thoughts. They were awfully young, Wendy and Peter, for death thoughts. Or, no, you were never too young, really. Long before you knew what death was you were wishing it on someone else. When you were two years old you were shooting people with cap pistols.

But this—the long, hot African veldt-the awful death in the jaws of a lion. And repeated again and again.

"Where are you going?"

He didn't answer Lydia. Preoccupied, he let the lights glow softly on ahead of him, extinguish behind him as he padded to the nursery door. He listened against it. Far away, a lion roared. He unlocked the door and opened it. Just before he stepped inside, he heard a faraway scream. And then another roar from the lions, which subsided quickly. He stepped into Africa. How many times in the last year had he opened this door and found Wonderland, Alice, the Mock Turtle, or Aladdin and his Magical Lamp, or Jack Pumpkinhead of Oz, or Dr. Doolittle, or the cow jumping over a very real-appearing moon-all the delightful contraptions of a make-believe world. How often had he seen Pegasus flying in the sky ceiling, or seen fountains of red fireworks, or heard angel voices singing. But now, this yellow hot Africa, this bake oven with murder in the heat. Perhaps Lydia was right. Perhaps they needed a little vacation from the fantasy which was growing a bit too real for ten-year-old children. It was all right to exercise one's mind with gymnastic fantasies, but when the lively child mind settled on one pattern . . . ? It seemed that, at a distance, for the past month, he had heard lions roaring, and smelled their strong odor seeping as far away as his study door. But, being busy, he had paid it no attention.

George Hadley stood on the African grassland alone. The lions looked up from their feeding, watching him. The only flaw to the illusion was the open door through which he could see his wife, far down the dark hall, like a framed picture, eating her dinner abstractedly.

"Go away," he said to the lions.

They did not go.

He knew the principle of the room exactly. You sent out your thoughts. Whatever you thought would appear. "Let's have Aladdin and his lamp," he snapped. The veldtland remained; the lions remained.

"Come on, room! I demand Aladdin!" he said.

Nothing happened. The lions mumbled in their baked pelts.

"Aladdin!"

He went back to dinner. "The fool room's out of order," he said. "It won't respond."

"Or—"

"Or what?"

"Or it can't respond," said Lydia, "because the children have thought about Africa and lions and killing so many days that the room's in a rut."

"Could be."

"Or Peter's set it to remain that way."

"Set it?"

"He may have got into the machinery and fixed something."

"Peter doesn't know machinery."

"He's a wise one for ten. That I.Q. of his -"

"Nevertheless -"

"Hello, Mom. Hello, Dad."

The Hadleys turned. Wendy and Peter were coming in the front door, cheeks like peppermint candy, eyes like bright blue agate marbles, a smell of ozone on their jumpers from their trip in the helicopter.

"You're just in time for supper," said both parents.

"We're full of strawberry ice cream and hot dogs," said the children, holding hands. "But we'll sit and watch."

"Yes, come tell us about the nursery," said George Hadley.

The brother and sister blinked at him and then at each other.

"Nursery?"

"All about Africa and everything," said the father with false joviality.

"I don't understand," said Peter.

"Your mother and I were just traveling through Africa with rod and reel; Tom Swift and his Electric Lion," said George Hadley.

"There's no Africa in the nursery," said Peter simply.

"Oh, come now, Peter. We know better."

"I don't remember any Africa," said Peter to Wendy. "Do you?"

"No."

"Run see and come tell."

She obeyed.

"Wendy, come back here!" said George Hadley, but she was gone. The house lights followed her like a flock of fireflies. Too late, he realized he had forgotten to lock the nursery door after his last inspection.

"Wendy'll look and come tell us," said Peter.

"She doesn't have to tell me. I've seen it."

"I'm sure you're mistaken, Father."

"I'm not, Peter. Come along now."

But Wendy was back. "It's not Africa," she said breathlessly.

"We'll see about this," said George Hadley, and they all walked down the hall together and opened the nursery door.

There was a green, lovely forest, a lovely river, a purple mountain, high voices singing, and Rima, lovely and mysterious, lurking in the trees with colorful flights of butterflies, like animated bouquets, lingering in her long hair. The African veldtland was gone. The lions were gone. Only Rima was here now, singing a song so beautiful that it brought tears to your eyes.

George Hadley looked in at the changed scene. "Go to bed," he said to the children. They opened their mouths.

"You heard me," he said.

They went off to the air closet, where a wind sucked them like brown leaves up the flue to their slumber rooms.

George Hadley walked through the singing glade and picked up something that lay in the comer near where the lions had been. He walked slowly back to his wife.

"What is that?" she asked.

"An old wallet of mine," he said.

He showed it to her. The smell of hot grass was on it and the smell of a lion. There were drops of saliva on it, it had been chewed, and there were blood smears on both sides. He closed the nursery door and locked it, tight.

In the middle of the night he was still awake and he knew his wife was awake.

"Do you think Wendy changed it?" she said at last, in the dark room.

"Of course."

"Made it from a veldt into a forest and put Rima there instead of lions?"

"Yes."

"Why?"

"I don't know. But it's staying locked until I find out."

"How did your wallet get there?"

"I don't know anything," he said, "except that I'm beginning to be sorry we bought that room for the children. If children are neurotic at all, a room like that -"

"It's supposed to help them work off their neuroses in a healthful way."

"I'm starting to wonder." He stared at the ceiling.

"We've given the children everything they ever wanted. Is this our reward-secrecy, disobedience?"

"Who was it said, 'Children are carpets; they should be stepped on occasionally'? We've never lifted a hand. They're insufferable—let's admit it. They come and go when they like; they treat us as if we were offspring. They're spoiled, and we're spoiled."

"They've been acting funny ever since you forbade them to take the rocket to New York a few months ago."

"They're not old enough to do that alone, I explained."

"Nevertheless, I've noticed they've been decidedly cool toward us since."

"I think I'll have David McClean come tomorrow morning to have a look at Africa."

"But it's not Africa now, it's Green Mansions country and Rima."

"I have a feeling it'll be Africa again before then."

A moment later they heard the screams.

Two screams. Two people screaming from downstairs. And then a roar of lions.

"Wendy and Peter aren't in their rooms," said his wife.

He lay in his bed with his beating heart. "No," he said. "They've broken into the nursery."

"Those screams—they sound familiar."

"Do they?"

"Yes, awfully."

And although their beds tried very hard, the two adults couldn't be rocked to sleep for another hour. A smell of cats was in the night air.

"Father?" said Peter.

"Yes."

Peter looked at his shoes. He never looked at his father any more, nor at his mother. "You aren't going to lock up the nursery for good, are you?"

"That all depends."

"On what?" snapped Peter.

"On you and your sister. If you intersperse this Africa with a little variety—oh, Sweden perhaps, or Denmark or China"

"I thought we were free to play as we wished."

"You are, within reasonable bounds."

"What's wrong with Africa, Father?"

"Oh, so now you admit you have been conjuring up Africa, do you?"

"I wouldn't want the nursery locked up," said Peter coldly. "Ever."

"Matter of fact, we're thinking of turning the whole house off for about a month. Live sort of a carefree one-for-all existence."

"That sounds dreadful! Would I have to tie my own shoes instead of letting the shoe tier do it? And brush my own teeth and comb my hair and give myself a bath?"

"It would be fun for a change, don't you think?"

"No, it would be horrid. I didn't like it when you took out the picture painter last month."

"That's because I wanted you to learn to paint all by yourself, son."

"I don't want to do anything but look and listen and smell; what else is there to do?"

"All right, go play in Africa."

"Will you shut off the house sometime soon?"

"We're considering it."

"I don't think you'd better consider it any more, Father."

"I won't have any threats from my son!"

"Very well." And Peter strolled off to the nursery.

"Am I on time?" said David McClean.

"Breakfast?" asked George Hadley.

"Thanks, had some. What's the trouble?"

"David, you're a psychologist."

"I should hope so."

"Well, then, have a look at our nursery. You saw it a year ago when you dropped by; did you notice anything peculiar about it then?"

"Can't say I did; the usual violences, a tendency toward a slight paranoia here or there, usual in children because they feel persecuted by parents constantly, but, oh, really nothing."

They walked down the hall. "I locked the nursery up," explained the father, "and the children broke back into it during the night. I let them stay so they could form the patterns for you to see."

There was a terrible screaming from the nursery.

"There it is," said George Hadley. "See what you make of it."

They walked in on the children without rapping.

The screams had faded. The lions were feeding.

"Run outside a moment, children," said George Hadley. "No, don't change the mental combination. Leave the walls as they are. Get!"

With the children gone, the two men stood studying the lions clustered at a distance, eating with great relish whatever it was they had caught.

"I wish I knew what it was," said George Hadley. "Sometimes I can almost see. Do you think if I brought high-powered binoculars here and -"

David McClean laughed dryly. "Hardly." He turned to study all four walls. "How long has this been going on?"

"A little over a month."

"It certainly doesn't feel good."

"I want facts, not feelings."

"My dear George, a psychologist never saw a fact in his life. He only hears about feelings; vague things. This doesn't feel good, I tell you. Trust my hunches and my instincts. I have a nose for something bad. This is very bad. My advice to you is to have the whole room torn down and your children brought to me every day during the next year for treatment."

"Is it that bad?"

"I'm afraid so. One of the original uses of these nurseries was so that we could study the patterns left on the walls by the child's mind, study at our leisure, and help the child. In this case, however, the room has become a channel toward destructive thoughts, instead of a release away from them."

"Didn't you sense this before?"

"I sensed only that you had spoiled your children more than most. And now you're letting them down in some way. What way?"

"I wouldn't let them go to New York."

"What else?"

"I've taken a few machines from the house and threatened them, a month ago, with closing up the nursery unless they did their homework. I did close it for a few days to show I meant business."

"Ah, ha!"

"Does that mean anything?"

"Everything. Where before they had a Santa Claus now they have a Scrooge. Children prefer Santas. You've let this room and this house replace you and your wife in your children's affections. This room is their mother and father, far more important in their lives than their real parents. And now you come along and want to shut it off. No wonder there's hatred here. You can feel it coming out of the sky. Feel that sun. George, you'll have to change your life. Like too many others, you've built it around creature comforts. Why, you'd starve tomorrow if something went wrong in your kitchen. You wouldn't know bow to tap an egg. Nevertheless, turn everything off. Start new. It'll take time. But we'll make good children out of bad in a year, wait and see."

"But won't the shock be too much for the children, shutting the room up abruptly, for good?"

"I don't want them going any deeper into this, that's all."

The lions were finished with their red feast.

The lions were standing on the edge of the clearing watching the two men.

"Now I'm feeling persecuted," said McClean. "Let's get out of here. I never have cared for these darned rooms. Make me nervous."

"The lions look real, don't they?" said George Hadley. I don't suppose there's any way—"

"What?"

"—that they could become real?"

"Not that I know."

"Some flaw in the machinery, a tampering or something?"

"No."

They went to the door.

"I don't imagine the room will like being turned off," said the father.

"Nothing ever likes to die—even a room."

"I wonder if it hates me for wanting to switch it off?"

"Paranoia is thick around here today," said David McClean. "You can follow it like a spoor. Hello." He bent and picked up a bloody scarf. "This yours?"

"No." George Hadley's face was rigid. "It belongs to Lydia."

They went to the fuse box together and threw the switch that killed the nursery.

The two children were in hysterics. They screamed and pranced and threw things. They yelled and sobbed and swore and jumped at the furniture.

"You can't do that to the nursery, you can't!"

"Now, children."

The children flung themselves onto a couch, weeping.

"George," said Lydia Hadley, "turn on the nursery, just for a few moments. You can't be so abrupt."

"No."

"You can't be so cruel . . ."

"Lydia, it's off, and it stays off. And the whole house dies as of here and now. The more I see of the mess we've put ourselves in, the more it sickens me. We've been contemplating our mechanical, electronic navels for too long. My goodness, how we need a breath of honest air!"

And he marched about the house turning off the voice clocks, the stoves, the heaters, the shoe shiners, the shoe lacers, the body scrubbers and swabbers and massagers, and every other machine be could put his hand to.

The house was full of dead machines, it seemed. It felt like a mechanical cemetery. So silent. None of the humming hidden energy of machines waiting to function at the tap of a button.

"Don't let them do it!" wailed Peter at the ceiling, as if he was talking to the house, the nursery. "Don't let Father kill everything." He turned to his father. "Oh, I hate you!"

"Insults won't get you anywhere."

"I wish you were dead!"

"We were, for a long while. Now we're going to really start living. Instead of being handled and massaged, we're going to live."

Wendy was still crying and Peter joined her again. "Just a moment, just one moment, just another moment of nursery," they wailed.

"Oh, George," said the wife, "it can't hurt."

"All right—all right, if they'll just shut up. One minute, mind you, and then off forever."

"Daddy, Daddy, Daddy!" sang the children, smiling with wet faces.

"And then we're going on a vacation. David McClean is coming back in half an hour to help us move out and get to the airport. I'm going to dress. You turn the nursery on for a minute, Lydia, just a minute, mind you."

And the three of them went babbling off while he let himself be vacuumed upstairs through the air flue and set about dressing himself. A minute later Lydia appeared.

"I'll be glad when we get away," she sighed.

"Did you leave them in the nursery?"

"I wanted to dress too. Oh, that horrid Africa. What can they see in it?"

"Well, in five minutes we'll be on our way to Iowa. Lord, how did we ever get in this house? What prompted us to buy a nightmare?"

"Pride, money, foolishness."

"I think we'd better get downstairs before those kids get engrossed with those darned beasts again."

Just then they heard the children calling, "Daddy, Mommy, come quick—quick!"

They went downstairs in the air flue and ran down the hall. The children were nowhere in sight. "Wendy? Peter!"

They ran into the nursery. The veldtland was empty save for the lions waiting, looking at them. "Peter, Wendy?"

The door slammed.

"Wendy, Peter!"

George Hadley and his wife whirled and ran back to the door.

"Open the door!" cried George Hadley, trying the knob. "Why, they've locked it from the outside! Peter!" He beat at the door. "Open up!"

He heard Peter's voice outside, against the door.

"Don't let them switch off the nursery and the house," he was saying.

Mr. and Mrs. George Hadley beat at the door. "Now, don't be ridiculous, children. It's time to go. Mr. McClean'll be here in a minute and . . ."

And then they heard the sounds.

The lions on three sides of them, in the yellow veldt grass, padding through the dry straw, rumbling and roaring in their throats.

The lions.

Mr. Hadley looked at his wife, and they turned and looked back at the beasts edging slowly forward crouching, tails stiff.

Mr. and Mrs. Hadley screamed.

And suddenly they realized why those other screams had sounded familiar.

"Well, here I am," said David McClean in the nursery doorway, "Oh, hello." He stared at the two children seated in the center of the open glade eating a little picnic lunch. Beyond them was the water hole and the yellow veldtland; above was the hot sun. He began to perspire. "Where are your father and mother?"

The children looked up and smiled. "Oh, they'll be here directly."

"Good, we must get going." At a distance Mr. McClean saw the lions fighting and clawing and then quieting down to feed in silence under the shady trees.

He squinted at the lions with his hand tip to his eyes.

Now the lions were done feeding. They moved to the water hole to drink.

A shadow flickered over Mr. McClean's hot face. Many shadows flickered. The vultures were dropping down the blazing sky.

"A cup of tea?" asked Wendy in the silence.

Questions for Discussion:

1. The family's home is described as that "which clothed and fed and rocked them to sleep and played and sang and was good to them." When you first read that line, did you think it was an odd way to describe the house? In what ways did you come to learn that these characteristics were not merely metaphorical?
2. How would you describe the relationship between George and Lydia and their children?
3. The theme of the story is technology. What do you think Bradbury means for the reader to understand about technology? Is there a moral to the story?
4. Ray Bradbury is widely known as the author for many scientific and horror stories, most notably, *Farenheit 451*. Although he wrote in the 1950's, much of his works center around his predictions of life in and around the year 2000. How do you think "The Veldt" translates to 21st-century culture? How close does the story's theme function as a realistic prediction of technology in our time?

"The Story of An Hour"

Kate Chopin

Author Biography: Born Katherine O'Flaherty in St. Louis, MO in 1850, Kate Chopin wrote short stories and novels that, while published in major publications, invited some controversy for subjects and characters that were ahead of their time. Much of her work is set in Louisiana and New Orleans, where she moved in 1870 after marrying. She died of a brain hemorrhage while visiting the St. Louis World's Fair in 1904.

Context: Some of Chopin's work was considered controversial or even immoral at the time it was published, as some of the themes and characters' actions conflicted with accepted behavior for the time. In fact, many who study her work believe her to be an early feminist who wrote about female characters who felt liberated being on their own and expressing their sexuality.

Literary Terms: theme, irony, paradox

Knowing that Mrs. Mallard was afflicted with a heart trouble, great care was taken to break to her as gently as possible the news of her husband's death.

It was her sister Josephine who told her, in broken sentences; veiled hints that revealed in half concealing. Her husband's friend Richards was there, too, near her. It was he who had been in the newspaper office when intelligence of the railroad disaster was received, with Brently Mallard's name leading the list of "killed." He had only taken the time to assure himself of its truth by a second telegram, and had hastened to forestall any less careful, less tender friend in bearing the sad message.

She did not hear the story as many women have heard the same, with a paralyzed inability to accept its significance. She wept at once, with sudden, wild abandonment, in her sister's arms. When the storm of grief had spent itself she went away to her room alone. She would have no one follow her.

There stood, facing the open window, a comfortable, roomy armchair. Into this she sank, pressed down by a physical exhaustion that haunted her body and seemed to reach into her soul.

She could see in the open square before her house the tops of trees that were all aquiver with the new spring life. The delicious breath of rain was in the air. In the street below a peddler was crying his wares. The notes of a distant song which some one was singing reached her faintly, and countless sparrows were twittering in the eaves.

There were patches of blue sky showing here and there through the clouds that had met and piled one above the other in the west facing her window.

She sat with her head thrown back upon the cushion of the chair, quite motionless, except when a sob came up into her throat and shook her, as a child who has cried itself to sleep continues to sob in its dreams.

She was young, with a fair, calm face, whose lines bespoke repression and even a certain strength. But now there was a dull stare in her eyes, whose gaze was fixed away off yonder on one of those patches of blue sky. It was not a glance of reflection, but rather indicated a suspension of intelligent thought.

There was something coming to her and she was waiting for it, fearfully. What was it? She did not know; it was too subtle and elusive to name. But she felt it, creeping out of the sky, reaching toward her through the sounds, the scents, the color that filled the air.

Now her bosom rose and fell tumultuously. She was beginning to recognize this thing that was approaching to possess her, and she was striving to beat it back with her will—as powerless as her two white slender hands would have been. When she abandoned herself a little whispered word escaped her slightly parted lips. She said it over and over under her breath: "free, free, free!" The vacant stare and the look of terror that had followed it went from her eyes. They stayed keen and bright. Her pulses beat fast, and the coursing blood warmed and relaxed every inch of her body.

She did not stop to ask if it were or were not a monstrous joy that held her. A clear and exalted perception enabled her to dismiss the suggestion as trivial. She knew that she would weep again when she saw the kind, tender hands folded in death; the face that had never looked save with love upon her, fixed and gray and dead. But she saw beyond that bitter moment a long procession of years to come that would belong to her absolutely. And she opened and spread her arms out to them in welcome.

There would be no one to live for during those coming years; she would live for herself. There would be no powerful will bending hers in that blind persistence with which men and women believe they have a right to impose a private will upon a fellow-creature. A kind intention or a cruel intention made the act seem no less a crime as she looked upon it in that brief moment of illumination.

And yet she had loved him—sometimes. Often she had not. What did it matter! What could love, the unsolved mystery, count for in the face of this possession of self-assertion which she suddenly recognized as the strongest impulse of her being!

"Free! Body and soul free!" she kept whispering.

Josephine was kneeling before the closed door with her lips to the keyhold, imploring for admission. "Louise, open the door! I beg; open the door—you will make yourself ill. What are you doing, Louise? For heaven's sake open the door."

"Go away. I am not making myself ill." No; she was drinking in a very elixir of life through that open window.

Her fancy was running riot along those days ahead of her. Spring days, and summer days, and all sorts of days that would be her own. She breathed a quick prayer that life might be long. It was only yesterday she had thought with a shudder that life might be long.

She arose at length and opened the door to her sister's importunities. There was a feverish triumph in her eyes, and she carried herself unwittingly like a goddess of Victory. She clasped her sister's waist, and together they descended the stairs. Richards stood waiting for them at the bottom.

Someone was opening the front door with a latchkey. It was Brently Mallard who entered, a little travel-stained, composedly carrying his grip-sack and umbrella. He had been far from the scene of the accident, and did not even know there had been one. He stood amazed at Josephine's piercing cry; at Richards' quick motion to screen him from the view of his wife.

When the doctors came they said she had died of heart disease—of the joy that kills.

Questions for Discussion:

1. Think about the title of this story. How do you think time functions as a central theme?
2. The narrator describes Mrs. Mallard as descending the stairs "like a goddess of Victory." Over what might she feel victorious?
3. The doctors declare that her heart problem was a disease of "the joy that kills." How do you interpret that?

"The Rocking-Horse Winner"

D. H. Lawrence

Author Biography: D.H. Lawrence was born in England in 1885. Though he is not usually grouped with the "Lost Generation" writers such as Hemingway, Fitzgerald, and Pound, Lawrence was deeply affected by the events of World War I and how modern life seemed to dehumanize others. He traveled around Europe frequently, accompanied by Frieda Weekley, who was married at the time they met. Accused of aiding Germany in the War, Lawrence was forced to move frequently, going on what he called a "savage pilgrimage." He died in France in 1930.

Context: Lawrence was a controversial figure while he was alive. Unlike many of the "Lost Generation" literary figures, Lawrence promoted a certain conservatism, bordering on fascism, in his writings. Many of his works were sexually explicit, leading some to label him a pornographer and chauvinist. Still, many saw and still see in Lawrence important critiques of modern life, which we see too in "The Rocking Horse Winner."

Literary Terms: theme, tone, imagery, metaphor

There was a woman who was beautiful, who started with all the advantages, yet she had no luck. She married for love, and the love turned to dust. She had bonny children, yet she felt they had been thrust upon her, and she could not love them. They looked at her coldly, as if they were finding fault with her. And hurriedly she felt she must cover up some fault in herself. Yet what it was that she must cover up she never knew. Nevertheless, when her children were present, she always felt the centre of her heart go hard. This troubled her, and in her manner she was all the more gentle and anxious for her children, as if she loved them very much. Only she herself knew that at the centre of her heart was a hard little place that could not feel love, no, not for anybody. Everybody else said of her: "She is such a good mother. She adores her children." Only she herself, and her children themselves, knew it was not so. They read it in each other's eyes.

There were a boy and two little girls. They lived in a pleasant house, with a garden, and they had discreet servants, and felt themselves superior to anyone in the neighbourhood.

Although they lived in style, they felt always an anxiety in the house. There was never enough money. The mother had a small income, and the father had a small income, but not nearly enough for the social position which they had to keep up. The father went into town to some office. But though he had good prospects, these prospects never materialised. There was always the grinding sense of the shortage of money, though the style was always kept up.

At last the mother said: "I will see if I can't make something." But she did not know where to begin. She racked her brains, and tried this thing and the other, but could not find anything successful. The failure made deep lines come into her face. Her children were growing up, they would have to go to school. There must be more money, there must be more money. The father, who was always very handsome and expensive in his tastes, seemed as if he never would be able to do anything worth doing. And the mother, who had a great belief in herself, did not succeed any better, and her tastes were just as expensive.

And so the house came to be haunted by the unspoken phrase: There must be more money! There must be more money! The children could hear it all the time though nobody said it aloud. They heard it at Christmas, when the expensive and splendid toys filled the nursery. Behind the shining modern rocking-horse, behind the smart doll's house, a voice would start whispering: "There must be more money! There must be more money!" And the children would stop playing, to listen for a moment. They would look into each other's eyes, to see if they had all heard. And each one saw in the eyes of the other two that they too had heard. "There must be more money! There must be more money!"

It came whispering from the springs of the still-swaying rocking-horse, and even the horse, bending his wooden, champing head, heard it. The big doll, sitting so pink and smirking in her new pram, could hear it quite plainly, and seemed to be smirking all the more self-consciously because of it. The foolish puppy, too, that took the place of the teddy-bear, he was looking so extraordinarily foolish for no other reason but that he heard the secret whisper all over the house: "There must be more money!"

Yet nobody ever said it aloud. The whisper was everywhere, and therefore no one spoke it. Just as no one ever says: "We are breathing!" in spite of the fact that breath is coming and going all the time.

"Mother," said the boy Paul one day, "why don't we keep a car of our own? Why do we always use uncle's, or else a taxi?"

"Because we're the poor members of the family," said the mother.

"But why are we, mother?"

"Well—I suppose," she said slowly and bitterly, "it's because your father has no luck."

The boy was silent for some time.

"Is luck money, mother?" he asked, rather timidly.

"No, Paul. Not quite. It's what causes you to have money."

"Oh!" said Paul vaguely. "I thought when Uncle Oscar said filthy lucker, it meant money."

"Filthy lucre does mean money," said the mother. "But it's lucre, not luck."

"Oh!" said the boy. "Then what is luck, mother?"

"It's what causes you to have money. If you're lucky you have money. That's why it's better to be born lucky than rich. If you're rich, you may lose your money. But if you're lucky, you will always get more money."

"Oh! Will you? And is father not lucky?"

"Very unlucky, I should say," she said bitterly.

The boy watched her with unsure eyes.

"Why?" he asked.

"I don't know. Nobody ever knows why one person is lucky and another unlucky."

"Don't they? Nobody at all? Does nobody know?"

"Perhaps God. But He never tells."

"He ought to, then. And aren't you lucky either, mother?"

"I can't be, it I married an unlucky husband."

"But by yourself, aren't you?"

"I used to think I was, before I married. Now I think I am very unlucky indeed."

"Why?"

"Well—never mind! Perhaps I'm not really," she said.

The child looked at her to see if she meant it. But he saw, by the lines of her mouth, that she was only trying to hide something from him.

"Well, anyhow," he said stoutly, "I'm a lucky person."

"Why?" said his mother, with a sudden laugh.

He stared at her. He didn't even know why he had said it.

"God told me," he asserted, brazening it out.

"I hope He did, dear!", she said, again with a laugh, but rather bitter.

"He did, mother!"

"Excellent!" said the mother, using one of her husband's exclamations.

The boy saw she did not believe him; or rather, that she paid no attention to his assertion. This angered him somewhere, and made him want to compel her attention.

He went off by himself, vaguely, in a childish way, seeking for the clue to 'luck'. Absorbed, taking no heed of other people, he went about with a sort of stealth, seeking inwardly for luck. He wanted luck, he wanted it, he wanted it. When the two girls were playing dolls in the nursery, he would sit on his big rocking-horse, charging madly into space, with a frenzy that made the little girls peer at him uneasily. Wildly the horse careered, the waving dark hair of the boy tossed, his eyes had a strange glare in them. The little girls dared not speak to him.

When he had ridden to the end of his mad little journey, he climbed down and stood in front of his rocking-horse, staring fixedly into its lowered face. Its red mouth was slightly open, its big eye was wide and glassy-bright.

"Now!" he would silently command the snorting steed. "Now take me to where there is luck! Now take me!"

And he would slash the horse on the neck with the little whip he had asked Uncle Oscar for. He knew the horse could take him to where there was luck, if only he forced it. So he would mount again and start on his furious ride, hoping at last to get there.

"You'll break your horse, Paul!" said the nurse.

"He's always riding like that! I wish he'd leave off!" said his elder sister Joan.

But he only glared down on them in silence. Nurse gave him up. She could make nothing of him. Anyhow, he was growing beyond her.

One day his mother and his Uncle Oscar came in when he was on one of his furious rides. He did not speak to them.

"Hallo, you young jockey! Riding a winner?" said his uncle.

"Aren't you growing too big for a rocking-horse? You're not a very little boy any longer, you know," said his mother.

But Paul only gave a blue glare from his big, rather close-set eyes. He would speak to nobody when he was in full tilt. His mother watched him with an anxious expression on her face.

At last he suddenly stopped forcing his horse into the mechanical gallop and slid down.

"Well, I got there!" he announced fiercely, his blue eyes still flaring, and his sturdy long legs straddling apart.

"Where did you get to?" asked his mother.

"Where I wanted to go," he flared back at her.

"That's right, son!" said Uncle Oscar. "Don't you stop till you get there. What's the horse's name?"

"He doesn't have a name," said the boy.

"Get's on without all right?" asked the uncle.

"Well, he has different names. He was called Sansovino last week."

"Sansovino, eh? Won the Ascot. How did you know this name?"

"He always talks about horse-races with Bassett," said Joan.

The uncle was delighted to find that his small nephew was posted with all the racing news. Bassett, the young gardener, who had been wounded in the left foot in the war and had got his present job through Oscar Cresswell, whose batman he had been, was a perfect blade of the 'turf'. He lived in the racing events, and the small boy lived with him.

Oscar Cresswell got it all from Bassett.

"Master Paul comes and asks me, so I can't do more than tell him, sir," said Bassett, his face terribly serious, as if he were speaking of religious matters.

"And does he ever put anything on a horse he fancies?"

"Well—I don't want to give him away—he's a young sport, a fine sport, sir. Would you mind asking him himself? He sort of takes a pleasure in it, and perhaps he'd feel I was giving him away, sir, if you don't mind.

Bassett was serious as a church.

The uncle went back to his nephew and took him off for a ride in the car.

"Say, Paul, old man, do you ever put anything on a horse?" the uncle asked.

The boy watched the handsome man closely.

"Why, do you think I oughtn't to?" he parried.

"Not a bit of it! I thought perhaps you might give me a tip for the Lincoln."

The car sped on into the country, going down to Uncle Oscar's place in Hampshire.

"Honour bright?" said the nephew.

"Honour bright, son!" said the uncle.

"Well, then, Daffodil."

"Daffodil! I doubt it, sonny. What about Mirza?"

"I only know the winner," said the boy. "That's Daffodil."

"Daffodil, eh?"

There was a pause. Daffodil was an obscure horse comparatively.

"Uncle!"

"Yes, son?"

"You won't let it go any further, will you? I promised Bassett."

"Bassett be damned, old man! What's he got to do with it?"

"We're partners. We've been partners from the first. Uncle, he lent me my first five shillings, which I lost. I promised him, honour bright, it was only between me and him; only you gave me that ten-shilling note I started winning with, so I thought you were lucky. You won't let it go any further, will you?"

The boy gazed at his uncle from those big, hot, blue eyes, set rather close together. The uncle stirred and laughed uneasily.

"Right you are, son! I'll keep your tip private. How much are you putting on him?"

"All except twenty pounds," said the boy. "I keep that in reserve."

The uncle thought it a good joke.

"You keep twenty pounds in reserve, do you, you young romancer? What are you betting, then?"

"I'm betting three hundred," said the boy gravely. "But it's between you and me, Uncle Oscar! Honour bright?"

"It's between you and me all right, you young Nat Gould," he said, laughing. "But where's your three hundred?"

"Bassett keeps it for me. We're partners."

"You are, are you! And what is Bassett putting on Daffodil?"

"He won't go quite as high as I do, I expect. Perhaps he'll go a hundred and fifty."

"What, pennies?" laughed the uncle.

"Pounds," said the child, with a surprised look at his uncle. "Bassett keeps a bigger reserve than I do."

Between wonder and amusement Uncle Oscar was silent. He pursued the matter no further, but he determined to take his nephew with him to the Lincoln races.

"Now, son," he said, "I'm putting twenty on Mirza, and I'll put five on for you on any horse you fancy. What's your pick?"

"Daffodil, uncle."

"No, not the fiver on Daffodil!"

"I should if it was my own fiver," said the child.

"Good! Good! Right you are! A fiver for me and a fiver for you on Daffodil."

The child had never been to a race-meeting before, and his eyes were blue fire. He pursed his mouth tight and watched. A Frenchman just in front had put his money on Lancelot. Wild with excitement, he flayed his arms up and down, yelling "Lancelot!, Lancelot!" in his French accent.

Daffodil came in first, Lancelot second, Mirza third. The child, flushed and with eyes blazing, was curiously serene. His uncle brought him four five-pound notes, four to one.

"What am I to do with these?" he cried, waving them before the boys eyes.

"I suppose we'll talk to Bassett," said the boy. "I expect I have fifteen hundred now; and twenty in reserve; and this twenty."

His uncle studied him for some moments.

"Look here, son!" he said. "You're not serious about Bassett and that fifteen hundred, are you?"

"Yes, I am. But it's between you and me, uncle. Honour bright?"

"Honour bright all right, son! But I must talk to Bassett."

"If you'd like to be a partner, uncle, with Bassett and me, we could all be partners. Only, you'd have to promise, honour bright, uncle, not to let it go beyond us three.

Bassett and I are lucky, and you must be lucky, because it was your ten shillings I started winning with . . ."

Uncle Oscar took both Bassett and Paul into Richmond Park for an afternoon, and there they talked.

"It's like this, you see, sir," Bassett said. "Master Paul would get me talking about racing events, spinning yarns, you know, sir. And he was always keen on knowing if I'd made or if I'd lost. It's about a year since, now, that I put five shillings on Blush of Dawn for him: and we lost. Then the luck turned, with that ten shillings he had from you: that we put on Singhalese. And since that time, it's been pretty steady, all things considering. What do you say, Master Paul?"

"We're all right when we're sure," said Paul. "It's when we're not quite sure that we go down."

"Oh, but we're careful then," said Bassett.

"But when are you sure?" smiled Uncle Oscar.

"It's Master Paul, sir," said Bassett in a secret, religious voice. "It's as if he had it from heaven. Like Daffodil, now, for the Lincoln. That was as sure as eggs."

"Did you put anything on Daffodil?" asked Oscar Cresswell.

"Yes, sir, I made my bit."

"And my nephew?"

Bassett was obstinately silent, looking at Paul.

"I made twelve hundred, didn't I, Bassett? I told uncle I was putting three hundred on Daffodil."

"That's right," said Bassett, nodding.

"But where's the money?" asked the uncle.

"I keep it safe locked up, sir. Master Paul he can have it any minute he likes to ask for it."

"What, fifteen hundred pounds?"

"And twenty! And forty, that is, with the twenty he made on the course."

"It's amazing!" said the uncle.

"If Master Paul offers you to be partners, sir, I would, if I were you: if you'll excuse me," said Bassett.

Oscar Cresswell thought about it.

"I'll see the money," he said.

They drove home again, and, sure enough, Bassett came round to the garden-house with fifteen hundred pounds in notes. The twenty pounds reserve was left with Joe Glee, in the Turf Commission deposit.

"You see, it's all right, uncle, when I'm sure! Then we go strong, for all we're worth, don't we, Bassett?"

"We do that, Master Paul."

"And when are you sure?" said the uncle, laughing.

"Oh, well, sometimes I'm absolutely sure, like about Daffodil," said the boy; "and sometimes I have an idea; and sometimes I haven't even an idea, have I, Bassett? Then we're careful, because we mostly go down."

"You do, do you! And when you're sure, like about Daffodil, what makes you sure, sonny?"

"Oh, well, I don't know," said the boy uneasily. "I'm sure, you know, uncle; that's all."

"It's as if he had it from heaven, sir," Bassett reiterated.

"I should say so!" said the uncle.

But he became a partner. And when the Leger was coming on Paul was 'sure' about Lively Spark, which was a quite inconsiderable horse. The boy insisted on putting a thousand on the horse, Bassett went for five hundred, and Oscar Cresswell two hundred. Lively Spark came in first, and the betting had been ten to one against him. Paul had made ten thousand.

"You see," he said. "I was absolutely sure of him."

Even Oscar Cresswell had cleared two thousand.

"Look here, son," he said, "this sort of thing makes me nervous."

"It needn't, uncle! Perhaps I shan't be sure again for a long time."

"But what are you going to do with your money?" asked the uncle.

"Of course," said the boy, "I started it for mother. She said she had no luck, because father is unlucky, so I thought if I was lucky, it might stop whispering."

"What might stop whispering?"

"Our house. I hate our house for whispering."

"What does it whisper?"

"Why—why"—the boy fidgeted—"why, I don't know. But it's always short of money, you know, uncle."

"I know it, son, I know it."

"You know people send mother writs, don't you, uncle?"

"I'm afraid I do," said the uncle.

"And then the house whispers, like people laughing at you behind your back. It's awful, that is! I thought if I was lucky—"

"You might stop it," added the uncle.

The boy watched him with big blue eyes, that had an uncanny cold fire in them, and he said never a word.

"Well, then!" said the uncle. "What are we doing?"

"I shouldn't like mother to know I was lucky," said the boy.

"Why not, son?"

"She'd stop me."

"I don't think she would."

"Oh!"—and the boy writhed in an odd way—"I don't want her to know, uncle."

"All right, son! We'll manage it without her knowing."

They managed it very easily. Paul, at the other's suggestion, handed over five thousand pounds to his uncle, who deposited it with the family lawyer, who was then to inform Paul's mother that a relative had put five thousand pounds into his hands, which sum was to be paid out a thousand pounds at a time, on the mother's birthday, for the next five years.

"So she'll have a birthday present of a thousand pounds for five successive years," said Uncle Oscar. "I hope it won't make it all the harder for her later."

Paul's mother had her birthday in November. The house had been 'whispering' worse than ever lately, and, even in spite of his luck, Paul could not bear up against it. He was very anxious to see the effect of the birthday letter, telling his mother about the thousand pounds.

When there were no visitors, Paul now took his meals with his parents, as he was beyond the nursery control. His mother went into town nearly every day. She had discovered that she had an odd knack of sketching furs and dress materials, so she worked secretly in the studio of a friend who was the chief 'artist' for the leading drapers. She drew the figures of ladies in furs and ladies in silk and sequins for the newspaper advertisements. This young woman artist earned several thousand pounds a year, but Paul's mother only made several hundreds, and she was again dissatisfied. She so wanted to be first in something, and she did not succeed, even in making sketches for drapery advertisements.

She was down to breakfast on the morning of her birthday. Paul watched her face as she read her letters. He knew the lawyer's letter. As his mother read it, her face hardened and became more expressionless. Then a cold, determined look came on her mouth. She hid the letter under the pile of others, and said not a word about it.

"Didn't you have anything nice in the post for your birthday, mother?" said Paul.

"Quite moderately nice," she said, her voice cold and hard and absent.

She went away to town without saying more.

But in the afternoon Uncle Oscar appeared. He said Paul's mother had had a long interview with the lawyer, asking if the whole five thousand could not be advanced at once, as she was in debt.

"What do you think, uncle?" said the boy.

"I leave it to you, son."

"Oh, let her have it, then! We can get some more with the other," said the boy.

"A bird in the hand is worth two in the bush, laddie!" said Uncle Oscar.

"But I'm sure to know for the Grand National; or the Lincolnshire; or else the Derby. I'm sure to know for one of them," said Paul.

So Uncle Oscar signed the agreement, and Paul's mother touched the whole five thousand. Then something very curious happened. The voices in the house suddenly went mad, like a chorus of frogs on a spring evening. There were certain new furnishings, and Paul had a tutor. He was really going to Eton, his father's school, in the following autumn. There were flowers in the winter, and a blossoming of the luxury Paul's mother had been used to. And yet the voices in the house, behind the sprays of mimosa and almond-blossom, and from under the piles of iridescent cushions, simply trilled and screamed in a sort of ecstasy: "There must be more money! Oh-h-h; there must be more money. Oh, now, now-w! Now-w-w—there must be more money! — more than ever! More than ever!"

It frightened Paul terribly. He studied away at his Latin and Greek with his tutor. But his intense hours were spent with Bassett. The Grand National had gone by: he had not 'known', and had lost a hundred pounds. Summer was at hand. He was in agony for the Lincoln. But even for the Lincoln he didn't 'know', and he lost fifty pounds. He became wild-eyed and strange, as if something were going to explode in him.

"Let it alone, son! Don't you bother about it!" urged Uncle Oscar. But it was as if the boy couldn't really hear what his uncle was saying.

"I've got to know for the Derby! I've got to know for the Derby!" the child reiterated, his big blue eyes blazing with a sort of madness.

His mother noticed how overwrought he was.

"You'd better go to the seaside. Wouldn't you like to go now to the seaside, instead of waiting? I think you'd better," she said, looking down at him anxiously, her heart curiously heavy because of him.

But the child lifted his uncanny blue eyes.

"I couldn't possibly go before the Derby, mother!" he said. "I couldn't possibly!"

"Why not?" she said, her voice becoming heavy when she was opposed. "Why not? You can still go from the seaside to see the Derby with your Uncle Oscar, if that that's what you wish. No need for you to wait here. Besides, I think you care too much about these races. It's a bad sign. My family has been a gambling family, and you won't know till you grow up how much damage it has done. But it has done damage. I shall have to send Bassett away, and ask Uncle Oscar not to talk racing to you, unless you promise to be reasonable about it: go away to the seaside and forget it. You're all nerves!"

"I'll do what you like, mother, so long as you don't send me away till after the Derby," the boy said.

"Send you away from where? Just from this house?"

"Yes," he said, gazing at her.

"Why, you curious child, what makes you care about this house so much, suddenly? I never knew you loved it."

He gazed at her without speaking. He had a secret within a secret, something he had not divulged, even to Bassett or to his Uncle Oscar.

But his mother, after standing undecided and a little bit sullen for some moments, said: "Very well, then! Don't go to the seaside till after the Derby, if you don't wish it. But promise me you won't think so much about horse-racing and events as you call them!"

"Oh no," said the boy casually. "I won't think much about them, mother. You needn't worry. I wouldn't worry, mother, if I were you."

"If you were me and I were you," said his mother, "I wonder what we should do!"

"But you know you needn't worry, mother, don't you?" the boy repeated.

"I should be awfully glad to know it," she said wearily.

"Oh, well, you can, you know. I mean, you ought to know you needn't worry," he insisted.

"Ought I? Then I'll see about it," she said.

Paul's secret of secrets was his wooden horse, that which had no name. Since he was emancipated from a nurse and a nursery-governess, he had had his rocking-horse removed to his own bedroom at the top of the house.

"Surely you're too big for a rocking-horse!" his mother had remonstrated.

"Well, you see, mother, till I can have a real horse, I like to have some sort of animal about," had been his quaint answer.

"Do you feel he keeps you company?" she laughed.

"Oh yes! He's very good, he always keeps me company, when I'm there," said Paul.

So the horse, rather shabby, stood in an arrested prance in the boy's bedroom.

The Derby was drawing near, and the boy grew more and more tense. He hardly heard what was spoken to him, he was very frail, and his eyes were really uncanny. His mother had sudden strange seizures of uneasiness about him. Sometimes, for half an hour, she would feel a sudden anxiety about him that was almost anguish. She wanted to rush to him at once, and know he was safe.

Two nights before the Derby, she was at a big party in town, when one of her rushes of anxiety about her boy, her first-born, gripped her heart till she could hardly speak. She fought with the feeling, might and main, for she believed in common sense. But it was too strong. She had to leave the dance and go downstairs to telephone to the country. The children's nursery-governess was terribly surprised and startled at being rung up in the night.

"Are the children all right, Miss Wilmot?"

"Oh yes, they are quite all right."

"Master Paul? Is he all right?"

"He went to bed as right as a trivet. Shall I run up and look at him?"

"No," said Paul's mother reluctantly. "No! Don't trouble. It's all right. Don't sit up. We shall be home fairly soon." She did not want her son's privacy intruded upon.

"Very good," said the governess.

It was about one o'clock when Paul's mother and father drove up to their house. All was still. Paul's mother went to her room and slipped off her white fur cloak. She had told her maid not to wait up for her. She heard her husband downstairs, mixing a whisky and soda.

And then, because of the strange anxiety at her heart, she stole upstairs to her son's room. Noiselessly she went along the upper corridor. Was there a faint noise? What was it?

She stood, with arrested muscles, outside his door, listening. There was a strange, heavy, and yet not loud noise. Her heart stood still. It was a soundless noise, yet rushing and powerful. Something huge, in violent, hushed motion. What was it? What in God's name was it? She ought to know. She felt that she knew the noise. She knew what it was.

Yet she could not place it. She couldn't say what it was. And on and on it went, like a madness.

Softly, frozen with anxiety and fear, she turned the door-handle.

The room was dark. Yet in the space near the window, she heard and saw something plunging to and fro. She gazed in fear and amazement.

Then suddenly she switched on the light, and saw her son, in his green pyjamas, madly surging on the rocking-horse. The blaze of light suddenly lit him up, as he urged the wooden horse, and lit her up, as she stood, blonde, in her dress of pale green and crystal, in the doorway.

"Paul!" she cried. "Whatever are you doing?"

"It's Malabar!" he screamed in a powerful, strange voice. "It's Malabar!"

His eyes blazed at her for one strange and senseless second, as he ceased urging his wooden horse. Then he fell with a crash to the ground, and she, all her tormented motherhood flooding upon her, rushed to gather him up.

But he was unconscious, and unconscious he remained, with some brain-fever. He talked and tossed, and his mother sat stonily by his side.

"Malabar! It's Malabar! Bassett, Bassett, I know! It's Malabar!"

So the child cried, trying to get up and urge the rocking-horse that gave him his inspiration.

"What does he mean by Malabar?" asked the heart-frozen mother.

"I don't know," said the father stonily.

"What does he mean by Malabar?" she asked her brother Oscar.

"It's one of the horses running for the Derby," was the answer.

And, in spite of himself, Oscar Cresswell spoke to Bassett, and himself put a thousand on Malabar: at fourteen to one.

The third day of the illness was critical: they were waiting for a change. The boy, with his rather long, curly hair, was tossing ceaselessly on the pillow. He neither slept nor regained consciousness, and his eyes were like blue stones. His mother sat, feeling her heart had gone, turned actually into a stone.

In the evening Oscar Cresswell did not come, but Bassett sent a message, saying could he come up for one moment, just one moment? Paul's mother was very angry at the intrusion, but on second thoughts she agreed. The boy was the same. Perhaps Bassett might bring him to consciousness.

The gardener, a shortish fellow with a little brown moustache and sharp little brown eyes, tiptoed into the room, touched his imaginary cap to Paul's mother, and stole to the bedside, staring with glittering, smallish eyes at the tossing, dying child.

"Master Paul!" he whispered. "Master Paul! Malabar came in first all right, a clean win. I did as you told me. You've made over seventy thousand pounds, you have; you've got over eighty thousand. Malabar came in all right, Master Paul."

"Malabar! Malabar! Did I say Malabar, mother? Did I say Malabar? Do you think I'm lucky, mother? I knew Malabar, didn't I? Over eighty thousand pounds! I call that lucky, don't you, mother? Over eighty thousand pounds! I knew, didn't I know I knew? Malabar came in all right. If I ride my horse till I'm sure, then I tell you, Bassett, you can go as high as you like. Did you go for all you were worth, Bassett?"

"I went a thousand on it, Master Paul."

"I never told you, mother, that if I can ride my horse, and get there, then I'm absolutely sure—oh, absolutely! Mother, did I ever tell you? I am lucky!"

"No, you never did," said his mother.

But the boy died in the night.

And even as he lay dead, his mother heard her brother's voice saying to her, "My God, Hester, you're eighty-odd thousand to the good, and a poor devil of a son to the bad. But, poor devil, poor devil, he's best gone out of a life where he rides his rocking-horse to find a winner."

Questions for Discussion:

1. The prose of the first paragraph begins as many fairy tales do. Explain. What does the reader expect from such a beginning?
2. Note Paul's eyes throughout the story, and write down how they are described in the progression of the tale. What is the author's purpose in using the imagery of Paul's eyes?
3. Uncle Oscar notes that Paul is a "poor devil" at the end of the story and that "he's best gone out of a life where he rides a rocking horse to find a winner." What is the significance of this statement?

"Woman Hollering Creek"

Sandra Cisneros

Author Biography: Sandra Cisneros was born in Chicago in 1954, but her family moved back and forth between Mexico and the United States frequently throughout her younger years. In Chicago, the family—of which she was the only daughter of seven children—lived in one of the poorest neighborhoods. Beginning to write at a young age, she has been a prolific author of novels and short stories that have garnered her the American Book Award and the MacArthur Fellowship.

Context: Having moved back and forth between Mexico and the U.S. so frequently, Cisneros has often written about not feeling at home in either country. That idea of a split self or sense of belonging pervades her work, as do other cultural themes such as the role of women and the expectations for them in society.

Literary Terms: theme, characterization, symbolism

T he day Don Serafín gave Juan Pedro Martínez Sánchez permission to take Cleófilas Enriqueta DeLeón Hernández as his bride, across her father's threshold, over several miles of dirt road and several miles of paved, over one border and beyond to a town *en el otro lado*—on the other side—already did he divine the morning his daughter would raise her hand over her eyes, look south, and dream of returning to the chores that never ended, six good-for-nothing brothers, and one old man's complaints.

He had said, after all, in the hubbub of parting: I am your father, I will never abandon you. He *had* said that, hadn't he, when he hugged and then let her go. But at the moment Cleófilas was busy looking for Chela, her maid of honor, to fulfill their bouquet conspiracy. She would not remember her father's parting words until later. *I am your father, I will never abandon you.*

Only now as a mother did she remember. Now, when she and Juan Pedrito sat by the creek's edge. How when a man and a woman love each other, sometimes that love sours. But a parent's love for a child, a child's for its parents, is another thing entirely.

This is what Cleófilas thought evenings when Juan Pedro did not come home, and she lay on her side of the bed listening to the hollow roar of the interstate, a distant dog barking, the pecan trees rustling like ladies in stiff petticoats—*shh-shh-shh, shh-shh-shh*—soothing her to sleep.

In the town where she grew up, there isn't very much to do except accompany the aunts and godmothers to the house of one or the other to play cards. Or walk to the cinema to see this week's film again, speckled and with one hair quivering annoyingly on the screen. Or to the center of town to order a milk shake that will appear in a day and a half as a pimple on her backside. Or to the girlfriend's house to watch the latest *telenovela* episode and try to copy the way women comb their hair, wear their makeup.

But what Cleófilas has been waiting for, has been whispering and sighing and giggling for, has been anticipating since she was old enough to lean against the window displays of gauze and butterflies and lace, is passion. Not the kind on the cover of the *¡Alarma!* magazines, mind you, where the lover is photographed with the bloody fork she used to salvage her good name. But passion in its purest crystalline essence. The kind the books and songs and *telenovelas* describe when one finds, finally, the great love of one's life, and does whatever one can, must do, at whatever cost.

Tú o Nadie. "You or No One." The title of the current *telenovela.* The beautiful Lucía Méndez having to put up with all kinds of hardships of the heart, separation and betrayal, and loving, always loving no matter what, because *that* is the important thing, and did you see Lucía Méndez on the Bayer aspirin commercials—wasn't she lovely? Does she dye her hair do you think? Cleófilas is going to go to the *farmacía* and buy a hair rinse; her girlfriend Chela will apply it—it's not that difficult at all.

Because you didn't watch last night's episode when Lucía confessed she loved him more than anyone in her life. In her life! And she sings the song "You or No One" in the beginning and the end of the show. *Tú o Nadie.* Somehow one ought to live one's life like that, don't you think? You or no one. Because to suffer for love is good. The pain all sweet somehow. In the end.

Seguín. She had like the sound of it. Far away and lovely. Not like *Monclova. Coahuia.* Ugly.

Seguín, Tejas. A nice sterling ring to it. The tinkle of money. She would get to wear outfits like the women on the *tele*, like Lucía Méndez. And have a lovely house, and wouldn't Chela be jealous.

And yes, they will drive all the way to Laredo to get her wedding dress. That's what they say. Because Juan Pedro wants to get married right away, without a long engagement since he can't take off too much time from work. He has a very important position in Seguin with, with…a beer company, I think. Or was it tires? Yes, he has to be back. So they will get married in the spring when he can take off work, and then they will drive off in his new pickup—did you see it?—to their new home in Seguin. Well, not exactly new, but they're going to repaint the house. You know newlyweds. New paint and new furniture. Why not? He can afford it. And later on add maybe a room or two for the children. May they be blessed with many.

Well, you'll see. Cleófilas has always been so good with her sewing machine. A little *rrr, rrr, rrr* of the machine and ¡*zas!* Miracles. She's always been so clever, that girl. Poor thing. And without even a mama to advise her on things like her wedding night. Well, may God help her. What with a father with a head like a burro, and those six clumsy brothers. Well, what do you think! Yes, I'm going to the wedding. Of course! The dress I want to wear just needs to be altered a teensy bit to bring it up to date. See, I saw a new style last night that I thought would suit me. Did you watch last night's episode of *The Rich Also Cry?* Well, did you notice the dress the mother was wearing?

La Gritona. Such a funny name for such a lovely *arroyo*. But that's what they called the creek that ran behind the house. Though no one could say whether the woman had hollered from anger or pain. The natives only knew the *arroyo* one crossed on the way to San Antonio, and then once again on the way back, was called Woman Hollering, a name no one from these parts questioned, little less understood. *Pues, allá de los indios, quién sabe*—who knows, the townspeople shrugged, because it was of no concern to their lives how this trickle of water received its curious name.

"What do you want to know for?" Trini the Laundromat attendant asked in the same gruff Spanish she always used whenever she gave Cleófilas change or yelled at her for something. First for putting too much soap in the machines. Later, for sitting on a washer. And still later, after Juan Pedrito was born, for not understanding that in this country you cannot let your baby walk around with no diaper and his pee-pee hanging out, it wasn't nice, *¿entiendes? Pues.*

How could Cleófilas explain to a woman like this why the name Woman Hollering fascinated her. Well, there was no sense talking to Trini.

On the other hand there were the neighbor ladies, one on either side of the house they rented near the *arroyo*. The woman Soledad on the left, the woman Dolores on the right.

The neighbor lady Soledad liked to call herself a widow, though how she came to be one was a mystery. Her husband had either died, or run away with an ice-house floozie, or simply gone out for cigarettes one afternoon and never came back. It was hard to say which since Soledad, as a rule, didn't mention him.

In the other house lived *la señora* Dolores, kind and very sweet, but her house smelled too much of incense and candles from the altars that burned continuously in memory of two sons who had died in the last war and one husband who had died shortly after from grief. The neighbor lady Dolores divided her time between the memory of these men and her garden, famous for its sunflowers—so tall they had to be supported with broom handles and old boards; red red cockscombs, fringed and bleeding a thick menstrual color; and, especially, roses whose sad scent reminded Cleófilas of the dead. Each Sunday *la señora* Dolores clipped the most beautiful of these flowers and arranged them on three modest headstones at the Seguin cemetery.

The neighbor ladies, Soledad, Dolores, they might've known once the name of the *arroyo* before it turned English but they did not know now. They were too busy remembering the men who had left through either choice or circumstance and would never come back.

Pain or rage, Cleófilas wondered when she drove over the bridge the first time as a newlywed and Juan Pedro had pointed it out. *La Gritona*, he had said, and she had laughed. Such a funny name for a creek so pretty and full of happily ever after.

The first time she had been so surprised she didn't cry out or try to defend herself. She had always said she would strike back if a man, any man, were to strike her.

But when the moment came, and he slapped her once, and then again, and again, until the lip split and bled an orchid of blood, she didn't fight back, she didn't break into tears, she didn't run away as she imagined she might when she saw such things in the *telenovelas*.

In her own home her parents had never raised a hand to each other or to their children. Although she admitted she may have been brought up a little leniently as an only daughter—*la consentida*, the princess—there were some things she would never tolerate. Ever.

Instead, when it happened for the first time, when they were barely man and wife, she had been so stunned, it left her speechless, motionless, numb. She had done nothing but reach up to the heat on her mouth and stare at the blood on her hand as if even then she didn't understand.

She could think of nothing to say, said nothing. Just stroked the dark curls of the man who wept and would weep like a child, his tears of repentance and shame, this time and each.

The men at the ice house. From what she can tell, from the times during her first year when still a newlywed she is invited and accompanies her husband, sits mute beside their conversation, waits and sips a beer until it grows warm, twists a paper napkin into a knot, then another into a fan, one into a rose, nods her head, smiles, yawns, politely grins, laughs at the appropriate moments, leans against her husband's sleeve, tugs at his elbow, and finally becomes good at predicting where the talk will lead, from this Cleófilas concludes each is nightly trying to find the truth lying at the bottom of the bottle like a gold doubloon on the sea floor.

They want to tell each other what they want to tell themselves. But what is bumping like a helium balloon at the ceiling of the brain never finds its way out. It bubbles and rises, it gurgles in the throat, it rolls across the surface of the tongue, and erupts from the lips—a belch.

If they are lucky, there are tears at the end of the long night. At any given moment, the fists try to speak. They are dogs chasing their own tails before lying down to sleep, trying to find a way, a route, an out, and—finally—get some peace.

In the morning sometimes before he opens his eyes. Or after they have finished loving. Or at times when he is simply across from her at the table putting pieces of food into his mouth and chewing. Cleófilas thinks, This is the man I have waited my whole life for.

Not that he isn't a good man. She has to remind herself why she loves him when she changes the baby's Pampers, or when she mops the bathroom floor, or tries to make the curtains for the doorways without doors, or whiten the linen. Or wonder a little when he kicks the refrigerator and says he hates this shitty house and is going out where he won't be bothered with the baby's howling and her suspicious questions, and her requests to fix this and this and this because if she had any brains in her head she'd realize he's been up before the rooster earning his living to pay for the food in her belly and the roof over her head and would have to wake up again early the next day so why can't you just leave me in peace, woman.

He is not very tall, no, and he doesn't look like the men on the *telenovelas*. His face still scarred from acne. And he has a bit of a belly from all the beer he drinks. Well, he's always been husky.

This man who farts and belches and snores as well as laughs and kisses and holds her. Somehow this husband whose whiskers she finds each morning in the sink, whose shoes she must air each evening on the porch, this husband who cuts his fingernails in public, laughs loudly, curses like a man, and demands each course of dinner be served on a separate plate like at his mother's, as soon as he gets home, on time or late, and who doesn't care at all for music or *telenovelas* or romance or roses or the moon floating pearly over the *arroyo*, or through the bedroom window for that matter, shut the blinds and go back to sleep, this man, this father, this rival, this keeper, this lord, this master, this husband till kingdom come.

A doubt. Slender as a hair. A washed cup set back on the shelf wrong-side-up. Her lipstick, and body talc, and hairbrush all arranged in the bathroom a different way.

No. Her imagination. The house the same as always. Nothing.

Coming home from the hospital with her new son, her husband. Something comforting in discovering her house slippers beneath the bed, the faded housecoat where she left it on the bathroom hook. Her pillow. Their bed.

Sweet sweet homecoming. Sweet as the scent of face powder in the air, jasmine, sticky liquor.

Smudged fingerprints on the door. Crushed cigarette in a glass. Wrinkle in the brain crumpling to a crease.

Sometimes she thinks of her father's house. But how could she go back there? What a disgrace. What would the neighbors say? Coming home like that with one baby on her hip and one in the oven. Where's your husband?

The town of gossips. The town of dust and despair. Which she has traded for this town of gossips. This town of dust, despair. Houses farther apart perhaps, though no more privacy because of it. No leafy *zócalo* in the center of the town, though the murmur of talk is clear enough all the same. No huddled whispering on the church steps each Sunday. Because here the whispering begins at sunset at the ice house instead.

This town with its silly pride for a bronze pecan the size of a baby carriage in front of the city hall. TV repair shop, drugstore, hardware, dry cleaner's, chiropractor's, liquor store, bail bonds, empty storefront, and nothing, nothing, nothing of interest. Nothing one could walk to, at any rate. Because the towns here are built so that you have to depend on husbands. Or you stay home. Or you drive. If you're rich enough to own, allowed to drive, your own car.

There is no place to go. Unless one counts the neighbor ladies. Soledad on one side, Dolores on the other. Or the creek.

Don't go out there after dark, *mi'jita*. Stay near the house. *No es bueno para la salud. Mala suerte.* Bad luck. *Mal aire.* You'll get sick and the baby too. You'll catch a fright wandering about in the dark, and then you'll see how right we were.

The stream sometimes only a muddy puddle in the summer, though now in the springtime, because of the rains, a good-size alive thing, a thing with a voice all its own, all day and all night calling in its high, silver voice. Is it La Llorona, the weeping woman? La Llorona, who drowned her own children. Perhaps La Llorona is the one they named the creek after, she thinks, remembering all the stories she learned as a child.

La Llorona is calling to her. She is sure of it. Cleófilas sets the baby's Donald Duck blanket on the grass. Listens. The day sky turning to night. The baby pulling up fistfuls of grass and laughing. La Llorona. Wonders if something as quiet as this drives a woman to the darkness under the trees.

What she needs is. . . and made a gesture as if to yank a woman's buttocks to his groin. Maximiliano, the foul-smelling fool from across the road, said this and set the men laughing, but Cleófilas just muttered, *Grosera*, and went on washing dishes.

She knew he said it not because it was true, but more because it was he who needed to sleep with a woman, instead of drinking each night at the ice house and stumbling home.

Maximiliano who was said to have killed his wife in an ice-house brawl when she came at him with a mop. I had to shoot, he had said—she was armed.

Their laughter outside the kitchen window. Her husband's, his friends'. Manolo, Beto, Efraín, el Perico. Maximiliano.

Was Cleófilas just exaggerating as her husband always had said? It seemed the newspapers were full of such stories. This woman found on the side of the interstate. This one pushed from a moving car. This one's cadaver, this one unconscious, this one beaten blue. Her ex-husband, her husband, her lover, her father, her brother, her uncle, her friend, her co-worker. Always. The same grisly news in the pages of the dailies. She dunked a glass under the soapy water for a moment—shivered.

He had thrown a book. Hers. From across the room. A hot welt across the cheek. She could forgive that. But what stung more was the fact that it was *her* book, a love story by Corín Tellado, what she loved most now that she lived in the U.S., without a television set, without the *telenovelas*.

Except now and again when her husband was away and she could manage it, the few episodes glimpsed at the neighbor lady Soledad's house because Dolores didn't care for that sort of thing, though Soledad was often kind enough to retell what had happened on what episode of *María de Nadie*, the poor Argentine country girl who had the ill fortune of falling in love with the beautiful son of the Arrocha family, the very family she worked for, whose roof she slept under and whose floors she vacuumed, while in that same house, with the dust brooms and floor cleaners as witnesses, the square-jawed Juan Carlos Arrocha had uttered words of love, I love you, María, listen to me, *mi querida*, but it was she who had to say No, no, we are not of the same class, and remind him it was not his place nor hers to fall in love, while all the while her heart was breaking, can you imagine.

Cleófilas thought her life would have to be like that, like a *telenovela*, only now the episodes got sadder and sadder. And there were no commercials in between for comic relief. And no happy ending in sight. She thought this when she sat with the baby out by the creek behind the house. Cleófilas de...? But somehow she would have to change her name to Topazio, or Yesenia, Cristal, Adriana, Stefania, Andrea, something more poetic than Cleófilas. Everything happened to women with names like jewels. But what happened to a Cleófilas? Nothing. But a crack in the face.

Because the doctor had said so. She has to go. To make sure the new baby is all right, so there won't be any problems when he's born, and the appointment card says next Tuesday. Could he please take her. And that's all.

No, she won't mention it. She promises. If the doctor asks she can say she fell down the front steps or slipped when she was out in the backyard, slipped out back, she could tell him that. She has to go back next Tuesday, Juan Pedro, please, for the new baby. For their child.

She would write to her father and ask maybe for money, just a loan, for the new baby's medical expenses. Well then if he'd rather she didn't. All right, she won't. Please don't anymore. Please don't. She knows it's difficult saving money with all the bills they have, but how else are they going to get out of debt with the truck payments? And after the rent and the food and the electricity and the gas and the water and the who-knows-what, well, there's hardly anything left. But please, at least for the doctor visit. She won't ask for anything else. She has to. Why is she so anxious? Because.

Because she is going to make sure the baby is not turned around backward this time to split her down the center. Yes. Next Tuesday at five-thirty. I'll have Juan Pedrito dressed and ready. But those are the only shoes he has. I'll polish them, and we'll be ready. As soon as you come from work. We won't make you ashamed.

Felice? It's me, Graciela.

No, I can't talk louder. I'm at work.

Look, I need a kind of favor. There's a patient, a lady here who's got a problem.

Well, wait a minute. Are you listening to me or what?

I can't talk real loud 'cause her husband's in the next room.

Well, would you just listen?

I was going to do this sonogram on her—she pregnant, right?—and she just starts crying on me. *Híjole*, Felice! This poor lady's got black-and-blue marks all over. I'm not kidding.

From her husband. Who else? Another one of those brides from across the border. And her family's all in Mexico.

Shit. You think they're going to help her? Give me a break. This lady doesn't even speak English. She hasn't been allowed to call home or write or nothing. That's why I'm calling you.

She needs a ride.

Not to Mexico, you goof. Just to the Greyhound. In San Anto.

No, just a ride. She's got her own money. All you'd have to do is drop her off in San Antonio on your way home. Come on, Felice. Please? If we don't help her, who will? I'd drive her myself, but she needs to be on that bus before her husband gets home from work. What do you say?

I don't know. Wait.

Right away, tomorrow even.

Well, if tomorrow's no good for you…

It's a date, Felice. Thursday. At the Cash N Carry off I-10. Noon. She'll be ready. Oh, and her name's Cleófilas.

I don't know. One of those Mexican saints, I guess. A martyr or something.

Cleófilas. C-L-E-O-F-I-L-A-S. Cle. I. Fi. Las. Write it down.

Thanks, Felice. When her kid's born she'll have to name her after us, right?

Yeah, you got it. A regular soap opera sometimes. *Qué vida, comadre. Bueno* bye.

All morning that flutter of half-fear, half-doubt. At any moment Juan Pedro might appear in the doorway. On the street. At the Cash N Carry. Like in the dreams she dreamed.

There was that to think about, yes, until the woman in the pickup drove up. Then there wasn't time to think about anything but the pickup pointed toward San Antonio. Put your bags in the back and get in.

But when they drove across the *arroyo*, the driver opened her mouth and let out a yell as loud as any mariachi. Which startled not only Cleófilas, but Juan Pedrito as well.

Pues, look how cute. I scared you two, right? Sorry. Should've warned you. Every time I cross that bridge I do that. Because of the name, you know. Woman Hollering. *Pues*, I holler. She said this in Spanish pocked with English and laughed. Did you ever notice, Felice continued, how nothing around here is named after a woman? Really. Unless she's the Virgin. I guess you're only famous if you're a virgin. She was laughing again.

That's why I like the name of that *arroyo*. Make you want to holler like Tarzan, right?

Everything about this woman, this Felice, amazed Cleófilas. The fact that she drove a pickup. A pickup, mind you, but when Cleófilas asked if it was her husband's, she said she didn't have a husband. The pickup was hers. She herself had chosen it. She herself was paying for it.

I used to have a Pontiac Sunbird. But those cars are for *viejas*. Pussy cars. Now this here is a *real* car.

What kind of talk was that coming from a woman? Cleófilas though. But then again, Felice was like no woman she'd ever met. Can you imagine, when we crossed the *arroyo* she just started yelling like a crazy, she would say later to her father and brothers. Just like that. Who would've thought?

Who would've? Pain or rage, perhaps, but not a hoot like the one Felice had just let go. Makes you want to holler like Tarzan, Felice had said.

Then Felice began laughing again, but it wasn't Felice laughing. It was gurgling out of her own throat, a long ribbon of laughter, like water.

Questions for Discussion:

1. What do you think is the significance of La Gritona? What does she symbolize?
2. What is the significance of the telenovelas in the story? Do you think they help to mold Cleófilas' desires and dreams? If so, what is this relationship?
3. Discuss the title of the story. What about the name of the creek so fascinated Cleófilas?

"Paul's Case: A Study in Temperament"

Willa Cather

> **Author Biography:** Willa Cather was born in 1873 in Virginia but moved to Nebraska when she was nine years old. Her home on the plains of the American Midwest became the backdrop and inspiration for much of her work, which often explores the contrasts between this rural American frontier and the growing American cities of the early and mid-twentieth centuries. Cather won the Pulitzer Prize in 1923 for her novel *One of Ours*.
>
> **Context:** Cather's work is often interested in exploring the personal development of characters who are finding their way through new environments, especially the city. In this work and others, we can almost see Cather engaging in a psychological experiment as she writes—what will this person do when confronted with the issues and dangers of the city? What has their background prepared them for, or not?
>
> **Literary Terms:** theme, characterization, tone, style, symbolism

It was Paul's afternoon to appear before the faculty of the Pittsburg High School to account for his various misdemeanors. He had been suspended a week ago, and his father had called at the principal's office and confessed his perplexity about his son. Paul entered the faculty room, suave and smiling. His clothes were a trifle outgrown, and the tan velvet on the collar of his open overcoat was frayed and worn; but, for all that, there was something of the dandy about him, and he wore an opal pin in his neatly knotted black four-in-hand, and a red carnation in his buttonhole. This latter adornment the faculty somehow felt was not properly significant of the contrite spirit befitting a boy under the ban of suspension.

Paul was tall for his age and very thin, with high, cramped shoulders and a narrow chest. His eyes were remarkable for a certain hysterical brilliancy, and he continually used them in a conscious, theatrical sort of way, peculiarly offensive in a boy. The pupils were abnormally large, as though he were addicted to belladonna, but there was a glassy glitter about them which that drug does not produce.

When questioned by the principal as to why he was there, Paul stated, politely enough, that he wanted to come back to school. This was a lie, but Paul was quite accustomed to lying—found it, indeed, indispensible for overcoming friction. His teachers were asked to state their respective charges, which they did with such a rancour and aggrievedness as evinced that this was not a usual case. Disorder and impertinence were among the offences named, yet each of his instructors felt that it was scarcely possible to put into words the real cause of the trouble, which lay in a sort of hysterically defiant manner of the boy's; in the contempt which they all knew he felt for them, and which he seemingly made not the least effort to conceal. Once, when he had been making a synopsis of a paragraph at the blackboard, his English teacher had stepped to his side and attempted to guide his hand. Paul had started back with a shudder, and thrust his hands violently behind him. The astonished woman could scarcely have been more hurt and embarrassed had he struck at her. The insult was so involuntary and definitely personal as to be unforgettable. In one way and another he had made all his teachers, men and women alike, conscious of the same feeling of physical aversion.

His teachers felt, this afternoon, that his whole attitude was symbolized by his shrug and his flippantly red carnation flower, and they fell upon him without mercy. He stood through it, smiling, his pale lips parted over his white teeth. (His lips were continually twitching, and he had a habit of raising his eyebrows that was contemptuous and irritating to the last degree.) Older boys than Paul had broken down and shed tears under that baptism of fire, but his set smile did not once desert him, and his only sign of discomfort was the nervous trembling of the fingers that toyed with the buttons of his overcoat, and an occasional jerking of the other hand that held his hat. Paul was always smiling, always glancing about him, seeming to feel that people might be watching him and trying to detect something. This conscious expression, since it was as far as possible from boyish mirthfulness, was usually attributed to insolence or "smartness."

As the inquisition proceeded, one of his instructors repeated an impertinent remark of the boy's, and the principal asked him whether he thought that a courteous speech to have made a woman. Paul shrugged his shoulders slightly and his eyebrows twitched.

"I don't know," he replied. "I didn't mean to be polite, or impolite, either. I guess it's a sort of way I have of saying things, regardless."

The principal, who was a sympathetic man, asked him whether he didn't think that a way it would be well to get rid of. Paul grinned and said he guessed so. When he was told that he could go, he bowed gracefully and went out. His bow was but a repetition of the scandalous red carnation.

His teachers were in despair, and his drawing-master voiced the feeling of them all when he declared there was something about the boy which none of them understood. He added: "I don't really believe that smile of his comes altogether from insolence; there's something sort of haunted about it. The boy is not strong, for one thing. I happen to know that he was born in Colorado, only a few months before his mother died out there of a long illness. There is something wrong about the fellow."

The drawing-master had come to realize that, in looking at Paul, one saw only his white teeth and the forced animation of his eyes. One warm afternoon the boy had gone to sleep at his drawing-board, and his master had noted with amazement what a white, blue-veined face it was; drawn and wrinkled like an old man's about the eyes, the lips twitching even in his sleep, and stiff with a nervous tension that drew them back from his teeth.

As for Paul, he ran down the hill whistling the soldiers' chorus from "Faust," looking wildly behind him, now and then, to see whether some of his teachers were not there to writhe under his light-heartedness. As it was now late in the afternoon, and Paul was on duty that evening as usher in Carnegie Hall, he decided that he would not go home to supper, but would hang about an Oakland tobacconist's shop until it was time to go to the concert hall.

When Paul reached the ushers' dressing-room at about half-past seven that evening, half a dozen boys were there already, and Paul began, excitedly, to tumble into his uniform. It was one of the few that at all approached fitting, and he thought it very becoming, though he knew that the tight, straight coat accentuated his narrow chest, about which he was exceedingly sensitive. He was always considerably excited while he dressed, twanging all over to the tuning of the strings and the preliminary flourishes of the horns in the music-room; but to-night he seemed quite beside himself, and he teased and plagued the boys until, telling him that he was crazy, they put him down on the floor and sat on him.

Somewhat calmed by his suppression, Paul dashed out to the front of the house to seat the early comers.

He was a model usher; gracious and smiling, he ran up and down the aisles; nothing was too much trouble for him; he carried messages and brought programs as though it were his greatest pleasure in life, and all the people in his section thought him a charming boy, feeling that he remembered and admired them. As the house filled, he grew more and more vivacious and animated, and the color came to his cheeks and lips. It was very much as though this were a great reception, and Paul were the host.

When the symphony began, Paul sank into one of the rear seats, with a long sigh of relief. It was not that symphonies, as such, meant anything in particular to Paul, but the first sigh of the instruments seemed to free some hilarious and potent spirit within him— something that struggled there like the Genius in the bottle found by the Arab fisherman. He felt a sudden zest of life; the lights danced before his eyes and the concert hall blazed into unimaginable splendor. When the soprano soloist came on, Paul half closed his eyes, and gave himself up to the peculiar stimulus such personages always had for him. The soloist chanced to be a German woman, by no means in her first youth and the mother of many children; but she wore an elaborate gown and a tiara, and above all, she had that indefinable air of achievement, that world-shine upon her, which, in Paul's eyes, made her a veritable queen of romance.

After a concert was over Paul was always irritable and wretched until he got to sleep, and to-night he was even more than usually restless. He had the feeling of not being able to let down, of its being impossible to give up this delicious excitement which was the only thing that could be called living at all. During the last number he withdrew, and, after hastily changing his clothes in the dressing-room, slipped out to the side door where the soprano's carriage stood. Here he began pacing rapidly up and down the walk, waiting to see her come out.

Over yonder the Schenley, in its vacant stretch, loomed big and square through the fine rain, the windows of its twelve stories glowing like those of a lighted cardboard house under a Christmas tree. All the actors and singers of the better class stayed there when they were in the city, and a number of the big manufacturers of the place lived there in the winter. Paul had often hung about the hotel, watching the people go in and out, longing to enter and leave school-masters and dull care behind him forever.

At last the singer came out, accompanied by the conductor who helped her into her carriage and closed the door with a cordial *auf wiedersehen*, which set Paul to wondering whether she were not an old sweetheart of his. Paul followed the carriage over to the hotel, walking so rapidly as not to be far from the entrance when the singer alighted and disappeared behind the swinging glass doors that were opened by a negro in a tall hat and a long coat. In the moment that the door was ajar, it seemed to Paul that he too entered. He seemed to feel himself go after her up the steps, into the warm, lighted building, into an exotic, a tropical world of shiny, glistening surfaces and basking ease. He reflected upon the mysterious dishes that were brought into the dining-room, the green bottles in buckets of ice, as he had seen them in the supper-party pictures of the Sunday *World* supplement. A quick gust of wind brought the rain down with sudden vehemence, and Paul was startled to find that he was still outside in the slush of the gravel driveway; that his boots were letting in the water, and his scanty overcoat was clinging wet about him; that the lights in front of the concert hall were out, and that the rain was driving in sheets between him and the orange glow of the windows above him. There it was, what he wanted—tangibly before him, like the fairy world of a Christmas pantomime, but mocking spirits stood guard at the doors, and, as the rain beat in his face, Paul wondered whether he were destined always to shiver in the black night outside, looking up at it.

He turned and walked reluctantly toward the car tracks. The end had to come sometime; his father in his night-clothes at the top of the stairs, explanations that did not explain, hastily improvised fictions that were forever tripping him up, his upstairs room and its horrible yellow Wallpaper, the creaking bureau with the greasy plush collar box and over his painted wooden bed the pictures of George Washington and John Calvin, and the framed motto, "Feed my Lambs," which had been worked in red worsted by his mother.

Half an hour later, Paul alighted from his car and went slowly down one of the side streets off the main thoroughfare. It was a highly respectable street, where all the houses were exactly alike, and where business men of moderate means begot and reared large families of children, all of whom went to Sabbath-school and learned the shorter catechism, and were interested in arithmetic; all of whom were as exactly alike as their homes, and of a piece with the monotony in which they lived. Paul never went up Cordelia Street without a shudder of loathing. His home was next to the house of the Cumberland minister. He approached it to-night with the nerveless sense of defeat, the hopeless feeling of sinking back forever into ugliness and commonness that he always had when he came home. The moment he turned into Cordelia Street he felt the waters close above his head. After each of these orgies of living, he experienced all the physical depression which follows a debauch; the loathing of respectable beds, of common food, of a house penetrated by kitchen odors; a shuddering repulsion for the flavorless, colorless mass of every-day existence; a morbid desire for cool things and soft lights and fresh flowers.

The nearer he approached the house, the more absolutely unequal Paul felt to the sight of it all; his ugly sleeping chamber, the cold bath-room, with the grimy zinc tub, the cracked mirror, the dripping spigots, his father at the top of the stairs, his hairy legs sticking out from his night-shirt, his feet thrust into carpet slippers. He was so much later than usual that there would certainly be inquiries and reproaches. Paul stopped short before the door. He felt that he could not be accosted by his father to-night, that he could not toss again on that miserable bed. He would not go in. He would tell his father that he had no car fare, and it was raining so hard he had gone home with one of the boys and stayed all night.

Meanwhile, he was wet and cold. He went around to the back of the house and tried one of the basement windows, found it open, raised it cautiously, and scrambled down the cellar wall to the floor. There he stood, holding his breath, terrified by the noise he had made, but the floor above him was silent, and there was no creak on the stairs. He found a soap box, and carried it over to the soft ring of light that streamed from the furnace door, and sat down. He was horribly afraid of rats, so he did not try to sleep, but sat looking distrustfully at the dark, still terrified least he might have awakened his father. In such reactions, after one of the experiences which made days and nights out of the dreary blanks of the calendar, when his senses were deadened, Paul's head was always singularly clear. Suppose his father had heard him getting in at the window, and come down and shot him for a burglar? Then, again, suppose his father had come down, pistol in hand, and he had cried out in time to save himself, and his father had been horrified to think how nearly he had killed him? Then, again, suppose a day should come when his father would remember that night, and wish there had been no warning cry to stay his hand? With this last supposition Paul entertained himself until daybreak.

The following Sunday was fine; the sodden November chill was broken by the last flash of autumnal summer. In the morning Paul had to go to church and Sabbath-school, as always. On seasonable Sunday afternoons the burghers of Cordelia Street always sat out on their front "stoops," and talked to their neighbors on the next stoop, or called to those across the street in neighborly fashion. The men usually sat on gay cushions placed upon the steps that led down to the sidewalk, while the women, in their Sunday "waists," sat in rockers on the cramped porches, pretending to be greatly at their ease. The children played in the streets; there were so many of them that the place resembled the recreation grounds of a kindergarten. The men on the steps—all in their shirt sleeves, their vests unbuttoned—sat with their legs well apart, their stomachs comfortably protruding, and talked of the prices of things, or told anecdotes of the sagacity of their various chiefs and overlords. They occasionally looked over the multitude of squabbling children, listened affectionately to their high-pitched, nasal voices, smiling to see their own proclivities reproduced in their offspring, and interspersed their legends of the iron kings with remarks about their sons' progress at school, their grades in arithmetic, and the amounts they had saved in their toy banks.

On this last Sunday of November, Paul sat all the afternoon on the lowest step of his "stoop," staring into the street, while his sisters, in their rockers, were talking to the minister's daughters next door about how many shirt-waists they had made in the last week, and how many waffles some one had eaten at the last church supper. When the weather was warm, and his father was in a particularly jovial frame of mind, the girls made lemonade, which was always brought out in a red glass pitcher, ornamented with forget-me-nots in blue enamel. This the girls thought very fine, and the neighbors always joked about the suspicious color of the pitcher.

To-day Paul's father sat on the top step, talking to a young man who shifted a restless baby from knee to knee. He happened to be the young man who was daily held up to Paul as a model, and after whom it was his father's dearest hope that he would pattern. This young man was of a ruddy complexion, with a compressed, red mouth, and faded, near-sighted eyes, over which he wore thick spectacles, with gold bows that curved about his ears. He was clerk to one of the magnates of a great steel corporation, and was looked upon in Cordelia Street as a young man with a future. There was a story that, some five years ago—he was now barely twenty-six—he had been a trifle dissipated, but in order to curb his appetites and save the loss of time and strength that a sowing of wild oats might have entailed, he had taken his chief's advice, oft reiterated to his employees, and at twenty-one, had married the first woman whom he could persuade to share his fortunes. She happened to be an angular schoolmistress, much older than he, who also wore thick glasses, and who had now borne him four children, all near-sighted, like herself.

The young man was relating how his chief, now cruising in the Mediterranean, kept in touch with all the details of the business, arranging his office hours on his yacht just as though he were at home, and "knocking off work enough to keep two stenographers busy." His father told, in turn, the plan his corporation was considering, of putting in an electric railway plant at Cairo. Paul snapped his teeth; he had an awful apprehension that they might spoil it all before he got there. Yet he rather liked to hear these legends of the iron kings, that were told and retold on Sundays and holidays; these stories of palaces in Venice, yachts on the Mediterranean, and high play at Monte Carlo appealed to his fancy, and he was interested in the triumphs of these cash-boys who had become famous, though he had no mind for the cash-boy stage.

After supper was over, and he had helped to dry the dishes, Paul nervously asked his father whether he could go to George's to get some help in his geometry, and still more nervously asked for car fare. This latter request he had to repeat, as his father, on principle, did not like to hear requests for money, whether much or little. He asked Paul whether he could not go to some boy who lived nearer, and told him that he ought not to leave his school work until Sunday; but he gave him the dime. He was not a poor man, but he had a worthy ambition to come up in the world. His only reason for allowing Paul to usher was, that he thought a boy ought to be earning a little.

Paul bounded up-stairs, scrubbed the greasy odor of the dish-water from his hands with the ill-smelling soap he hated, and then shook over his fingers a few drops of violet water from the bottle he kept hidden in his drawer. He left the house with his geometry conspicuously under his arm, and the moment he got out of Cordelia Street and boarded a downtown car, he shook off the lethargy of two deadening days, and began to live again.

The leading juvenile of the permanent stock company which played at one of the downtown theatres was an acquaintance of Paul's, and the boy had been invited to drop in at the Sunday-night rehearsals whenever he could. For more than a year Paul had spent every available moment loitering about Charley Edwards's dressing-room. He had won a place among Edwards's following, not only because the young actor, who could not afford to employ a dresser, often found the boy very useful, but because he recognized in Paul something akin to what Churchmen term 'vocation.'

It was at the theatre and at Carnegie Hall that Paul really lived; the rest was but a sleep and a forgetting. This was Paul's fairy tale, and it had for him all the allurement of a secret love. The moment he inhaled the gassy, painty, dusty odor behind the scenes, he breathed like a prisoner set free, and felt within him the possibility of doing or saying splendid, brilliant, poetic things. The moment the cracked orchestra beat out the overture from "Martha", or jerked at the serenade from "Rigoletto," all stupid and ugly things slid from him, and his senses were deliciously, yet delicately, fired.

Perhaps it was because, in Paul's world, the natural nearly always wore the guise of ugliness, that a certain element of artificiality seemed to him necessary in beauty.

Perhaps it was because his experience of life elsewhere was so full of Sabbath-school picnics, petty economies, wholesome advice as to how to succeed in life, and the unescapable odors of cooking, that he found this existence so alluring, these smartly clad men and women so attractive, that he was so moved by these starry apple orchards that bloomed perennially under the lime-light.

It would be difficult to put it strongly enough how convincingly the stage entrance of that theatre was for Paul the actual portal of Romance. Certainly none of the company ever suspected it, least of all Charley Edwards. It was very like the old stories that used to float about London of fabulously rich Jews, who had subterranean halls there; with palms, and fountains, and soft lamps, and richly appareled women who never saw the disenchanting light of London day. So, in the midst of that smoke-palled city, enamored of figures and grimy toil, Paul had his secret temple, his wishing carpet, his bit of blue-and-white Mediterranean shore bathed in perpetual sunshine.

Several of Paul's teachers had a theory that his imagination had been perverted by garish fiction, but the truth was that he scarcely ever read at all. The books at home were not such as would either tempt or corrupt a youthful mind, and as for reading the novels that some of his friends urged upon him—well, he got what he wanted much more quickly from music; any sort of music, from an orchestra to a barrel-organ. He needed only the spark, the indescribable thrill that made his imagination master of his senses, and he could make plots and pictures enough of his own. It was equally true that he was not stage-struck—not, at any rate, in the usual acceptation of that expression. He had no desire to become an actor, any more than he had to become a musician. He felt no necessity to do any of these things; what he wanted was to see, to be in the atmosphere, float on the wave of it, to be carried out, blue league after blue league, away from everything.

After a night behind the scenes, Paul found the school-room more than ever repulsive: the bare floors and naked walls, the prosy men who never wore frock-coats, or violets in their button-holes; the women with their dull gowns, shrill voices, and pitiful seriousness about prepositions that govern the dative. He could not bear to have the other pupils think, for a moment, that he took these people seriously; he must convey to them that he considered it all trivial, and was there only by way of a jest, anyway. He had autograph pictures of all the members of the stock company, which he showed his classmates, telling them the most incredible stories of his familiarity with these people, of his acquaintance with the soloists who came to Carnegie Hall, his suppers with them and the flowers he sent them. When these stories lost their effect, and his audience grew listless, he became desperate and would bid all the boys good-night, announcing that he was going to travel for a while, going to Naples, to Venice, to Egypt. Then, next Monday, he would slip back, conscious, and nervously smiling; his sister was ill, and he should have to defer his voyage until spring.

Matters went steadily worse with Paul at school. In the itch to let his instructors know how heartily he despised them and their homilies, and how thoroughly he was appreciated elsewhere, he mentioned once or twice that he had no time to fool with theorems; adding, with a twitch of the eyebrows and a touch of that nervous bravado which so perplexed them, that he was helping the people down at the stock company; they were old friends of his.

The upshot of the matter was, that the principal went to Paul's father, and Paul was taken out of school and put to work. The manager at Carnegie Hall was told to get another usher in his stead, the doorkeeper at the theatre was warned not to admit him to the house, and Charley Edwards remorsefully promised the boy's father not to see him again.

The members of the stock company were vastly amused when some of Paul's stories reached them—especially the women. They were hard-working women, most of them supporting indigent husbands or brothers, and they laughed rather bitterly at having stirred the boy to such fervid and florid inventions. They agreed with the faculty and with his father that Paul's was a bad case.

II

The east-bound train was plowing through a January snow-storm; the dull dawn was beginning to show gray, when the engine whistled a mile out of Newark. Paul started up from the seat where he had lain curled in uneasy slumber, rubbed the breath-misted window-glass with his hand, and peered out. The snow was whirling in curling eddies above the white bottom-lands, and the drifts lay already deep in the fields and along the fences, while here and there the long dead grass and dried weed stalks protruded black above it. Lights shone from the scattered houses, and a gang of laborers who stood beside the track waved their lanterns.

Paul had slept very little, and he felt grimy and uncomfortable. He had made the all-night journey in a day coach, partly because he was ashamed, dressed as he was, to go into a Pullman, and partly because he was afraid of being seen there by some Pittsburg business man, who might have noticed him in Denny & Carson's office. When the whistle awoke him, he clutched quickly at his breast pocket, glancing about him with an uncertain smile. But the little, clay-bespattered Italians were still sleeping, the slatternly women across the aisle were in open-mouthed oblivion, and even the crumby, crying babies were for the nonce stilled. Paul settled back to struggle with his impatience as best he could.

When he arrived at the Jersey City station, Paul hurried through his breakfast, manifestly ill at ease and keeping a sharp eye about him. After he reached the Twenty-third Street station, he consulted a cabman, and had himself driven to a men's furnishing establishment that was just opening for the day. He spent upward of two hours there, buying with endless reconsidering and great care. His new street suit he put on in the fitting-room; the frock-coat and dress-clothes he had bundled into the cab with his linen. Then he drove to a hatter's and a shoe house. His next errand was at Tiffany's, where he selected his silver and a new scarf-pin. He would not wait to have his silver marked, he said. Lastly, he stopped at a trunk shop on Broadway, and had his purchases packed into various traveling bags.

It was a little after one o'clock when he drove up to the Waldorf, and after settling with the cabman, went into the office. He registered from Washington; said his mother and father had been abroad, and that he had come down to await the arrival of their steamer. He told his story plausibly and had no trouble, since he volunteered to pay for them in advance, in engaging his rooms, a sleeping-room, sitting-room and bath.

Not once, but a hundred times, Paul had planned this entry into New York. He had gone over every detail of it with Charley Edwards, and in his scrap-book at home there were pages of description about New York hotels, cut from the Sunday papers. When he was shown to his sitting-room on the eighth floor, he saw at a glance that everything was as it should be; there was but one detail in his mental picture that the place did not realize, so he rang for the bell-boy and sent him down for flowers. He moved about nervously until the boy returned, putting away his new linen and fingering it delightedly as he did so. When the flowers came, he put them hastily into water, and then tumbled into a hot bath. Presently he came out of his white bath-room, resplendent in his new silk underwear, and playing with the tassels of his red robe. The snow was whirling so fiercely outside his windows that he could scarcely see across the street but within the air was deliciously soft and fragrant. He put the violets and jonquils on the taboret beside the couch, and threw himself down, with a long sigh, covering himself with a Roman blanket. He was thoroughly tired; he had been in such haste, had stood up to such a strain, covered so much ground in the last twenty-four hours, that he wanted to think how it had all come about. Lulled by the sound of the wind, the warm air, and the cool fragrance of the flowers, he sank into deep, drowsy retrospection.

It had been wonderfully simple; when they had shut him out of the theatre and concert hall, when they had taken away his bone, the whole thing was virtually determined. The rest was a mere matter of opportunity. The only thing that at all surprised him was his own courage, for he realized well enough that he had always been tormented by fear, a sort of apprehensive dread that, of late years, as the meshes of the lies he had told closed about him, had been pulling the muscles of his body tighter and tighter. Until now, he could not remember the time when he had not been dreading something. Even when he was a little boy, it was always there—behind him, or before, or on either side. There had always been the shadowed corner, the dark place into which he dared not look, but from which something seemed always to be watching him—and Paul had done things that were not pretty to watch, he knew.

But now he had a curious sense of relief, as though he had at last thrown down the gauntlet to the thing in the corner.

Yet it was but a day since he had been sulking in the traces; but yesterday afternoon that he had been sent to the bank with Denny & Carson's deposits as usual—but this time he was instructed to leave the book to be balanced. There were above two thousand dollars in checks, and nearly a thousand in the bank-notes which he had taken from the book and quietly transferred to his pocket. At the bank he had made out a new deposit slip. His nerves had been steady enough to permit of his returning to the office, where he had finished his work and asked for a full day's holiday tomorrow, Saturday, giving a perfectly reasonable pretext. The bank-book, he knew, would not be returned before Monday or Tuesday, and his father would be out of town for the next week. From the time he slipped the bank-notes into his pocket until he boarded the night train for New York, he had not known a moment's hesitation. It was not the first time Paul had steered through treacherous waters.

How astonishingly easy it had all been; here he was, the thing done, and this time there would be no awakening, no figure at the top of the stairs. He watched the snow-flakes whirling by his window until he fell asleep.

When he awoke, it was three o'clock in the afternoon. He bounded up with a start; half of one of his precious days gone already! He spent more than an hour in dressing, watching every stage of his toilet carefully in the mirror. Everything was quite perfect; he was exactly the kind of boy he had always wanted to be.

When he went down-stairs, Paul took a carriage and drove up Fifth Avenue toward the Park. The snow had somewhat abated, carriages and tradesmen's wagons were hurrying to and fro in the winter twilight, boys in woollen mufflers were shovelling off the doorsteps, the avenue stages made fine spots of color against the white street. Here and there on the corners were stands, with whole flower gardens blooming under glass cases, against the sides of which the snow-flakes stuck and melted; violets, roses, carnations, lilies of the valley, somehow vastly more lovely and alluring that they blossomed thus unnaturally in the snow. The Park itself was a wonderful stage winter-piece.

When he returned, the pause of the twilight had ceased, and the tune of the streets had changed. The snow was falling faster, lights streamed from the hotels that reared their dozen stories fearlessly up into the storm, defying the raging Atlantic winds. A long, black stream of carriages poured down the avenue, intersected here and there by other streams, tending horizontally. There were a score of cabs about the entrance of his hotel, and his driver had to wait. Boys in livery were running in and out of the awning that was stretched across the sidewalk, up and down the red velvet carpet laid from the door to the street. Above, about, within it all was the rumble and roar, the hurry and toss of thousands of human beings as hot for pleasure as himself, and on every side of him towered the glaring affirmation of the omnipotence of wealth.

The boy set his teeth and drew his shoulders together in a spasm of realization; the plot of all dramas, the text of all romances, the nerve-stuff of all sensations was whirling about him like the snow-flakes. He burnt like a faggot in a tempest.

When Paul went down to dinner, the music of the orchestra came floating up the elevator shaft to greet him. His head whirled as he stepped into the thronged corridor, and he sank back into one of the chairs against the wall to get his breath. The lights, the chatter, the perfumes, the bewildering medley of color—he had for a moment the feeling of not being able to stand it. But only for a moment; these were his own people, he told himself. He went slowly about the corridors, through the writing-rooms, smoking-rooms, reception-rooms, as though he were exploring the chambers of an enchanted palace, built and peopled for him alone.

When he reached the dining-room he sat down at a table near a window. The flowers, the white linen, the many-colored wine glasses, the gay toilettes of the women, the low popping of corks, the undulating repetitions of the "Blue Danube" from the orchestra, all flooded Paul's dream with bewildering radiance. When the rosy tinge of his champagne was added—that cold, precious, bubbling stuff that creamed and foamed in his glass—Paul wondered that there were honest men in the world at all. This was what all the world was fighting for, he reflected; this was what all the struggle was about. He doubted the reality of his past. Had he ever known a place called Cordelia Street, a place where fagged-looking business men got on the early car; mere rivets in a machine, they seemed to Paul—sickening men, with combings of children's hair always hanging to their coats, and the smell of cooking in their clothes. Cordelia Street—Ah! that belonged to another time and country; had he not always been thus, had he not sat here night after night, from as far back as he could remember, looking pensively over just such shimmering textures and slowly twirling the stem of a glass like this one between his thumb and middle finger? He rather thought he had.

He was not in the least abashed or lonely. He had no especial desire to meet or to know any of these people; all he demanded was the right to look on and conjecture, to watch the pageant. The mere stage properties were all he contended for. Nor was he lonely later in the evening, in his *loge* at the Metropolitan. He was now entirely rid of his nervous misgivings, of his forced aggressiveness, of the imperative desire to show himself different from his surroundings. He felt now that his surroundings explained him. Nobody questioned the purple; he had only to wear it passively. He had only to glance down at his attire to reassure himself that here it would be impossible for anyone to humiliate him.

He found it hard to leave his beautiful sitting-room to go to bed that night, and sat long watching the raging storm from his turret window. When he went to sleep, it was with the lights turned on in his bedroom; partly because of his old timidity and partly so that, if he should wake in the night, there would be no wretched moment of doubt, no horrible suspicion of yellow Wallpaper, or of Washington and Calvin above his bed.

Sunday morning the city was practically snow-bound. Paul breakfasted late, and in the afternoon he fell in with a wild San Francisco boy, a freshman at Yale, who said he had run down for a "little flyer" over Sunday. The young man offered to show Paul the night side of the town, and the two boys went out together after dinner, not returning to the hotel until seven o'clock the next morning. They had started out in the confiding warmth of a champagne friendship, but their parting in the elevator was singularly cool. The freshman pulled himself together to make his train and Paul went to bed. He awoke at two o'clock in the afternoon, very thirsty and dizzy, and rang for ice-water, coffee, and the Pittsburg papers.

On the part of the hotel management, Paul excited no suspicion. There was this to be said for him, that he wore his spoils with dignity and in no way made himself conspicuous. Even under the glow of his wine he was never boisterous, though he found the stuff like a magician's wand for wonder-building. His chief greediness lay in his ears and eyes, and his excesses were not offensive ones. His dearest pleasures were the gray winter twilights in his sitting-room; his quiet enjoyment of his flowers, his clothes, his wide divan, his cigarette, and his sense of power. He could not remember a time when he had felt so at peace with himself. The mere release from the necessity of petty lying, lying every day and every day, restored his self-respect. He had never lied for pleasure, even at school, but to be noticed and admired, to assert his difference from other Cordelia Street boys; and he felt a good deal more manly, more honest even, now that he had no need for boastful pretensions, now that he could, as his actor friends used to say, "dress the part." It was characteristic that remorse did not occur to him. His golden days went by without a shadow, and he made each as perfect as he could.

On the eighth day after his arrival in New York, he found the whole affair exploited in the Pittsburg papers, exploited with a wealth of detail which indicated that local news of a sensational nature was at a low ebb. The firm of Denny & Carson announced that the boy's father had refunded the full amount of the theft, and that they had no intention of prosecuting. The Cumberland minister had been interviewed, and expressed his hope of yet reclaiming the motherless boy, and his Sabbath-school teacher declared that she would spare no effort to that end. The rumor had reached Pittsburg that the boy had been seen in a New York hotel, and his father had gone East to find him and bring him home.

Paul had just come in to dress for dinner; he sank into a chair, weak to the knees, and clasped his head in his hands. It was to be worse than jail, even; the tepid waters of Cordelia Street were to close over him finally and forever. The gray monotony stretched before him in hopeless, unrelieved years; Sabbath-school, Young People's Meeting, the yellow-papered room, the damp dish-towels; it all rushed back upon him with a sickening vividness. He had the old feeling that the orchestra had suddenly stopped, the sinking sensation that the play was over. The sweat broke out on his face, and he sprang to his feet, looked about him with his white, conscious smile, and winked at himself in the mirror. With something of the old childish belief in miracles with which he had so often gone to class, all his lessons unlearned, Paul dressed and dashed whistling down the corridor to the elevator.

He had no sooner entered the dining-room and caught the measure of the music than his remembrance was lightened by his old elastic power of claiming the moment, mounting with it, and finding it all-sufficient. The glare and glitter about him, the mere scenic accessories had again, and for the last time, their old potency. He would show himself that he was game, he would finish the thing splendidly. He doubted, more than ever, the existence of Cordelia Street, and for the first time he drank his wine recklessly. Was he not, after all, one of those fortunate beings born to the purple, was he not still himself and in his own place? He drummed a nervous accompaniment to the Pagliacci music and looked about him, telling himself over and over that it had paid.

He reflected drowsily, to the swell of the music and the chill sweetness of his wine, that he might have done it more wisely. He might have caught an outbound steamer and been well out of their clutches before now. But the other side of the world had seemed too far away and too uncertain then; he could not have waited for it; his need had been too sharp. If he had to choose over again, he would do the same thing tomorrow. He looked affectionately about the dining-room, now gilded with a soft mist. Ah, it had paid indeed!

Paul was awakened next morning by a painful throbbing in his head and feet. He had thrown himself across the bed without undressing, and had slept with his shoes on. His limbs and hands were lead heavy, and his tongue and throat were parched and burnt. There came upon him one of those fateful attacks of clear-headedness that never occurred except when he was physically exhausted and his nerves hung loose. He lay still and closed his eyes and let the tide of things wash over him.

His father was in New York; "stopping at some joint or other," he told himself. The memory of successive summers on the front stoop fell upon him like a weight of black water. He had not a hundred dollars left; and he knew now, more than ever, that money was everything, the wall that stood between all he loathed and all he wanted. The thing was winding itself up; he had thought of that on his first glorious day in New York, and had even provided a way to snap the thread. It lay on his dressing-table now; he had got it out last night when he came blindly up from dinner, but the shiny metal hurt his eyes, and he disliked the looks of the thing.

He rose and moved about with a painful effort, succumbing now and again to attacks of nausea. It was the old depression exaggerated; all the world had become Cordelia Street. Yet somehow, he was not afraid of anything, was absolutely calm; perhaps because he had looked into the dark corner at last and knew. It was bad enough, what he saw there, but somehow not so bad as his long fear of it had been. He saw everything clearly now. He had a feeling that he had made the best of it, that he had lived the sort of life he was meant to live, and for half an hour he sat staring at the revolver. But he told himself that was not the way, so he went down stairs and took a cab to the ferry.

When Paul arrived at Newark, he got off the train and took another cab, directing the driver to follow the Pennsylvania tracks out of the town. The snow lay heavy on the roadways and had drifted deep in the open fields. Only here and there the dead grass or dried weed stalks projected, singularly black, above it. Once well into the country, Paul dismissed the carriage and walked, floundering along the tracks, his mind a medley of irrelevant things. He seemed to hold in his brain an actual picture of everything he had seen that morning. He remembered every feature of both his drivers, of the toothless old woman from whom he had bought the red flowers in his coat, the agent from whom he had got his ticket, and all of his fellow-passengers on the ferry. His mind, unable to cope with vital matters near at hand, worked feverishly and deftly at sorting and grouping these images. They made for him a part of the ugliness of the world, of the ache in his head, and the bitter burning on his tongue. He stooped and put a handful of snow into his mouth as he walked, but that, too, seemed hot. When he reached a little hillside, where the tracks ran through a cut some twenty feet below him, he stopped and sat down.

The carnations in his coat were drooping with the cold, he noticed, their red glory all over. It occurred to him that all the flowers he had seen in the glass cases that first night must have gone the same way, long before this. It was only one splendid breath they had, in spite of their brave mockery at the winter outside the glass, and it was a losing game in the end, it seemed, this revolt against the homilies by which the world is run. Paul took one of the blossoms carefully from his coat and scooped a little hole in the snow, where he covered it up. Then he dozed a while, from his weak condition, seemingly insensible to the cold.

The sound of an approaching train awoke him, and he started to his feet, remembering only his resolution, and afraid lest he should be too late. He stood watching the approaching locomotive, his teeth chattering, his lips drawn away from them in a frightened smile; once or twice he glanced nervously sidewise, as though he were being watched. When the right moment came, he jumped. As he fell, the folly of his haste occurred to him with merciless clearness, the vastness of what he had left undone. There flashed through his brain, clearer than ever before, the blue of Adriatic water, the yellow of Algerian sands.

He felt something strike his chest, and that his body was being thrown swiftly through the air, on and on, immeasurably far and fast, while his limbs were gently relaxed. Then, because the picture-making mechanism was crushed, the disturbing visions flashed into black, and Paul dropped back into the immense design of things.

Questions for Discussion:

1. What do you learn about Paul from the description of his physical features and clothes in the first seven paragraphs?
2. What could the red carnation in Paul's buttonhole represent? What could the color of the carnation signify?
3. What does New York represent in the story? In what ways does it differ from Cordelia Street?
4. Discuss how the story ends. What happens to Paul? Comment on Paul's function in the story as a playwright, as an actor, and as audience.

"Revelation"

Flannery O'Connor

> **Author Biography:** Flannery O'Connor was born in Savannah, Georgia in 1925. Showing an aptitude for writing on her high school newspaper, O'Connor finished an accelerated degree program at what was then the Georgia College for Women. After, she attended the prestigious Iowa Writers' Workshop and began to publish there and after, both novels and short stories. She was diagnosed with lupus in 1952, and died in 1964.
>
> **Context:** O'Connor never left her Southern roots behind in her work and is known as one of the foremost Southern writers along with Faulkner. Like Faulkner in many ways, O'Connor's work is thought of as Southern gothic, her work peppered with monstrous or shocking characters.
>
> **Literary Terms:** theme, imagery, symbolism, characterization

The doctor's waiting room, which was very small, was almost full when the Turpins entered and Mrs. Turpin, who was very large, made it look even smaller by her presence. She stood looming at the head of the magazine table set in the center of it, a living demonstration that the room was inadequate and ridiculous. Her little bright black eyes took in all the patients as she sized up the seating situation. There was one vacant chair and a place on the sofa occupied by a blond child in a dirty blue romper who should have been told to move over and make room for the lady. He was five or six, but Mrs. Turpin saw at once that no one was going to tell him to move over. He was slumped down in the seat, his arms idle at his sides and his eyes idle in his head; his nose ran unchecked.

Mrs. Turpin put a firm hand on Claud's shoulder and said in a voice that included anyone who wanted to listen, "Claud, you sit in that chair there," and gave him a push down into the vacant one. Claud was florid and bald and sturdy, somewhat shorter than Mrs. Turpin, but he sat down as if he were accustomed to doing what she told him to.

Mrs. Turpin remained standing. The only man in the room besides Claud was a lean stringy old fellow with a rusty hand spread out on each knee, whose eyes were closed as if he were asleep or dead or pretending to be so as not to get up and offer her his seat. Her gaze settled agreeably on a well-dressed grey-haired lady whose eyes met hers and whose expression said: if that child belonged to me, he would have some manners and move over—there's plenty of room there for you and him too.

Claud looked up with a sigh and made as if to rise.

"Sit down," Mrs. Turpin said. "You know you're not supposed to stand on that leg. He has an ulcer on his leg," she explained.

Claud lifted his foot onto the magazine table and rolled his trouser leg up to reveal a purple swelling on a plump marble-white calf.

"My!" the pleasant lady said. "How did you do that?"

"A cow kicked him," Mrs. Turpin said.

"Goodness!" said the lady.

Claud rolled his trouser leg down.

"Maybe the little boy would move over," the lady suggested, but the child did not stir.

"Somebody will be leaving in a minute," Mrs. Turpin said. She could not understand why a doctor—with as much money as they made charging five dollars a day to just stick their head in the hospital door and look at you—couldn't afford a decent-sized waiting room. This one was hardly bigger than a garage. The table was cluttered with limp-looking magazines and at one end of it there was a big green glass ash tray full of cigarette butts and cotton wads with little blood spots on them. If she had had anything to do with the running of the place, that would have been emptied every so often. There were no chairs against the wall at the head of the room. It had a rectangular-shaped panel in it that permitted a view of the office where the nurse came and went and the secretary listened to the radio. A plastic fern in a gold pot sat in the opening and trailed its fronds down almost to the floor. The radio was softly playing gospel music.

Just then the inner door opened and a nurse with the highest stack of yellow hair Mrs. Turpin had ever seen put her face in the crack and called for the next patient. The woman sitting beside Claud grasped the two arms of her chair and hoisted herself up; she pulled her dress free from her legs and lumbered through the door where the nurse had disappeared.

Mrs. Turpin eased into the vacant chair, which held her tight as a corset. "I wish I could reduce," she said, and rolled her eyes and gave a comic sigh.

"Oh, *you* aren't fat," the stylish lady said.

"Ooooo I am too," Mrs. Turpin said. "Claud he eats all he wants to and never weighs over one hundred and seventy-five pounds, but me I just look at something good to eat and I gain some weight," and her stomach and shoulders shook with laughter. "You can eat all you want to, can't you, Claud?" she asked, turning to him.

Claud only grinned.

"Well, as long as you have such a good disposition," the stylish lady said, "I don't think it makes a bit of difference what size you are. You just can't beat a good disposition."

Next to her was a fat girl of eighteen or nineteen, scowling into a thick blue book which Mrs. Turpin saw was entitled *Human Development*. The girl raised her head and directed her scowl at Mrs. Turpin as if she did not like her looks. She appeared annoyed that anyone should speak while she tried to read. The poor girl's face was blue with acne and Mrs. Turpin thought how pitiful it was to have a face like that at that age. She gave the girl a friendly smile but the girl only scowled the harder. Mrs. Turpin herself was fat but she had always had good skin, and, though she was forty-seven years old, there was not a wrinkle in her face except around her eyes from laughing too much.

Next to the ugly girl was the child, still in exactly the same position, and next to him was a thin leathery old woman in a cotton print dress. She and Claud had three sacks of chicken feed in their pump house that was in the same print. She had seen from the first that the child belonged with the old woman. She could tell by the way they sat—kind of vacant and white-trashy, as if they would sit there until Doomsday if nobody called and told them to get up. And at right angles but next to the well-dressed pleasant lady was a lank-faced woman who was certainly the child's mother. She had on a yellow sweat shirt and wine-colored slacks, both gritty-looking, and the rims of her lips were stained with snuff. Her dirty yellow hair was tied behind with a little piece of red paper ribbon. Worse than niggers any day, Mrs. Turpin thought.

The gospel hymn playing was, "When I looked up and He looked down," and Mrs. Turpin, who knew it, supplied the last line mentally, "And wona these days I know I'll we-eara crown."

Without appearing to, Mrs. Turpin always noticed people's feet. The well-dressed lady had on red and grey suede shoes to match her dress. Mrs. Turpin had on her good black patent leather pumps. The ugly girl had on Girl Scout shoes and heavy socks. The old woman had on tennis shoes and the white-trashy mother had on what appeared to be bedroom slippers, black straw with gold braid threaded through them—exactly what you would have expected her to have on.

Sometimes at night when she couldn't go to sleep, Mrs. Turpin would occupy herself with the question of who she would have chosen to be if she couldn't have been herself. If Jesus had said to her before he made her, "There's only two places available for you. You can either be a nigger or white-trash," what would she had said? "Please Jesus, please," she would have said, "just let me wait until there's another place available," and he would have said, "No, you have to go right now and I have only those two places so make up your mind." She would have wiggled and squirmed and begged and pleaded but it would have been no use and finally she would have said, "All right, make me a nigger then—but that don't mean a trashy one." And he would have made her a neat clean respectable Negro woman, herself but black.

Next to the child's mother was a red-headed youngish woman, reading one of the magazines and working a piece of chewing gum, hell for leather, as Claud would say. Mrs. Turpin could not see the woman's feet. She was not white-trash, just common. Sometimes Mrs. Turpin occupied herself at night naming the classes of people. On the bottom of the heap were most colored people, not the kind she would have been if she had been one, but most of them; then next to them—not above, just away from— were the white-trash; then above them were the home-owners, and above them the home-and-land owners, to which she and Claud belonged. Above she and Claud were people with a lot of money and much bigger houses and much more land. But here the complexity of it would begin to bear in on her, for some of the people with a lot of money were common and ought to be below she and Claud and some of the people who had good blood had lost their money and had to rent and then there were colored people who owned their homes and land as well. There was a colored dentist in town who had two red Lincolns and a swimming pool and a farm with registered white-face cattle on it. Usually by the time she had fallen asleep all the classes of people were moiling and roiling around in her head, and she would dream they were all crammed in together in a box car, being ridden off to be put in a gas oven.

"That's a beautiful clock," she said and nodded to her right. It was a big wall clock, the face encased in a brass sunburst.

"Yes, it's very pretty," the stylish lady said agreeably. "And right on the dot too," she added, glancing at her watch.

The ugly girl beside her cast an eye upward at the clock, smirked, then looked directly at Mrs. Turpin and smirked again. Then she returned her eyes to her book. She was obviously the lady's daughter because, although they didn't look anything alike as to disposition, they both had the same shape of face and the same blue eyes. On the lady they sparkled pleasantly but in the girl's seared face they appeared alternately to smolder and to blaze.

What if Jesus had said, "All right, you can be white-trash or a nigger or ugly!"

Mrs. Turpin felt an awful pity for the girl, though she thought it was one thing to be ugly and another to act ugly.

The woman with the snuff-stained lips turned around in her chair and looked up at the clock. Then she turned back and appeared to look a little to the side of Mrs. Turpin. There was a cast in one of her eyes. "You want to know where you can get you one of themther clocks?" she asked in a loud voice.

"No, I already have a nice clock," Mrs. Turpin said. Once somebody like her got a leg in the conversation, she would be all over it.

"You can get you one with green stamps," the woman said. "That's most likely wher he got hisn. Save you up enough, you can get you most anythang. I got me some joo'ry."

Ought to have got you a wash rag and some soap, Mrs. Turpin thought.

"I get contour sheets with mine," the pleasant lady said.

The daughter slammed her book shut. She looked straight in front of her, directly through Mrs. Turpin and on through the yellow curtain and the plate glass window which made the wall behind her. The girl's eyes seemed lit all of a sudden with a peculiar light, an unnatural light like night road signs give. Mrs. Turpin turned her head to see if there was anything going on outside that she should see, but she could not see anything. Figures passing cast only a pale shadow through the curtain. There was no reason the girl should single her out for her ugly looks.

"Miss Finley," the nurse said, cracking the door. The gum-chewing woman got up and passed in front of her and Claud and went into the office. She had on red high-heeled shoes.

Directly across the table, the ugly girl's eyes were fixed on Mrs. Turpin as if she had some very special reason for disliking her.

"This is wonderful weather, isn't it?" the girl's mother said.

"It's good weather for cotton if you can get the niggers to pick it," Mrs. Turpin said, "but niggers don't want to pick cotton any more. You can't get the white folks to pick it and now you can't get the niggers—because they got to be right up there with the white folks."

"They gonna *try* anyways," the white-trash woman said, leaning forward.

"Do you have one of those cotton-picking machines?" the pleasant lady asked.

"No," Mrs. Turpin said, "they leave half the cotton in the field. We don't have much cotton anyway. If you want to make it farming now, you have to have a little of every-thing. We got a couple of acres of cotton and a few hogs and chickens and just enough white-face that Claud can look after them himself.

"One thang I don't want," the white-trash woman said, wiping her mouth with the back of her hand. "Hogs. Nasty stinking things, a-gruntin and a-rootin all over the place."

Mrs. Turpin gave her the merest edge of her attention. "Our hogs are not dirty and they don't stink," she said. "They're cleaner than some children I've seen. Their feet never touch the ground. We have a pig-parlor—that's where you raise them on concrete," she explained to the pleasant lady, "and Claud scoots them down with the hose every afternoon and washes off the floor." Cleaner by far than that child right there, she thought. Poor nasty little thing. He had not moved except to put the thumb of his dirty hand into his mouth.

The woman turned her face away from Mrs. Turpin. "I know I wouldn't scoot down no hog with no hose," she said to the wall.

You wouldn't have no hog to scoot down, Mrs. Turpin said to herself.

"A-gruntin and a-rootin and a-groanin," the woman muttered.

"We got a little of everything," Mrs. Turpin said to the pleasant lady. "It's no use in having more than you can handle yourself with help like it is. We found enough niggers to pick our cotton this year but Claud he has to go after them and take them home again in the evening. They can't walk that half a mile. No they can't. I tell you," she said and laughed merrily, "I sure am tired of buttering up niggers, but you got to love em if you want em to work for you. When they come in the morning, I run out and I say, "Hi yawl this morning?" and when Claud drives them off to the field I just wave to beat the band and they just wave back." And she waved her hand rapidly to illustrate.

"Like you read out of the same book," the lady said, showing she understood perfectly.

"Child, yes," Mrs. Turpin said. "And when they come in from the field, I run out with a bucket of icewater. That's the way it's going to be from now on," she said. "You may as well face it."

"One thang I know," the white-trash woman said. "Two thangs I ain't going to do: love no niggers or scoot down no hog with no hose." And she let out a bark of contempt.

The look that Mrs. Turpin and the pleasant lady exchanged indicated they both understood that you had to *have* certain things before you could *know* certain things. But every time Mrs. Turpin exchanged a look with the lady, she was aware that the ugly girl's peculiar eyes were still on her, and she had trouble bringing her attention back to the conversation.

"When you got something," she said, "you got to look after it." And when you ain't got a thing but breath and britches, she added to herself, you can afford to come to town every morning and just sit on the Court House coping and spit.

A grotesque revolving shadow passed across the curtain behind her and was thrown palely on the opposite wall. Then a bicycle clattered down against the outside of the building. The door opened and a colored boy glided in with a tray from the drug store. It had two large red and white paper cups on it with tops on them. He was a tall, very black boy in discolored white pants and a green nylon shirt. He was chewing gum slowly, as if to music. He set the tray down in the office opening next to the fern and stuck his head through to look for the secretary. She was not in there. He rested his arms on the ledge and waited, his narrow bottom stuck out, swaying slowly to the left and right. He raised a hand over his head and scratched the base of his skull.

"You see that button there, boy?" Mrs. Turpin said. "You can punch that and she'll come. She's probably in the back somewhere."

"Is that right?" the boy said agreeably, as if he had never seen the button before. He leaned to the right and put his finger on it. "She sometime out," he said and twisted around to face his audience, his elbows behind him on the counter. The nurse appeared and he twisted back again. She handed him a dollar and he rooted in his pocket and made the change and counted it out to her. She gave him fifteen cents for a tip and he went out with the empty tray. The heavy door swung to slowly and closed at length with the sound of suction. For a moment no one spoke.

"They ought to send all them niggers back to Africa," the white-trash woman said. "That's wher they come from in the first place."

"Oh, I couldn't do without my good colored friends," the pleasant lady said.

"There's a heap of things worse than a nigger," Mrs. Turpin agreed. "It's all kinds of them just like it's all kinds of us."

"Yes, and it takes all kinds to make the world go round," the lady said in her musical voice.

As she said it, the raw-complexioned girl snapped her teeth together. Her lower lip turned downwards and inside out, revealing the pale pink inside of her mouth. After a second it rolled back up. It was the ugliest face Mrs. Turpin had ever seen anyone make and for a moment she was certain that the girl had made it at her. She was looking at her as if she had known and disliked her all her life—all of Mrs. Turpin's life, it seemed too, not just all the girl's life. Why, girl, I don't even know you, Mrs. Turpin said silently.

She forced her attention back to the discussion. "It wouldn't be practical to send them back to Africa," she said. "They wouldn't want to go. They got it too good here."

"Wouldn't be what they wanted—if I had anythang to do with it," the woman said.

"It wouldn't be a way in the world you could get all the niggers back over there," Mrs. Turpin said. "They'd be hiding out and lying down and turning sick on you and wailing and hollering and raring and pitching. It wouldn't be a way in the world to get them over there."

"They got over here," the trashy woman said. "Get back like they got over."

"It wasn't so many of them then," Mrs. Turpin explained.

The woman looked at Mrs. Turpin as if here was an idiot indeed but Mrs. Turpin was not bothered by the look, considering where it came from.

"Nooo," she said, "they're going to stay here where they can go to New York and marry white folks and improve their color. That's what they all want to do, every one of them, improve their color."

"You know what comes of that, don't you?" Claud asked.

"No, Claud, what?" Mrs. Turpin said.

Claud's eyes twinkled. "White-faced niggers," he said with never a smile.

Everybody in the office laughed except the white-trash and the ugly girl. The girl gripped the book in her lap with white fingers. The trashy woman looked around her from face to face as if she thought they were all idiots. The old woman in the feed sack dress continued to gaze expressionless across the floor at the high-top shoes of the man opposite her, the one who had been pretending to be asleep when the Turpins came in. He was laughing heartily, his hands still spread out on his knees. The child had fallen to the side and was lying now almost face down in the old woman's lap.

While they recovered from their laughter, the nasal chorus on the radio kept the room from silence.

"You go to blank blank
And I'll go to mine
But we'll all blank along
To-geth-ther,
And all along the blank
We'll help each other out
Smile-ling in any kind of
Weath-ther!"

Mrs. Turpin didn't catch every word but she caught enough to agree with the spirit of the song and it turned her thoughts sober. To help anybody out that needed it was her philosophy of life. She never spared herself when she found somebody in need, whether they were white or black, trash or decent. And of all she had to be thankful for, she was most thankful that this was so. If Jesus said, "You can be high society and have all the money you want and be thin and svelte-like, but you can't be a good woman with it," she would have to say, "Well don't make me that then. Make me a good woman and it don't matter what else, how fat or how ugly or how poor!" Her heart rose. He had not made her a nigger or white-trash or ugly! He had made her herself and given her a little of everything. Jesus, thank you! she said. Thank you thank you thank you! Whenever she counted her blessings she felt as buoyant as if she weighed one hundred and twenty-five pounds instead of one hundred and eighty.

"What's wrong with your little boy?" the pleasant lady asked the white-trashy woman.

"He has a ulcer," the woman said proudly. "He ain't give me a minute's peace since he was born. Him and her are just alike," she said, nodding at the old woman, who was running her leathery fingers through the child's pale hair. "Look like I can't get nothing down them two but Co'Cola and candy."

That's all you try to get down em, Mrs. Turpin said to herself. Too lazy to light the fire. There was nothing you could tell her about people like them that she didn't know already. And it was not just that they didn't have anything. Because if you gave them everything, in two weeks it would all be broken or filthy or they would have chopped it up for lightwood. She knew all this from her own experience. Help them you must, but help them you couldn't.

All at once the ugly girl turned her lips inside out again. Her eyes were fixed like two drills on Mrs. Turpin. This time there was no mistaking that there was something urgent behind them.

Girl, Mrs. Turpin exclaimed silently, I haven't done a thing to you! The girl might be confusing her with somebody else. There was no need to sit by and let herself be intimidated. "You must be in college," she said boldly, looking directly at the girl. "I see you reading a book there."

The girl continued to stare and pointedly did not answer.

Her mother blushed at this rudeness. "The lady asked you a question, Mary Grace," she said under her breath.

"I have ears," Mary Grace said.

The poor mother blushed again. "Mary Grace goes to Wellesley College," she explained. She twisted one of the buttons on her dress. "In Massachusetts," she added with a grimace. "And in the summer she just keeps right on studying. Just reads all the time, a real book worm. She's done real well at Wellesley; she's taking English and Math and History and Psychology and Social Studies," she rattled on, "and I think it's too much. I think she ought to get out and have fun."

The girl looked as if she would like to hurl them all through the plate glass window.

"Way up north," Mrs. Turpin murmured and thought, well, it hasn't done much for her manners.

"I'd almost rather to have him sick," the white-trash woman said, wrenching the attention back to herself. "He's so mean when he ain't. Look like some children just take natural to meanness. It's some gets bad when they get sick but he was the opposite. Took sick and turned good. He don't give me no trouble now. It's me waitin to see the doctor," she said.

If I was going to send anybody back to Africa, Mrs. Turpin thought, it would be your kind, woman. "Yes, indeed," she said aloud, but looking up at the ceiling, "it's a heap of things worse than a nigger." And dirtier than a hog, she added to herself.

"I think people with bad dispositions are more to be pitied than anyone on earth," the pleasant lady said in a voice that was decidedly thin.

"I thank the Lord he has blessed me with a good one," Mrs. Turpin said. "The day has never dawned that I couldn't find something to laugh at."

"Not since she married me anyways," Claud said with a comical straight face.

Everybody laughed except the girl and the white-trash.

Mrs. Turpin's stomach shook. "He's such a caution," she said, "that I can't help but laugh at him."

The girl made a loud ugly noise through her teeth.

Her mother's mouth grew thin and tight. "I think the worst thing in the world," she said, "is an ungrateful person. To have everything and not appreciate it. I know a girl," she said, "who has parents who would give her anything, a little brother who loves her dearly, who is getting a good education, who wears the best clothes, but who can never say a kind word to anyone, who never smiles, who just criticizes and complains all day long."

"Is she too old to paddle?" Claud asked.

The girl's face was almost purple.

"Yes," the lady said, "I'm afraid there's nothing to do but leave her to her folly. Some day she'll wake up and it'll be too late."

"It never hurt anyone to smile," Mrs. Turpin said. "It just makes you feel better all over."

"Of course," the lady said sadly, "but there are just some people you can't tell anything to. They can't take criticism."

"If it's one thing I am," Mrs. Turpin said with feeling, "it's grateful. When I think who all I could have been besides myself and what all I got, a little of everything, and a good disposition besides, I just feel like shouting, 'Thank you, Jesus, for making everything the way it is!' It could have been different!" For one thing, somebody else could have got Claud. At the thought of this, she was flooded with gratitude and a terrible pang of joy ran through her. "Oh thank you, Jesus, Jesus, thank you!" she cried aloud.

The book struck her directly over her left eye. It struck almost at the same instant that she realized the girl was about to hurl it. Before she could utter a sound, the raw face came crashing across the table toward her, howling. The girl's fingers sank like clamps into the soft flesh of her neck. She heard the mother cry out and Claud shout, "Whoa!" There was an instant when she was certain that she was about to be in an earthquake.

All at once her vision narrowed and she saw everything as if it were happening in a small room far away, or as if she were looking at it through the wrong end of a telescope. Claud's face crumpled and fell out of sight. The nurse ran in, then out, then in again. Then the gangling figure of the doctor rushed out of the inner door. Magazines flew this way and that as the table turned over. The girl fell with a thud and Mrs. Turpin's vision suddenly reversed itself and she saw everything large instead of small. The eyes of the white-trashy woman were staring hugely at the floor. There the girl, held down on one side by the nurse and on the other by her mother, was wrenching and turning in their grasp. The doctor was kneeling astride her, trying to hold her arms down. He managed after a second to sink a long needle into it.

Mrs. Turpin felt entirely hollow except for her heart which swung from side to side as if it were agitated in a great empty drum of flesh.

"Somebody that's not busy call for the ambulance," the doctor said in the off-hand voice young doctors adopt for terrible occasions.

Mrs. Turpin could not have moved a finger. The old man who had been sitting next to her skipped nimbly into the office and made the call, for the secretary still seemed to be gone.

"Claud!" Mrs. Turpin called.

He was not in his chair. She knew she must jump up and find him but she felt like some one trying to catch a train in a dream, when everything moves in slow motion and the faster you try to run the slower you go.

"Here I am," a suffocated voice, very unlike Claud's, said.

He was doubled up in the corner on the floor, pale as paper, holding his leg. She wanted to get up and go to him but she could not move. Instead, her gaze was drawn slowly downward to the churning face on the floor, which she could see over the doctor's shoulder.

The girl's eyes stopped rolling and focused on her. They seemed a much lighter blue than before, as if a door that had been tightly closed behind them was now open to admit light and air.

Mrs. Turpin's head cleared and her power of motion returned. She leaned forward until she was looking directly into the fierce brilliant eyes. There was no doubt in her mind that the girl did know her, knew her in some intense and personal way, beyond time and place and condition. "What you got to say to me?" she asked hoarsely and held her breath, waiting, as for a revelation.

The girl raised her head. Her gaze locked with Mrs. Turpin's. "Go back to hell where you came from, you old wart hog," she whispered. Her voice was low but clear. Her eyes burned for a moment as if she saw with pleasure that her message had struck its target.

Mrs. Turpin sank back in her chair.

After a moment the girl's eyes closed and she turned her head wearily to the side. The doctor rose and handed the nurse the empty syringe. He leaned over and put both hands for a moment on the mother's shoulders, which were shaking. She was sitting on the floor, her lips pressed together, holding Mary Grace's hand in her lap. The girl's fingers were gripped like a baby's around her thumb. "Go on to the hospital," he said. "I'll call and make the arrangements."

"Now let's see that neck," he said in a jovial voice to Mrs. Turpin. He began to inspect her neck with his first two fingers. Two little moon-shaped lines like pink flesh bones were indented over her windpipe. There was the beginning of an angry red swelling above her eye. His fingers passed over this also.

"Lea' me be," she said thickly and shook him off. "See about Claud. She kicked him."

"I'll see about him in a minute," he said and felt her pulse. He was a thin grey-haired man, given to pleasantries. "Go home and have yourself a vacation the rest of the day," he said and patted her on the shoulder.

Quit your pattin me, Mrs. Turpin growled to herself.

"And put an ice pack over that eye," he said. Then he went and squatted down beside Claud and looked at his leg. After a moment he pulled him up and Claud limped after him into the office.

Until the ambulance came, the only sounds in the room were the tremulous moans of the girl's mother, who continued to sit on the floor. The white-trash woman did not take her eyes off the girl. Mrs. Turpin looked straight ahead at nothing. Presently the ambulance drew up, a long dark shadow, behind the curtain. The attendants came in and set the stretcher down beside the girl and lifted her expertly onto it and carried her out. The nurse helped the mother gather up her things. The shadow of the ambulance moved silently away and the nurse came back in the office.

"That ther girl is going to be a lunatic, ain't she?" the white-trash woman asked the nurse, but the nurse kept on to the back and never answered her.

"Yes. She's going to be a lunatic," the white-trash woman said to the rest of them.

"Po' critter," the old woman murmured. The child's face was still in her lap. His eyes looked idly out over her knees. He had not moved during the disturbance except to draw one leg up under him.

"I thank Gawd," the white-trash woman said fervently, "I ain't a lunatic."

Claud came limping out and the Turpins went home.

As their pick-up truck turned into their own dirt road and made the crest of the hill, Mrs. Turpin gripped the window ledge and looked out suspiciously. The land sloped gracefully down through a field dotted with lavender weeds and at the start of the rise their small yellow frame house, with its little flower beds spread out around it like a fancy apron, sat primly in its accustomed place between two giant hickory trees. She would not have been startled to see a burnt wound between two blackened chimneys.

Neither of them felt like eating so they put on their house clothes and lowered the shade in the bedroom and lay down, Claud with his leg on a pillow and herself with a damp washcloth over her eye. The instant she was flat on her back, the image of a razor-backed hog with warts on its face and horns coming out behind its ears snorted into her head. She moaned, a low quiet moan.

"I am not," she said tearfully, "a wart hog. From hell." But the denial had no force. The girl's eyes and her words, even the tone of her voice, low but clear, directed only to her, brooked no repudiation. She had been singled out for the message, though there was trash in the room to whom it might justly have been applied. The full force of this fact struck her only now. There was a woman there who was neglecting her own child but she had been overlooked. The message had been given to Ruby Turpin, a respectable, hard-working, church-going woman. The tears dried. Her eyes began to burn instead with wrath.

She rose on her elbow and the washcloth fell into her hand. Claud was lying on his back, snoring. She wanted to tell him what the girl had said. At the same time, she did not wish to put the image of herself as a wart hog from hell into his mind.

"Hey, Claud," she muttered and pushed his shoulder.

Claud opened one pale baby blue eye.

She looked into it warily. He did not think about anything. He just went his way.

"Wha, whasit?" he said and closed the eye again.

"Nothing," she said. "Does your leg pain you?"

"Hurts like hell," Claud said.

"It'll quit terreckly," she said and lay back down. In a moment Claud was snoring again. For the rest of the afternoon they lay there. Claud slept. She scowled at the ceiling. Occasionally she raised her fist and made a small stabbing motion over her chest as if she was defending her innocence to invisible guests who were like the comforts of Job, reasonable-seeming but wrong.

About five-thirty Claud stirred. "Got to go after those niggers," he sighed, not moving.

She was looking straight up as if there were unintelligible handwriting on the ceiling. The protuberance over her eye had turned a greenish-blue. "Listen here," she said.

"What?"

"Kiss me."

Claud leaned over and kissed her loudly on the mouth. He pinched her side and their hands interlocked. Her expression of ferocious concentration did not change. Claud got up, groaning and growling, and limped off. She continued to study the ceiling.

She did not get up until she heard the pick-up truck coming back with the Negroes. Then she rose and thrust her feet in her brown oxfords, which she did not bother to lace, and stumped out onto the back porch and got her red plastic bucket. She emptied a tray of ice cubes into it and filled it half full of water and went out into the back yard. Every afternoon after Claud brought the hands in, one of the boys helped him put out hay and the rest waited in the back of the truck until he was ready to take them home. The truck was parked in the shade under one of the hickory trees.

"Hi yawl this evening?" Mrs. Turpin asked grimly, appearing with the bucket and the dipper. There were three women and a boy in the truck.

"Us doin nicely," the oldest woman said. "Hi you doin?" and her gaze stuck immediately on the dark lump on Mrs. Turpin's forehead. "You done fell down, ain't you?" she asked in a solicitous voice. The old woman was dark and almost toothless. She had on an old felt hat of Claud's set back on her head. The other two women were younger and lighter and they both had new bright green sun hats. One of them had hers on her head; the other had taken hers off and the boy was grinning beneath it.

Mrs. Turpin set the bucket down on the floor of the truck. "Yawl hep yourselves," she said. She looked around to make sure Claud had gone. "No, I didn't fall down," she said, folding her arms. "It was something worse than that."

"Ain't nothing bad happen to you!" the old woman said. She said it as if they all knew that Mrs. Turpin was protected in some special way by Divine Providence. "You just had you a little fall."

"We were in town at the doctor's office for where the cow kicked Mr. Turpin," Mrs. Turpin said in a flat tone that indicated they could leave off their foolishness. "And there was this girl there. A big fat girl with her face all broke out. I could look at that girl and tell she was peculiar but I couldn't tell how. And me and her mama were just talking and going along and all of the sudden WHAM! She throws this big book she was reading at me and . . ."

"Naw!" the old woman cried out.

"And then she jumps over the table and commences to choke me."

"Naw!" they all exclaimed, "naw!"

"Hi come she do that?" the old woman asked. "What ail her?"

Mrs. Turpin only glared in front of her.

"Somethin ail her," the old woman said.

"They carried her off in an ambulance," Mrs. Turpin continued, "but before she went she was rolling on the floor and they were trying to hold her down to give her a shot and she said something to me." She paused. "You know what she said to me?"

"What she say?" they asked.

"She said," Mrs. Turpin began, and stopped, her face very dark and heavy. The sun was getting whiter and whiter, blanching the sky overhead so that the leaves of the hickory tree were black in the face of it. She could not bring forth the words. "Something real ugly," she muttered.

"She sho shouldn't said nothing ugly to you," the old woman said. "You so sweet. You the sweetest lady I know."

"She pretty too," the one with the hat on said.

"And stout," the other one said. "I never knowed no sweeter white lady."

"That's the truth befo' Jesus," the old woman said. "Amen! You des as sweet and pretty as you can be."

Mrs. Turpin knew just exactly how much Negro flattery was worth and it added to her rage. "She said," she began again and finished this time with a fierce rush of breath, "that I was an old wart hog from hell."

There was an astounded silence.

"Where she at?" the youngest woman cried in a piercing voice.

"Lemme see her. I'll kill her!"

"I'll kill her with you!" the other one cried.

"She b'long in the sylum," the old woman said emphatically. "You the sweetest white lady I know."

"She pretty too," the other two said. "Stout as she can be and sweet. Jesus satisfied with her!"

"Deed he is," the old woman declared.

Idiots! Mrs. Turpin growled to herself. You could never say anything intelligent to a nigger. You could talk at them but not with them. "Yawl ain't drunk your water," she said shortly. "Leave the bucket in the truck when you're finished with it. I got more to do than just stand around and pass the time of day," and she moved off and into the house.

She stood for a moment in the middle of the kitchen. The dark protuberance over her eye looked like a miniature tornado cloud which might any moment sweep across the horizon of her brow. Her lower lip protruded dangerously. She squared her massive shoulders. Then she marched into the front of the house and out the side door and started down the road to the pig parlor. She had the look of a woman going single-handed, weaponless, into battle.

The sun was a deep yellow now like a harvest moon and was riding westward very fast over the far tree line as if it meant to reach the hogs before she did. The road was rutted and she kicked several good-sized stones out of her path as she strode along. The pig parlor was on a little knoll at the end of a lane that ran off from the side of the barn. It was a square of concrete as large as a small room, with a board fence about four feet high around it. The concrete floor sloped slightly so that the hog wash could drain off into a trench where it was carried to the field for fertilizer. Claud was standing on the outside, on the edge of the concrete, hanging onto the top board, hosing down the floor inside. The hose was connected to the faucet of a water trough nearby.

Mrs. Turpin climbed up beside him and glowered down at the hogs inside. There were seven long-snouted bristly shoats in it—tan with liver-colored spots—and an old sow a few weeks off from farrowing. She was lying on her side grunting. The shoats were running about shaking themselves like idiot children, their little slit pig eyes searching the floor for anything left. She had read that pigs were the most intelligent animal. She doubted it. They were supposed to be smarter than dogs. There had even been a pig astronaut. He had performed his assignment perfectly but died of a heart attack afterwards because they left him in his electric suit, sitting upright throughout his examination when naturally a hog should be on all fours.

A-gruntin and a-rootin and a-groaning.

"Gimme that hose," she said, yanking it away from Claud. "Go on and carry them niggers home and then get off that leg."

"You look like you might have swallowed a mad dog," Claud observed, but he got down and limped off. He paid no attention to her humors.

Until he was out of earshot, Mrs. Turpin stood on the side of the pen, holding the hose and pointing the stream of water at the hind quarters of any shoat that looked as if it might try to lie down. When he had had time to get over the hill, she turned her head slightly and her wrathful eyes scanned the path. He was nowhere in sight. She turned back again and seemed to gather herself up. Her shoulders rose and she drew in her breath.

"What do you send me a message like that for?" she said in a low fierce voice, barely above a whisper but with the force of a shout in its concentrated fury. "How am I a hog and me both? How am I saved and from hell too?" Her free fist was knotted and with the other she gripped the hose, blindly pointing the stream of water in and out of the eye of the old sow whose outraged squeal she did not hear.

The pig parlor commanded a view of the back pasture where their twenty beef cows were gathered around the hay-bales Claud and the boy had put out. The freshly cut pasture clopped down to the highway. Across it was their cotton field and beyond that a dark green dusty wood which they owned as well. The sun was behind the wood, very red, looking over the paling of trees like a farmer inspecting his own hogs.

"Why me?" she rumbled. "It's no trash around here, black or white, that I haven't given to. And break my back to the bone every day working. And do for the church."

She appeared to be the right size woman to command the arena before her. "How am I a hog?" she demanded. "Exactly how am I like them?" and she jabbed the stream of water at the shoats. "There was plenty of trash there. It didn't have to be me.

"If you like trash better, go get yourself some trash then," she railed. "You could have made me trash. Or a nigger. If trash is what you wanted why didn't you make me trash?" She shook her first with the hose in it and a watery snake appeared momentarily in the air. "I could quit working and take it easy and be filthy," she growled. "Lounge about the sidewalks all day drinking root beer. Dip snuff and spit in every puddle and have it all over my face. I could be nasty.

"Or you could have made me a nigger. It's too late for me to be a nigger," she said with deep sarcasm, "but I could act like one. Lay down in the middle of the road and stop traffic. Roll on the ground."

In the deepening light everything was taking on a mysterious hue. The pasture was growing a peculiar glassy green and the streak of highway had turned lavender. She braced herself for a final assault and this time her voice rolled out over the pasture. "Go on," she yelled, "call me a hog! Call me a hog again. From hell. Call me a wart hog from hell. Put that bottom rail on top. There'll still be a top and bottom!"

A garbled echo returned to her.

A final surge of fury shook her and she roared, "Who do you think you are?"

The color of everything, field and crimson sky, burned for a moment with a transparent intensity. The question carried over the pasture and across the highway and the cotton field and returned to her clearly like an answer from beyond the wood.

She opened her mouth but no sound came out of it.

A tiny truck, Claud's, appeared on the highway, heading rapidly out of sight. Its gears scraped thinly. It looked like a child's toy. At any moment a bigger truck might smash into it and scatter Claud and the niggers' brains all over the road.

Mrs. Turpin stood there, her gaze fixed on the highway, all her muscles rigid, until in five or six minutes the truck reappeared, returning. She waited until it had had time to turn into their own road. Then like a monumental statue coming to life, she bent her head slowly and gazed, as if through the very heart of mystery, down into the pig parlor at the hogs. They had settled all in one corner around the old sow who was grunting softly. A red glow suffused them. They appeared to pant with a secret life.

Until the sun slipped finally behind the tree line, Mrs. Turpin remained there with her gaze bent to them, as if she were absorbing some abysmal life-giving knowledge. At last she lifted her head. There was only a purple streak in the sky, cutting through a field of crimson and leading, like an extension of the highway, into the descending dusk. She raised her hands from the side of the pen in a gesture hieratic and profound. A visionary light settled in her eyes. She saw the streak as a vast swinging bridge extending upward from the earth through a field of living fire. Upon it a vast horde of souls were rumbling toward heaven. There were whole companies of white-trash, clean for the first time in their lives, and bands of black niggers in white robes, and battalions of freaks and lunatics shouting and clapping and leaping like frogs. And bringing up the end of the procession was a tribe of people whom she recognized at once as those who, like herself and Claud, had always had a little of everything and the God-given wit to use it right.

She leaned forward to observe them closer. They were marching behind the others with great dignity, accountable as they had always been for good order and common sense and respectable behavior. They alone were on key. Yet she could see by their shocked and altered faces that even their virtues were being burned away. She lowered her hands and gripped the rail of the hog pen, her eyes small but fixed unblinkingly on what lay ahead. In a moment the vision faded but she remained where she was, immobile.

At length she got down and turned off the faucet and made her slow way on the darkening path to the house. In the woods around her the invisible cricket choruses had struck up, but what she heard were the voices of the souls climbing upward into the starry field and shouting hallelujah.

Questions for Discussion:

1. What does social class mean to Mrs. Turpin? Throughout the story, she characterizes people in a variety of ways. What do you think this says about how she identifies herself?
2. What do you think is Mrs. Turpin's major flaw? What examples from the story give evidence of this flaw?
3. What do you think prompted Mary Grace's unexpected attack on Mrs. Turpin?
4. How do the pigs function symbolically in the story? Use examples to support your ideas.

"Hills Like White Elephants"

Ernest Hemingway

Author Biography: Ernest Hemingway was born in Oak Park, Illinois in 1899, right at the turn of the century. After high school he worked as a journalist with the *Kansas City Star* but soon after enlisted in World War I on the Italian front, where he was severely injured. After recovering he returned to the States but was urged to visit Europe and Paris as a correspondent for the *Toronto Star*. In Paris Hemingway became a member of the lost generation, mingling with modernist artists and writers such as Gertrude Stein, James Joyce, Ezra Pound, F. Scott Fitzgerald, and more. It was here he threw himself into writing and became a fairly prolific writer of short stories and novels. He would live in Key West, Cuba, and Idaho throughout his life, and worked in both the Spanish Civil War and World War II. He received the Nobel Prize in Literature in 1954.

Context: Hemingway learned a lot from his jobs in the press, and the journalist's creed of short and clear writing can be seen in all his work. Indeed, Hemingway is known for his short, terse style—often considered a very masculine style to match the machismo present in much of his writing. Hemingway also subscribed to the "iceberg" theory of writing—just as only the tip of an iceberg shows above water, Hemingway wanted to only show his readers the very top of the story and have nearly all of the meaning underneath that small surface. "Hills Like White Elephants" encompasses that theory to the extreme.

Literary Terms: theme, symbolism, characterization, setting

The hills across the valley of the Ebro were long and white. On this side there was no shade and no trees and the station was between two lines of rails in the sun. Close against the side of the station there was the warm shadow of the building and a curtain, made of strings of bamboo beads, hung across the open door into the bar, to keep out flies. The American and the girl with him sat at a table in the shade, outside the building. It was very hot and the express from Barcelona would come in forty minutes. It stopped at this junction for two minutes and went on to Madrid.

"What should we drink?" the girl asked. She had taken off her hat and put it on the table.

"It's pretty hot," the man said.

"Let's drink beer."

"Dos cervezas," the man said into the curtain.

"Big ones?" a woman asked from the doorway.

"Yes. Two big ones."

The woman brought two glasses of beer and two felts pads. She put the felt pads and the beer glasses on the table and looked at the man and the girl. The girl was looking off at the line of hills. They were white in the sun and the country was brown and dry.

"They look like white elephants," she said.

"I've never seen one," the man drank his beer.

"No, you wouldn't have."

"I might have," the man said. "Just because you say I wouldn't have doesn't prove anything."

The girl looked at the bead curtain. "They've painted something on it," she said. "What does it say?"

"Anis del Toro. It's a drink."

"Could we try it?"

The man called "Listen" through the curtain. The woman came out from the bar.

"Four reales."

"We want two Anis del Toro."

"With water?"

"Do you want it with water?"

"I don't know," the girl said. "Is it good with water?"

"It's all right."

"You want them with water?" asked the woman.

"Yes, with water."

"It tastes like licorice," the girl said and put the glass down.

"That's the way with everything."

"Yes," said the girl. "Everything tastes of licorice. Especially all the things you've waited so long for, like absinthe."

"Oh, cut it out."

"You started it," the girl said. "I was being amused. I was having a fine time."

"Well, let's try and have a fine time."

"All right. I was trying. I said the mountains looked like white elephants. Wasn't that bright?"

"That was bright."

"I wanted to try this new drink. That's all we do, isn't it—look at things and try new drinks?"

"I guess so."

The girl looked across at the hills.

"They're lovely hills," she said. "They don't really look like white elephants. I just meant the coloring of their skin through the trees."

"Should we have another drink?"

"All right."

The warm wind blew the bead curtain against the table.

"The beer's nice and cool," the man said.

"It's lovely," the girl said.

"It's really an awfully simple operation, Jig," the man said. "It's not really an operation at all."

The girl looked at the ground the table legs rested on.

"I know you wouldn't mind it, Jig. It's really not anything. It's just to let the air in."

The girl did not say anything.

"I'll go with you and I'll stay with you all the time. They just let the air in and then it's all perfectly natural."

"Then what will we do afterward?"

"We'll be fine afterward. Just like we were before."

"What makes you think so?"

"That's the only thing that bothers us. It's the only thing that's made us unhappy."

The girl looked at the bead curtain, put her hand out and took hold of two of the strings of beads.

"And you think then we'll be all right and be happy."

"I know we will. You don't have to be afraid. I've known lots of people that have done it."

"So have I," said the girl. "And afterward they were all so happy."

"Well," the man said, "if you don't want to you don't have to. I wouldn't have you do it if you didn't want to. But I know it's perfectly simple."

"And you really want to?"

"I think it's the best thing to do. But I don't want you to do it if you don't really want to."

"And if I do it you'll be happy and things will be like they were and you'll love me?"

"I love you now. You know I love you."

"I know. But if I do it, then it will be nice again if I say things are like white elephants, and you'll like it?"

"I'll love it. I love it now but I just can't think about it. You know how I get when I worry."

"If I do it you won't ever worry?"

"I won't worry about that because it's perfectly simple."

"Then I'll do it. Because I don't care about me."

"What do you mean?"

"I don't care about me."

"Well, I care about you."

"Oh, yes. But I don't care about me. And I'll do it and then everything will be fine."

"I don't want you to do it if you feel that way."

The girl stood up and walked to the end of the station. Across, on the other side, were fields of grain and trees along the banks of the Ebro. Far away, beyond the river, were mountains. The shadow of a cloud moved across the field of grain and she saw the river through the trees.

"And we could have all this," she said. "And we could have everything and every day we make it more impossible."

"What did you say?"

"I said we could have everything."

"No, we can't."

"We can have the whole world."

"No, we can't."

"We can go everywhere."

"No, we can't. It isn't ours any more."

"It's ours."

"No, it isn't. And once they take it away, you never get it back."

"But they haven't taken it away."

"We'll wait and see."

"Come on back in the shade," he said. "You mustn't feel that way."

"I don't feel any way," the girl said. "I just know things."

"I don't want you to do anything that you don't want to do—"

"Nor that isn't good for me," she said. "I know. Could we have another beer?"

"All right. But you've got to realize—"

"I realize," the girl said. "Can't we maybe stop talking?"

They sat down at the table and the girl looked across at the hills on the dry side of the valley and the man looked at her and at the table.

"You've got to realize," he said, "that I don't want you to do it if you don't want to. I'm perfectly willing to go through with it if it means anything to you."

"Doesn't it mean anything to you? We could get along."

"Of course it does. But I don't want anybody but you. I don't want anyone else. And I know it's perfectly simple."

"Yes, you know it's perfectly simple."

"It's all right for you to say that, but I do know it."

"Would you do something for me now?"

"I'd do anything for you."

"Would you please please please please please please please stop talking?"

He did not say anything but looked at the bags against the wall of the station. There were labels on them from all the hotels where they had spent nights.

"But I don't want you to," he said, "I don't care anything about it."

"I'll scream," the girl said.

The woman came out through the curtains with two glasses of beer and put them down on the damp felt pads. "The train comes in five minutes," she said.

"What did she say?" asked the girl.

"That the train is coming in five minutes."

The girl smiled brightly at the woman, to thank her.

"I'd better take the bags over to the other side of the station," the man said. She smiled at him.

"All right. Then come back and we'll finish the beer."

He picked up the two heavy bags and carried them around the station to the other tracks. He looked up the tracks but could not see the train. Coming back, he walked through the barroom, where people waiting for the train were drinking. He drank an Anis at the bar and looked at the people. They were all waiting reasonably for the train. He went out through the bead curtain. She was sitting at the table and smiled at him.

"Do you feel better?" he asked.

"I feel fine," she said. "There's nothing wrong with me. I feel fine."

Questions for Discussion:

1. What is the "awfully simple operation" that the man is talking the girl into? How do they each feel about it?
2. How would you characterize the relationship between the man and the girl? Give specific examples from the story to support your characterization.
3. Consider the title of the story. How are the "white elephants" symbolic?

"1.7 to Tennessee"
from *I Want to Show You More*

Jamie Quatro

Author Biography: Jamie Quatro lives in Lookout Mountain, Georgia with her family and holds M.A. and M.F.A. degrees. She is a contributing editor at the *Oxford American Magazine,* and her work has appeared in numerous national outlets and anthologies, including *The New York Review of Books* and the *O. Henry Prize Stories 2013.* She has received numerous awards for her fiction.

Context: This story is from Quatro's first story collection, *I Want to Show You More,* which features female protagonists dealing with issues of love, sex, illness, death, and more. Quatro's work is often tied to place.

Literary Terms: theme, setting, metaphor, characterization

Eva Bock made her way along the shoulder of Lula Lake Road. She was eighty-nine—tall, bent forward from the waist. Her white pants hung from her hips so the hemlines of the legs pooled onto the tops of her tennis shoes. Her narrow lips were painted orange-red, and her steel-gray hair, tied up in a bun, smelled faintly of lemon. Loose strands hung about her cheeks and trailed down her spine. She wore a pair of headphones that created a furrow across the center pile of her hair. The cord fed into a chunky cassette deck/FM radio hooked onto the waistband of her pants. She was listening to NPR.

In her pocket was a letter, addressed: *Pres. George W. Bush, Penn. Ave., Wash. D.C.* Seven envelopes she had thrown away before she felt her handwriting passed for that of an adult. The letter itself she dictated to Quentin Jenkins, one of the McCallie boys who went down the mountain for her groceries. Quentin wrote in cursive on a college-ruled sheet of paper. She preferred he type it, and considered offering to pay him an extra dollar to do so, but when she finished her dictation and Quentin read the letter back to her, she grew excited and snatched the paper from him, folding and stuffing it into an envelope. Then she realized she hadn't signed the letter, so she had to open the envelope and borrow the boy's pen. Quentin offered to mail it for her but she had made up her mind to deliver it to the post office herself. She took great pride in the fact that she, an eighty-nine-year-old woman, still had things to say to the President of the United States. It was a formal letter, protesting the war. She felt it her duty to place it, personally, into the hands of the government.

A yellow Penske truck approached, honking. Eva set her feet a little ways apart and froze, looking straight ahead. She swayed from side to side, as if holding her balance on a log. In her freckled hand she carried a furled green umbrella, the tip of which she planted into the pavement to steady herself against the truck's tailwind.

When it passed she continued on, watching her feet take turns appearing and vanishing beneath her. One of her shoelaces was untied. The Lookout Mountain residents never honked. She had been walking this route, mornings, for as long as she could remember. Most locals slowed and made half-circles around her so she wouldn't feel obliged to step off the pavement. The tourists would run her off the road if she did not stand her ground to remind them this was a residential suburb, where folks lived and worked and took morning walks.

Eva felt short of breath, a bit light-headed. She'd been unable to finish her toast that morning, so eager she'd been to set off upon her errand. Three houses before the elementary school she stopped to tie her shoe. Sitting on the stone retaining wall beside the Sutherlands' driveway, she crossed her left foot over her right knee. The angle was awkward; the laces draped against her inside arch. She rested, looking up Lula Lake Road, visualizing her route. Just past the school's pillared entrance were a small pond and wooden gazebo; beyond the gazebo she could see the spire of the Methodist church, and beyond that were the bakery, City Hall, gas station, and convenience mart. Next came the Mountain Market and Bed and Breakfast. A brief stretch of houses. And then—with difficulty, Eva pictured herself reaching it—the four-way stop where Lookout Mountain, Georgia, became Lookout Mountain, Tennessee.

It was here, at the border, that Eva usually turned around, so that by the time she came home to the Adirondack rocker on her front patio, she had covered just over a mile of ground. Today would be different. The post office was on the Tennessee side, 1.7 miles from her front door. She'd had Quentin look it up on his laptop computer. Round trip: 3.4. She had not walked this far in twenty years.

She stood and, clutching the handle of her umbrella, again began her slow, measured steps. With her free hand she brushed off the backs of her pant legs and adjusted her top. She was wearing a threadbare sweater with an orange "P" knitted into the black fabric. It had been a gift from her son Thomas, who, after one semester at Princeton, joined the Army and was killed in a village in the Batangan Peninsula when he went into the jungle to relieve himself and stepped onto a booby-trapped 105 round. One arm was found hanging by its sleeve from a branch twenty feet above the ground. At least this was the story she heard coming out of her mouth when people asked about the sweater. Sometimes she forgot and said she didn't know where the sweater came from, and when she said this, it was as true as when she told the story about the dead son. She wasn't always sure if the thing had actually happened or if it was just something she read in a book. When she told the story, she felt she had not even known the boy in the jungle; she told it without emotion, as if describing a scene from a stage play, the boy who stepped onto the booby trap just an actor who was now carrying on another life somewhere.

When she finished telling the story she would berate herself. "His own mother," she would think. *What kind of mother stops feeling grief for her son? What kind of mother must I have been?* She could not remember. And there was no one left whom she could ask.

But no one talked to her about the sweater anymore. If anyone spoke to her at all, it was, "Miss Eva, why must you take your walk along this busy road? You know when the fog sets in we can't see you coming or going. Miss Eva, you're going to get yourself run over." But most people in town could not imagine what it would be like to drive along Lula Lake without watching for Miss Eva. Single-handedly, between 7:30 and 8:45 A.M., Eva Bock kept the speed limit in check.

The truth was she could no longer remember why she walked this road. "It's the way I know," she said when people asked. When she'd formed the habit, Lula Lake was not paved. Where the gas station and pharmacy stood had once been a grove of peach trees. But these were details that, most of the time, she could not recall. This morning, for example, she could think back only as far as yesterday's walk, when Phyllis Driver came out of the convenience mart and offered her a cup of Barnies coffee. She turned it down. The cup was brown with a picture of a man wearing glasses drawn in yellow lines. Phyllis was wearing a watch for people with vision trouble, large black numbers on an oversized white face. It read 8:10. Eva could remember these things—the time, watch, cup, "Barnies." She could not remember her own son.

Sometimes she did remember things, usually when the season was in a time of change, but they were memories from her childhood. When one of these memories broke over her she would laugh and clap her hands against her thighs. One October morning, she stepped into the Mountain Market, flushed and shaking. Loran Ellis, the cashier, put out her cigarette. "Gambling!" Eva shouted. "At the college!" Except for smears of red in the corners, her lips were colorless and wet with saliva. The skin on her face was like a delicate system of roots. Miss Eva beckoned and Lorna followed her out onto the stoop. With her umbrella, Eva pointed to the ridge above the Methodist church, where the trees around the Westminster campus shone red and yellow. "That's where Granddaddy showed me how to play blackjack. Held me on his knee and taught me to add up cards."

When she did remember her son, Eva Bock prayed. It was the only time she prayed, and since she rarely remembered, she prayed infrequently. She began with the Lord's Prayer but usually wound up arguing about the funeral with Hugh, her husband, dead thirty-two years now. "Thy will be done, on earth as it is in Heaven," she would recite, imagining Thomas's soul continuing to fly upward while the rest of him fell back to earth. "And get rid of the flag," she told Hugh. "It's sullying his coffin." When they sent Thomas home in a bag with a zipper, Hugh oversaw the entire affair: the guns, flag-folding, honors from a country that served Thomas up in the name of—what? It was a question she'd asked so many times it was boiled down, the feeling refined out of it. Just a quiet string of words she wished God would tell her the answer to. Sometimes during these prayers, when she got to the part where she meant to argue about the funeral, a young Hugh Bock would appear before her, expressionless and shining in a white linen suit. He was handsome and when she saw him like this she would forget what it was she wanted to say. She would feel girlish and shy and want to adorn him in some way, perhaps slide a daisy into the buttonhole on his lapel.

Today she did not remember Hugh or her son. She thought only of hand-delivering the letter in her pocket. It was cold out, close to freezing, in fact, and her knuckles ached around the handle of the umbrella. *Should have put on my coat. But there's no sense in turning around.* She was passing the pond and gazebo beside the school. Children—looking impossibly tiny to her, dwarfed by oversized backpacks—were emerging from side streets and parked cars. They wore brightly colored rubber shoes and hats with tassels. Mothers and fathers looked at her but did not wave or say hello, which was the way Eva wanted it. It was the reason she'd started wearing the headphones. The muscles of her face no longer betrayed any expression, so that it was difficult for anyone to tell if she was feeling friendly, which she usually was not. More than anything else, while she walked, Eva Bock wanted to be left alone.

Two boys wearing hooded sweatshirts flicked thin branches over the pond like fly rods. Sunlight and shadow spotted the muddy water, the surface of which buoyed a thousand brightly colored leaves. A yellow dog sat on the bank beside the boys.

"Careful," Eva said. She had not intended to say the word aloud.

They turned to look at her. One boy laughed, then leaned over and said something to the other.

"What are you listening to?" the second boy called out.

Eva kept up her wide, even steps. "Floods in Mexico," she said. "A mountain fell into the sea and the wave washed away a village in Chiapas."

The bell rang. The boys ran across the school's front lawn, the dog following, their shoes kicking up little moist tufts of grass.

Something in the way the boys ran off...Eva felt as if a stack of papers were shifting inside her head. *Remember.* But as soon as she tried there was only the road ahead of her, a line up of late-coming cars, children's faces like pale moons in backseat windows. Eva planted her feet and stood, waiting for the cars to pass. She listened to the British announcer reporting the collapse of a bridge in Dubai. She thought of her letter and reached into her pocket, afraid she might forget her errand and turn around at the four-way stop. She rubbed her fingers along the edge of the envelope, feeling the stamps. She'd had to lick four of them to make enough postage. Almost a half-dollar to mail a letter to the President.

She continued on, past City Hall with its wooden sign hanging by only one hook so the words *Lookout Mountain, Ga.* had to be read sideways. She passed the Fairy Bakery with its morning smells of cinnamon rolls and coffee. The bakery had opened in September and some mornings the line came out the door.

At the McFarland intersection, in front of the gas station, she had to stop to rest. There was a bench in the tiny center island, placed there by the Fairyland Garden Club. Violas had been planted around the bench and Eva accidentally crushed two of them beneath her shoe. She sat down, folding her hands around her knees. *Only a quarter-mile, Miss Eva. How are you going to make it all the way into Tennessee?* Little black spots dotted the outside edges of her vision. She swiped at them with her hand.

Coming toward her, crossing Lula Lake from Oberon Road, was the new family— the professor's wife and her two children. Eva had seen them before. They were late for school but the mother did not seem in a hurry. The boy had hair like a mushroom cap and carried a long stick. The girl's brown hair was pulled into pigtails and she wore a skirt with stockings. The mother watched the boy, who, when they reached the island, pointed the stick at Eva and pretended to fire. The mother said something and Eva pushed back an earphone.

"Sorry to interrupt. We've seen you out walking." She put her hands on the tops of the children's heads. "This is Myra and Grady. I'm Jocelyn Corley." She held out a hand. She seemed eager to be touched.

Eva took her hand and looked up. The woman had a scarf tied around her neck. *Sarkozy*, Eva heard in one ear, *like President Bush, is a teetotaler. He enjoys mountain biking. He and Bush are discussing a Franco-American holiday in honor of Lafayette.*

"We've been so charmed, seeing you out here every day," the mother said. "We even made up a limerick about it. We thought, with your permission, we could send it to the *Mountain Mirror.*"

"Let's hear it then," Eva said. She was annoyed by this distraction from her errand and by the fact that these new folks had already formed opinions about her. Again she reached to feel for the letter in her pocket. In one ear Sarkozy was speaking. *France was there for the United States at the beginning. United States was there for France during the wars in Europe. We must remind our people of this.*

The little girl stepped behind her mother, shy; but Jocelyn and the boy recited:

"There once was a woman named Bock,
who every day went for a walk.
Rain or snow,
still she would go,
each step like the tick of a clock."

"Carrying a dirty sock," said the boy. "Looking for a cool rock."

"He comes up with alternate endings," the mother said.

"What's on your Ipod?" the girl asked. When Eva didn't answer the girl pointed to her hip.

"Oh. It's a radio." She lifted the corner of her sweater so the girl could see the cassette player. "I've got my news program on. The war."

The boy sat down on the bench and unzipped his backpack. "Are you for blue or gray?"

Eva wiped her eyes with the back of her hand. The spots were elongating, drifting toward the center of her vision.

"Watch this," said the boy, pulling something from his bag. It was a large magnolia seedpod. He turned it over in his hand. "Incoming!" he said. He plunked the seedpod down onto the bed of violas and made a crackling noise inside his mouth.

Eva removed her headphones. "Where did you learn that?"

"Since we moved here he's become obsessed with weapons," the mother said. "All this Civil War history everywhere."

For a moment Eva thought she might reach out and shake the boy by the shoulders. *In the name of what?* But then she could not remember what her question meant.

Now the mother was smiling; she was taking the children away. As they crossed McFarland the boy looked back and waved.

Eva lifted her chin and put her headphones back on.

On she went, past the Mountain Market with its green awning and smells of pipe tobacco and lard from the deep fryer, past the Garden Walk Inn with its trellised porch and dollhouse mailbox. And now began the stretch of large homes set back from the road. Two more blocks and she would reach the four-way stop. This was still familiar ground. But Eva was beginning to worry.

In the first place, she realized, now that she was near the border, she could not remember if the post office in Tennessee was actually on Lula Lake Road. She thought there might be a turn somewhere. In the second place—whether from excitement or just the anticipation of the extra length of her walk—her heart was clattering beneath her sweater like teeth in the cold. She turned off the radio, though she left the headphones on to discourage talkers. She put her hand into her pocket and rubbed the letter between her thumb and forefinger. The black spots floated up, and up, in front of her.

Past Elfin, past Robin Hood Trail. She had to stop three times to steady herself for passing cars, all of which slowed and crossed the double yellow line into the opposite lane. She saw Megan Compson wave from inside her silver van. Eva walked on, trying not to bend her knees too much. Beside the road were smears of color, red and yellow, purple and orange; twiggy bushes and small trees with dead brown leaves under them; low stone walls and white fences with latched gates. Vines with chalky periwinkle berries dragged at her sleeve and pant legs. The sun laid orange slats of light across rooftops. Dogs strolled out from porches and sniffed at her legs; the ones that barked she held off with her umbrella.

She rounded the last curve and saw the single pulsing red light above the intersection of Lula Lake and Lee Avenue. She could not remember why she was supposed to cross rather than turn around. Something about solemn duty and the government.

She reached the intersection and stood, breathing. Her lips felt dry. Beside her was a wrought-iron sign with arrows and words: LOOKOUT MOUNTAIN BIRD SANCTUARY, POINT PARK, CRAVENS HOUSE, RUBY FALLS. Another sign, shaped like a choo-choo train, read TAKE SCENIC HIGHWAY DOWN TO HISTORIC CHATTANOOGA!

Something about the government. Something about a funeral. The post office. She was going to tell President Johnson how she felt about things in North…She reached into her pocket and her heart rattled beneath her ribs. Surely the post office would not be in the direction of all those damned tourist traps. She turned onto Lee.

After walking thirty yards Eva realized she had made a mistake. The road curved and began to climb a hill. She had not planned on climbing any hills. She turned to go back to the intersection and the asphalt rushed up toward her. She would have fallen were it not for the umbrella, which she threw out in front of her and held on to with both hands—she had to lean back and squat to avoid falling. There was nothing for it but to continue uphill, and to do so she was forced to lean forward and bend her knees, using her umbrella like a cane. She was considerably irked by the black spots, which moved around and around in the trees on either side of her. Pinestraw blanketed the pavement beneath her; it was slippery and she moved toward the center of the road. Why wasn't she on Lula Lake Road? Why wasn't she on her way home? The sun was already above the tops of the tallest pines.

The hill became steeper; now if she stopped at all she would not be able to hold her balance. Eva made up her mind to signal the next car that drove past and request a ride back home. No, that wasn't right. She was supposed to mail a letter. She would request a ride to the post office, and then home. She removed her headphones and left them hanging in an arc about her neck.

Ahead of her was a sharp blind curve. If she didn't cross the street she might be struck by an oncoming vehicle. Eva listened for cars; hearing nothing, with slow steps she crossed to the right side of the road.

Where the pavement ended, there was a steep drop-off. Below, fifty yards down the rocky hillside, Eva could see a track. A woman was running laps. Next to the track was a baseball diamond, the grass still green. Silver bleachers gleamed on either side of the baselines; beyond the field was a playground with swings and picnic tables. The Commons, on the Tennessee/Georgia border *grass stains on his pants. The smell of leather oil and sweat. Watch this hit, I'll fly it to the moon. Crepe myrtle blossoms in a jar on the kitchen table*...and now a black dog was bounding up the hillside. Eva saw him for only a second before he reached her. She did not have time to steady herself. She hit at him with her umbrella, then lost her balance and fell. Her thin body hurtled down the side of the hill toward the baseball field until she struck the trunk of a maple tree with her left hip bone.

She lay on her side among rocks and fallen leaves. For a space of time—seconds? hours?—she thought she had finished with her walk and was now resting in her own bed, and for this she felt an overwhelming gratitude. Interrupting her sleep was a dog's bark, abrupt like the scrape of a chair being pushed back from a table. A leaf blower droned, a bird sang. The sifting of leaves, then a quick panting, very close to her ear.

She opened her eyes. The black dog was in front of her; she saw his paws, toes spread on the uneven rocky hillside, cluster of silver tags hanging from a purple collar. He barked and Eva threw an arm over the ear that was facing upward.

The sleeve of her sweater was torn and pocked with hitchhiker burrs. She noticed her earphones were gone. The dog stopped barking and began to sniff around her face. Warm tongue on her cheek. The dog whimpered and backed away, then disappeared down the hillside.

The trunk before her was twisted about with a vine of bright pink leaves. In her confusion, Eva thought they were hands clamoring to reach the top branches, each leaf five fingers pressing into the bark, staking its claim. She rolled her head and saw that the vine ended halfway up the trunk; at the top of the tree the branches were thin and white, with only a few yellow leaves still attached. Through the branches the sky was an exhilarating blue.

She remembered: She was going to the post office in Tennessee. She was going to deliver a letter to President Bush.

What foolishness! She should never have attempted such a thing. Twenty years she had stood up to speeding tourists, and all anyone would remember was that she had fallen off the side of the road because of a dog. And what did she know about the war? Listening to NPR had only given her ideas, had made her forget who she was. She was an eighty-nine-year-old pacifist who could not find her way to the post office. Who could not remember her own son.

What do you know about the decisions of our government? It was Hugh's voice. He was standing in the driveway next to her; in her hand was the garden hose.

I know our son is dead. Cheated out of his birthright by his own country. I know the President is a liar.

Hugh slapped her across the face. She stumbled backward into the hydrangea bush. *Your son died in the name of this country. And here you are, setting your goddamn table with goddamn linen napkins.* She lay in the bush, looking up at the sky.

But something was not right with the sky. The black spots had returned and now swirled in front of the blue and branches and the yellow dangling leaves. Eva let her head roll back so she was again looking at the vine on the tree trunk and the black spots came with her, they went out to join the leaves, or the leaves peeled off and joined the spots, she couldn't tell. They were coming together, the colors merging into a subdued gray, approaching her, arranging themselves in a dark processional.

In her mind, Eva righted herself to meet them.

The spots drifting toward her were soldiers in uniform. They were all identical—all her son. She cried out and tried to touch one of them but the sons did not look at her as they came on. As they neared, Eva saw Thomas's face over and over again—his high cheekbones; the slight depression across the bridge of his nose, left there when he broke it against the handlebars of his two-wheel bicycle; the scar below the downy blond arch of his right eyebrow; the cowlick at the center of his part above his forehead. She used to wet down the cowlick Sunday mornings before church. His hair was soft and during the sermons she twirled it through her fingertips.

The faces came on. She could see the green and gold of Thomas's eyes. None of them saw her. The sons drifted past and out of her vision in a regular, stolid rhythm.

"Look at me," she said. "I want to ask you a question."

One of them stopped and turned his head. His face remained expressionless and the others waited patiently behind. She understood that he was waiting for her to ask the question and it was terrible, this passionless waiting man who was her son, terrible that he did not recognize her. She felt certain that, were she able to kiss his cheek, she would remember how to feel sadness and grief, love and longing.

In his gray uniform the son continued to wait. Eva could bear it no longer. "In the name of *what?*" she cried out to the son in front of her. "Of *what?*" she asked the waiting ones behind him. The son smiled and for a moment Eva thought he would comfort her. She saw his lips move but no sound came out. The others smiled in exactly the same way as the first.

And then they were pulling back, all of them, one by one. With horror she realized they were leaving her and she felt at the very least she should say something to put Thomas at rest. But the sons were not at rest—they were only apart, winnowed from victories and failures. While she watched they withdrew into the sky, grown dark now. They began to circle above her with a hard, impartial energy, like the stars.

Now the dark sky and circling soldiers started to descend and she understood that the darkness would cover her like a hood. Eva saw the last gray soldier turn. This time it was Hugh Bock's face before her and when he spoke it was only a whisper.

"Unanswerable," he said. And the host of orbiting sons repeated the word until it became a kind of song, the sound of air moving in summer trees. *Unanswerable, unanswerable.*

Beneath them, Eva listened.

The dog was, in fact, a female retriever named Pearl. Her barking alerted her owner, Sharon Miller, who was running laps on the track at the Commons. Pearl led her up the hillside to Eva Bock's body, her leg wrapped around the trunk of a tree. One of her shoes was missing and her thin foot in its dirty white stocking looked like a child's. Her hair was spread out across the rocks and colored leaves in a way that would have been almost sensual had she been merely asleep. Her eyes were open, wide and antique, and there was a vertical gash shaped like a parallelogram from her temple to her jaw. The frail skin looked as if it had been freshly shucked. Sharon Miller could see the grayish skullbone. She vomited, then called 911 and the Lookout Mountain, Georgia City Hall. She also called her husband, who called Liza at the *Mountain Mirror*. Assuming Miss Eva had been, as long predicted, run off the road by a tourist, Liza posted the information on the *Mountain Mirror*'s website, so that, for a time after her death, the Lookout Mountain residents felt a sense of indignation at the license plates from anywhere but Georgia or Tennessee.

Because she had fallen on the Tennessee side, the ambulance came not from the Walker County, Georgia, response unit six miles away, but from St. Elmo at the base of the mountain. It took seventeen minutes, during which time residents gathered and peered down the side of the hill. Dr. Bailey was called—he was young and took the steep hillside with ease—and was able to determine that Miss Eva was, indeed, dead. Just the same, he administered CPR until the EMTs came. Everyone felt it was a heroic gesture.

Before the night-shift CNA at Memorial Hospital threw out the white pants— bloody at the knees, both pant legs cut off the victim from the hemline up through the waistband—he found the envelope in the pocket. He was an immigrant from Haiti, nineteen years old, and had never seen 15-cent stamps. He felt this must be an important letter; he was surprised the EMTs had not removed it from the pocket for the next-of-kin. He could not read the words on the front but he opened the letter to see if there was any money inside. Then, feeling guilty and superstitious, he went into the supply closet and resealed the envelope with Scotch tape.

When he clocked out the next morning, the CNA gave the letter to the woman who volunteered at the front desk, who placed it in a stack of outgoing mail.

Seven months after Eva Bock's funeral (during which the local police closed 58 South to tourists, to ensure that the funeral procession could head down to the cemetery in St. Elmo unimpeded; the residents, who had already simplified Miss Eva the way the living do, felt it was her final triumph), a letter in an eight-by-ten white linen stock envelope, addressed to Mrs. Eva Bock, arrived at the Lookout Mountain Post Office. Steven Ruske, Receiving, had never seen a letter from the White House. He was supposed to shred it (there was no next-of-kin listed on the Bock account) but who would know?

On his lunch break, despite the fact that it was a felony—didn't he, of all people, know it!—Steven Ruske took the letter out to his car, which was parked on Lula Lake Road across from the post office. He opened the envelope beneath his steering wheel. It was only a form letter with a stamped signature. He read it anyhow.

Dear Mrs. Eva Bock,

Thank you for writing to express your concerns regarding our efforts to improve the lives of the Iraqi people. I want to assure you, personally, that I and my administration are doing everything within our power to minimize casualties, both military and civilian. Please continue to keep our troops in your thoughts and prayers as we look forward to a future in which the freedoms we enjoy as Americans—including the freedom of speech, which allows citizens like yourself to speak out against oppression and injustice—are made available to our fellow citizens at the far reaches of the globe.

Sincerely,
President George W. Bush

Steven Ruske slid the letter back into the envelope. He finished eating his sandwich, placing the letter in his lap to catch the crumbs. He stuffed the leftover crusts, foil wrapper, and envelope into his brown lunch sack. Then he crossed the street and, before returning to work, tossed the sack into the dumpster next to the Lookout Mountain Café.

Questions for Discussion:

1. Why is the setting of this story significant? Could the story have taken place in any city?
2. What was the purpose of Eva's trip to the post office? What obstacles did she face in her way?
3. What parallels can you draw between this story and Eudora Welty's "A Worn Path"?

"Sticks"

George Saunders

Author Biography: George Saunders was born in Amarillo, Texas in 1958 and grew up near Chicago. He earned a B.S. in geophysical engineering and later an M.A. in creative writing. Mainly a fiction writer of short stories and novels, Saunders has also been published for his nonfiction as well. He has won the National Magazine Award for fiction four times and received a MacArthur Fellowship in 2006.

Context: Saunders' work is often strange and perhaps a bit mysterious for a reader but so often contains deep cultural criticism and moral investigation. He has been compared at times to Kurt Vonnegut for this reason and because his work is characterized by irony, absurdity, and tragic-comical mannerisms.

Literary Terms: theme, symbolism, tone, imagery

Every year Thanksgiving night we flocked out behind Dad as he dragged the Santa suit to the road and draped it over a kind of crucifix he'd built out of metal pole in the yard. Super Bowl week the pole was dressed in a jersey and Rod's helmet and Rod had to clear it with Dad if he wanted to take the helmet off. On the Fourth of July the pole was Uncle Sam, on Veteran's Day a soldier, on Halloween a ghost. The pole was Dad's only concession to glee. We were allowed a single Crayola from the box at a time. One Christmas Eve he shrieked at Kimmie for wasting an apple slice. He hovered over us as we poured ketchup saying: good enough good enough good enough. Birthday parties consisted of cupcakes, no ice cream. The first time I brought a date over she said: what's with your dad and that pole? and I sat there blinking.

We left home, married, had children of our own, found the seeds of meanness blooming also within us. Dad began dressing the pole with more complexity and less discernible logic. He draped some kind of fur over it on Groundhog Day and lugged out a floodlight to ensure a shadow. When an earthquake struck Chile he lay the pole on its side and spray painted a rift in the earth. Mom died and he dressed the pole as Death and hung from the crossbar photos of Mom as a baby. We'd stop by and find odd talismans from his youth arranged around the base: army medals, theater tickets, old sweatshirts, tubes of Mom's makeup. One autumn he painted the pole bright yellow. He covered it with cotton swabs that winter for warmth and provided offspring by hammering in six crossed sticks around the yard. He ran lengths of string between the pole and the sticks, and taped to the string letters of apology, admissions of error, pleas for understanding, all written in a frantic hand on index cards. He painted a sign saying LOVE and hung it from the pole and another that said FORGIVE? and then he died in the hall with the radio on and we sold the house to a young couple who yanked out the pole and the sticks and left them by the road on garbage day.

Questions for Discussion:

1. What is the significance of the story's title?
2. Describe the narrator's tone in this story. What does it indicate about his or her reaction to Dad?
3. How does the way Dad decorates the pole change throughout the years? Why do you think these change occur?

"Everyday Use"

Alice Walker

Author Biography: Alice Walker was born in 1944 in Georgia, the daughter of a share-cropper and a maid still living under Jim Crow laws. Walker was valedictorian of her high school class, received a full-ride scholarship to Spelman College, and graduated later from Sarah Lawrence College. In the 1960s, Walker was involved in the Civil Rights Movement, inspired by a meeting with Martin Luther King, Jr. She began writing even in college, but achieved major success with her 1982 novel, *The Color Purple*, which won the Pulitzer Prize and the National Book Award. Walker continues to write fiction and poetry.

Context: "Everyday Use" is set in the late 1960s/early 1970s, a time in which American culture and African-American culture were undergoing some dramatic changes. After the Civil Rights Movement, a Black Power movement had emerged, which advocated a stronger response to injustice and a reinvigorated pride in African heritage. Here and in much of her work, Walker explores these issues, as well as those of feminism and family bonds.

Literary Terms: theme, setting, point of view, symbolism

I will wait for her in the yard that Maggie and I made so clean and wavy yesterday afternoon. A yard like this is more comfortable than most people know. It is not just a yard. It is like an extended living room. When the hard clay is swept clean as a floor and fine sand around the edges lined with tiny, irregular grooves, anyone can come and sit and look up into the elm tree and wait for the breezes that never come inside the house.

Maggie will be nervous until after her sister goes: she will stand hopelessly in corners, homely and ashamed of the burn scars down her arms and legs, eying her sister with a mixture of envy and awe. She thinks her sister has held life always in the palm of her hand, that "no" is a word the world never learned to say to her.

You've no doubt seen those TV shows where the child who has "made it" is confronted, as a surprise, by her own mother and father, tottering in weakly from back-stage. (A pleasant surprise, of course: What would they do if parent and child came on the show only to curse out and insult each other?) On TV mother and child embrace and smile into each other's faces. Sometimes the mother and father weep, the child wraps them in her arms and leans across the table to tell how she would not have made it without their help. I have seen those programs.

Sometimes I dream a dream in which Dee and I are suddenly brought together on a TV program of this sort. Out of a dark and soft-seated limousine I am ushered into a bright room filled with many people. There I meet a smiling, gray, sporty man like

Johnny Carson who shakes my hand and tells me what a fine girl I have. Then we are on the stage and Dee is embracing me with tears in her eyes. She pins on my dress a large orchid, even though she has told me once that she thinks orchids are tacky flowers.

In real life I am a large, big-boned woman with rough, man-working hands. In the winter I wear flannel nightgowns to bed and overalls during the day. I can kill and clean a hog as mercilessly as a man. My fat keeps me hot in zero weather. I can work outside all day, breaking ice to get water for washing; I can eat pork liver cooked over the open fire minutes after it comes steaming from the hog. One winter I knocked a bull calf straight in the brain between the eyes with a sledge hammer and had the meat hung up to chill before nightfall. But of course all this does not show on television. I am the way my daughter would want me to be: a hundred pounds lighter, my skin like an uncooked barley pancake. My hair glistens in the hot bright lights. Johnny Carson has much to do to keep up with my quick and witty tongue.

But that is a mistake. I know even before I wake up. Who ever knew a Johnson with a quick tongue? Who can even imagine me looking a strange white man in the eye? It seems to me I have talked to them always with one foot raised in flight, with my head turned in whichever way is farthest from them. Dee, though. She would always look anyone in the eye. Hesitation was not part of her nature.

"How do I look, Mama?" Maggie says, showing just enough of her thin body enveloped in pink skirt and red blouse for me to know she's there, almost hidden by the door.

"Come out into the yard," I say.

Have you ever seen a lame animal, perhaps a dog run over by some careless person rich enough to own a car, sidle up to someone who is ignorant enough to be kind to him? That is the way my Maggie walks. She has been like this, chin on chest, eyes on ground, feet in shuffle, ever since the fire that burned the other house to the ground.

Dee is lighter than Maggie, with nicer hair and a fuller figure. She's a woman now, though sometimes I forget. How long ago was it that the other house burned? Ten, twelve years? Sometimes I can still hear the flames and feel Maggie's arms sticking to me, her hair smoking and her dress falling off her in little black papery flakes. Her eyes seemed stretched open, blazed open by the flames reflected in them. And Dee. I see her standing off under the sweet gum tree she used to dig gum out of; a look of concentration on her face as she watched the last dingy gray board of the house fall in toward the red-hot brick chimney. Why don't you do a dance around the ashes? I'd wanted to ask her. She had hated the house that much.

I used to think she hated Maggie, too. But that was before we raised the money, the church and me, to send her to Augusta to school. She used to read to us without pity; forcing words, lies, other folks' habits, whole lives upon us two, sitting trapped and ignorant underneath her voice. She washed us in a river of make-believe, burned us with a lot of knowledge we didn't necessarily need to know. Pressed us to her with the serious way she read, to shove us away at just the moment, like dimwits, we seemed about to understand.

Dee wanted nice things. A yellow organdy dress to wear to her graduation from high school; black pumps to match a green suit she'd made from an old suit somebody gave me. She was determined to stare down any disaster in her efforts. Her eyelids would not flicker for minutes at a time. Often I fought off the temptation to shake her. At sixteen she had a style of her own: and knew what style was.

I never had an education myself. After second grade the school was closed down. Don't ask me why: in 1927 colored asked fewer questions than they do now. Sometimes Maggie reads to me. She stumbles along good-naturedly but can't see well. She knows she is not bright. Like good looks and money, quickness passed her by. She will marry John Thomas (who has mossy teeth in an earnest face) and then I'll be free to sit here and I guess just sing church songs to myself. Although I never was a good singer. Never could carry a tune. I was always better at a man's job. I used to love to milk till I was hooked in the side in '49. Cows are soothing and slow and don't bother you, unless you try to milk them the wrong way.

I have deliberately turned my back on the house. It is three rooms, just like the one that burned, except the roof is tin; they don't make shingle roofs any more. There are no real windows, just some holes cut in the sides, like the portholes in a ship, but not round and not square, with rawhide holding the shutters up on the outside. This house is in a pasture, too, like the other one. No doubt when Dee sees it she will want to tear it down. She wrote me once that no matter where we "choose" to live, she will manage to come see us. But she will never bring her friends. Maggie and I thought about this and Maggie asked me, "Mama, when did Dee ever have any friends?"

She had a few. Furtive boys in pink shirts hanging about on washday after school. Nervous girls who never laughed. Impressed with her they worshipped the well-turned phrase, the cute shape, the scalding humor that erupted like bubbles in lye. She read to them.

When she was courting Jimmy T she didn't have much time to pay to us, but turned all her faultfinding power on him. He *flew* to marry a cheap city girl from a family of ignorant flashy people. She hardly had time to recompose herself.

When she comes I will meet—but there they are!

Maggie attempts to make a dash for the house, in her shuffling way, but I stay her with my hand. "Come back here," I say. And she stops and tries to dig a well in the sand with her toe.

It is hard to see them clearly through the strong sun. But even the first glimpse of leg out of the car tells me it is Dee. Her feet were always neat-looking, as if God himself had shaped them with a certain style. From the other side of the car comes a short, stocky man. Hair is all over his head a foot long and hanging from his chin like a kinky mule tail. I hear Maggie suck in her breath. "Uhnnnh," is what it sounds like. Like when you see the wriggling end of a snake just in front of your foot on the road. "Uhnnnh."

Dee next. A dress down to the ground, in this hot weather. A dress so loud it hurts my eyes. There are yellows and oranges enough to throw back the light of the sun. I feel my whole face warming from the heat waves it throws out. Earrings gold, too, and hanging down to her shoulders. Bracelets dangling and making noises when she moves her arm up to shake the folds of the dress out of her armpits. The dress is loose and flows, and as she walks closer, I like it. I hear Maggie go "Uhnnnh" again. It is her sister's hair. It stands straight up like the wool on a sheep. It is black as night and around the edges are two long pig-tails that rope about like small lizards disappearing behind her ears.

"Wa-su-zo-Tean-o!" she says, coming on in that gliding way the dress makes her move. The short stocky fellow with the hair to his navel is all grinning and he follows up with "Asalamalakim, my mother and sister!" He moves to hug Maggie but she falls back, right up against the back of my chair. I feel her trembling there and when I look up I see the perspiration falling off her chin.

"Don't get up," says Dee. Since I am stout it takes something of a push. You can see me trying to move a second or two before I make it. She turns, showing white heels through her sandals, and goes back to the car. Out she peeks next with a Polaroid. She stoops down quickly and lines up picture after picture of me sitting there in front of the house with Maggie cowering behind me. She never takes a shot without making sure the house is included. When a cow comes nibbling around the edge of the yard she snaps it and me and Maggie *and* the house. Then she puts the Polaroid in the back seat of the car, and comes up and kisses me on the forehead.

Meanwhile Asalamalakim is going through motions with Maggie's hand. Maggie's hand is as limp as a fish, and probably as cold, despite the sweat, and she keeps trying to pull it back. It looks like Asalamalakim wants to shake hands but wants to do it fancy. Or maybe he don't know how people shake hands. Anyhow, he soon gives up on Maggie.

"Well," I say. "Dee."

"No, Mama," she says. "Not 'Dee,' Wangero Leewanika Kemanjo!"

"What happened to 'Dee'?" I wanted to know.

"She's dead," Wangero said. "I couldn't bear it any longer, being named after the people who oppress me."

"You know as well as me you was named after your aunt Dicie," I said. Dicie is my sister. She named Dee. We called her "Big Dee" after Dee was born.

"But who was she named after?" asked Wangero.

"I guess after Grandma Dee," I said.

"And who was she named after?" asked Wangero.

"Her mother," I said, and saw Wangero was getting fired. "That's about as far back as I can trace it," I said. Though, in fact, I probably could have carried it back beyond the Civil War through the branches.

"Well," said Asalamalakim, "there you are."

"Uhnnnh," I heard Maggie say.

"There I was not," I said, "before 'Dicie' cropped up in our family, so why should I try to trace it that far back?"

He just stood there grinning, looking down on me like somebody inspecting a Model A car. Every once in a while he and Wangero sent eye signals over my head.

"How do you pronounce this name?" I asked.

"You don't have to call me by it if you don't want to," said Wangero.

"Why shouldn't I?" I asked. "If that's what you want us to call you, we'll call you."

"I know it might sound awkward at first," said Wangero.

"I'll get used to it," I said. "Ream it out again."

Well, soon we got the name out of the way. Asalamalakim had a name twice as long and three times as hard. After I tripped over it two or three times he told me to just call him Hakim-a-barber. I wanted to ask him was he a barber, but I didn't really think he was, so I didn't ask.

"You must belong to those beef-cattle peoples down the road," I said. They said "Asalamalakim" when they met you, too, but they didn't shake hands. Always too busy: feeding the cattle, fixing the fences, putting up salt-lick shelters, throwing down hay. When the white folks poisoned some of the herd the men stayed up all night with rifles in their hands. I walked a mile and a half just to see the sight.

Hakim-a-barber said, "I accept some of their doctrines, but farming and raising cattle is not my style." (They didn't tell me, and I didn't ask, whether Wangero (Dee) had really gone and married him.)

We sat down to eat and right away he said he didn't eat collards and pork was unclean. Wangero, though, went on through the chitlins and corn bread, the greens and everything else. She talked a blue streak over the sweet potatoes. Everything delighted her. Even the fact that we still used the benches her daddy made for the table when we couldn't afford to buy chairs.

"Oh Mama!" she cried. Then turned to Hakim-a-barber. "I never knew how lovely these benches are. You can feel the rump prints," she said, running her hands underneath her and along the bench. Then she gave a sigh and her hand closed over Grandma Dee's butter dish. "That's it!" she said. "I knew there was something I wanted to ask you if I could have." She jumped up from the table and went over in the corner where the churn stood, the milk in it clabber by now. She looked at the churn and looked at it.

"This churn top is what I need," she said. "Didn't Uncle Buddy whittle it out of a tree you all used to have?"

"Yes," I said.

"Uh huh," she said happily. "And I want the dasher, too."

"Uncle Buddy whittle that, too?" asked the barber.

Dee (Wangero) looked up at me.

"Aunt Dee's first husband whittled the dash," said Maggie so low you almost couldn't hear her. "His name was Henry, but they called him Stash."

"Maggie's brain is like an elephant's," Wangero said, laughing. "I can use the churn top as a centerpiece for the alcove table," she said, sliding a plate over the churn, "and I'll think of something artistic to do with the dasher."

When she finished wrapping the dasher the handle stuck out. I took it for a moment in my hands. You didn't even have to look close to see where hands pushing the dasher up and down to make butter had left a kind of sink in the wood. In fact, there were a lot of small sinks; you could see where thumbs and fingers had sunk into the wood. It was beautiful light yellow wood, from a tree that grew in the yard where Big Dee and Stash had lived.

After dinner Dee (Wangero) went to the trunk at the foot of my bed and started rifling through it. Maggie hung back in the kitchen over the dishpan. Out came Wangero with two quilts. They had been pieced by Grandma Dee and then Big Dee and me had hung them on the quilt frames on the front porch and quilted them. One was in the Lone Star pattern. The other was Walk Around the Mountain. In both of them were scraps of dresses Grandma Dee had worn fifty and more years ago. Bits and pieces of Grandpa Jarrell's paisley shirts. And one teeny faded blue piece, about the size of a penny matchbox, that was from Great Grandpa Ezra's uniform that he wore in the Civil War.

"Mama," Wangero said sweet as a bird. "Can I have these old quilts?"

I heard something fall in the kitchen, and a minute later the kitchen door slammed.

"Why don't you take one or two of the others?" I asked. "These old things was just done by me and Big Dee from some tops your grandma pieced before she died."

"No," said Wangero. "I don't want those. They are stitched around the borders by machine."

"That'll make them last better," I said.

"That's not the point," said Wangero. "These are all pieces of dresses Grandma used to wear. She did all this stitching by hand. Imagine!" She held the quilts securely in her arms, stroking them.

"Some of the pieces, like those lavender ones, come from old clothes her mother handed down to her," I said, moving up to touch the quilts. Dee (Wangero) moved back just enough so that I couldn't reach the quilts. They already belonged to her.

"Imagine!" she breathed again, clutching them closely to her bosom. "The truth is," I said, "I promised to give them quilts to Maggie, for when she marries John Thomas."

She gasped like a bee had stung her.

"Maggie can't appreciate these quilts!" she said. "She'd probably be backward enough to put them to everyday use."

"I reckon she would," I said. "God knows I been saving 'em for long enough with nobody using 'em. I hope she will!" I didn't want to bring up how I had offered Dee (Wangero) a quilt when she went away to college. Then she had told me they were old-fashioned, out of style.

"But they're priceless!" she was saying now, furiously; for she has a temper. "Maggie would put them on the bed and in five years they'd be in rags. Less than that!"

"She can always make some more," I said. "Maggie knows how to quilt."

Dee (Wangero) looked at me with hatred. "You just will not understand. The point is these quilts, these quilts!"

"Well," I said, stumped. "What would you do with them?"

"Hang them," she said. As if that was the only thing you could do with quilts.

Maggie by now was standing in the door. I could almost hear the sound her feet made as they scraped over each other.

"She can have them, Mama," she said, like somebody used to never winning anything, or having anything reserved for her. "I can 'member Grandma Dee without the quilts."

I looked at her hard. She had filled her bottom lip with checkerberry snuff and it gave her face a kind of dopey, hangdog look. It was Grandma Dee and Big Dee who taught her how to quilt herself. She stood there with her scarred hands hidden in the folds of her skirt. She looked at her sister with something like fear but she wasn't mad at her. This was Maggie's portion. This was the way she knew God to work.

When I looked at her like that something hit me in the top of my head and ran down to the soles of my feet. Just like when I'm in church and the spirit of God touches me and I get happy and shout. I did something I never had done before: hugged Maggie to me, then dragged her on into the room, snatched the quilts out of Miss Wangero's hands and dumped them into Maggie's lap. Maggie just sat there on my bed with her mouth open.

"Take one or two of the others," I said to Dee.

But she turned without a word and went out to Hakim-a-barber.

"You just don't understand," she said, as Maggie and I came out to the car.

"What don't I understand?" I wanted to know.

"Your heritage," she said. And then she turned to Maggie, kissed her, and said, "You ought to try to make something of yourself, too, Maggie. It's really a new day for us. But from the way you and Mama still live you'd never know it."

She put on some sunglasses that hid everything above the tip of her nose and her chin.

Maggie smiled; maybe at the sunglasses. But a real smile, not scared. After we watched the car dust settle I asked Maggie to bring me a dip of snuff. And then the two of us sat there just enjoying, until it was time to go in the house and go to bed.

Questions for Discussion:

1. How does the title hint at the central theme of the story? What other evidence in the story hints at the central theme? What is that central theme? What in the story helps especially to bring the theme to life for you and keep it from becoming an abstract idea?

2. What is the point of view in "Everyday Use"? How does the style of writing reflect the character of the person who tells the story? That is, look at the language of the speaker. What are characteristics of that language and how do those characteristics reflect the personality of the speaker?

3. What do the quilts symbolize? What other evidence in the story leads us to see the quilts as symbols of a bigger issue? How does the climactic ending turn the tables on Dee's use of terms like "backward" and "heritage"? What is ironic about Dee's use of these words?

Poetry is figurative language that communicates human experiences. Narrative poetry tells our stories. Lyrical poetry sings the songs of us. Dramatic poetry acts out our characters in words.

Poetry is a language of the senses, of emotions, and of ideas. It is the language of likes and differences. It can inspire, conform, rebel, build, demolish, reveal, entice, enrage, heal, empower, and enlighten. Its expressions can be accessible or unfathomable, rhythmic or erratic, colloquial or pretentious, but it uses words to capture and release the reader's imagination, to soothe and inflame the reader's emotions, to create or affirm the reader's understanding of truth. From memories, recalled by words, poetry creates dreams in the mind and feelings in the heart.

Poetry's use of words for more than their meanings make it unlike any other literary genre, for poetry becomes a language in itself, like music or dance or painting, a language of rhythms and rhymes and images. Through this language, poets continue to find new ways to express ageless ideas, and readers continue to find new ways to understand themselves, others, and the world around them.

"The Panther"

Rainer Maria Rilke

Author Biography: Rainer Maria Rilke was born in Prague in 1875. His parents divorced when he was young, and he spent much of his life traveling around Europe and writing. When World War I broke out, Rainer was drafted, but friends with some political pull kept him out of the actual fighting. Later in his life, he retreated to Switzerland, where he lived for nearly a decade before succumbing to leukemia in 1926.

Context For These Works: Rilke is known for the powerful and substantial imagery in his poetry and other fiction; early in his career, his work is thought of as Romantic and lyrical. Throughout his life, though, Rilke was deeply interested in philosophy and the place of humanity in the world. A serious depression during and after World War I tinges much of his work with an investigation of the darker aspects of life, bordering on existentialism. "The Panther" was written when Rilke was the secretary for the sculptor Auguste Rodin, and the two visited a captive panther at a show in Paris.

Literary Terms: formalism, free verse, end stop, enjambment, imagery

His vision, from the constantly passing bars,
has grown so weary that it cannot hold
anything else. It seems to him there are
a thousand bars; and behind the bars, no world.

As he paces in cramped circles, over and over,
the movement of his powerful soft strides
is like a ritual dance around a center
in which a mighty will stands paralyzed.

Only at times, the curtain of the pupils
lifts, quietly—. An image enters in,
rushes down through the tensed, arrested muscles,
plunges into the heart and is gone.

Questions for Discussion:

1. What is the tension or conflict in the poem? What words convey the ideas of opposing forces?
2. According to the speaker, what is the relationship between what the panther sees and how the panther perceives?

"The Raven"

Edgar Allan Poe

Author Biography: Edgar Allan Poe was born in Boston in 1809, a child of two actors. His mother died when he was young, however, and his father left; Poe was unofficially adopted by the Allan family in Richmond, Virginia. Poe had a short military career but later dropped out of West Point to pursue writing. Though he met some success during his life, he was constantly saddled with debt, and the untimely death of his young wife pushed Poe into alcoholism. He died in Baltimore in 1849 after being found delirious in the street.

Context: Poe is often regarded as an American Romanticist, but his work has strong elements of the gothic, bordering on horror and even science fiction. Poe is also considered one of the first creators of detective fiction, which was a new genre that burgeoned in the nineteenth century with the creation of police forces and the rise of science. One sees throughout much of his work the mysterious and the paranormal.

Literary Terms: syzygy, repetition, masculine rhyme, feminine rhyme

Once upon a midnight dreary, while I pondered, weak and weary,
Over many a quaint and curious volume of forgotten lore—
    While I nodded, nearly napping, suddenly there came a tapping,
As of some one gently rapping, rapping at my chamber door.
5 "'Tis some visitor," I muttered, "tapping at my chamber door—
        Only this and nothing more."

Ah, distinctly I remember it was in the bleak December;
And each separate dying ember wrought its ghost upon the floor.
    Eagerly I wished the morrow;—vainly I had sought to borrow
10   From my books surcease of sorrow—sorrow for the lost Lenore—
For the rare and radiant maiden whom the angels name Lenore—
        Nameless *here* for evermore.

And the silken, sad, uncertain rustling of each purple curtain
Thrilled me—filled me with fantastic terrors never felt before;
15   So that now, to still the beating of my heart, I stood repeating
        "'Tis some visitor entreating entrance at my chamber door—
Some late visitor entreating entrance at my chamber door;—
        This it is and nothing more."

Presently my soul grew stronger; hesitating then no longer,
20 "Sir," said I, "or Madam, truly your forgiveness I implore;
    But the fact is I was napping, and so gently you came rapping,
    And so faintly you came tapping, tapping at my chamber door,
That I scarce was sure I heard you"—here I opened wide the door;—
        Darkness there and nothing more.

²⁵ Deep into that darkness peering, long I stood there wondering, fearing,
Doubting, dreaming dreams no mortal ever dared to dream before;
　　But the silence was unbroken, and the stillness gave no token,
　　And the only word there spoken was the whispered word, "Lenore?"
This I whispered, and an echo murmured back the word, "Lenore!"—
³⁰ 　　　Merely this and nothing more.

Back into the chamber turning, all my soul within me burning,
Soon again I heard a tapping somewhat louder than before.
　　"Surely," said I, "surely that is something at my window lattice;
　　Let me see, then, what thereat is, and this mystery explore—
³⁵ Let my heart be still a moment and this mystery explore;—
　　　'Tis the wind and nothing more!"

Open here I flung the shutter, when, with many a flirt and flutter,
In there stepped a stately Raven of the saintly days of yore;
　　Not the least obeisance made he; not a minute stopped or stayed he;
⁴⁰ 　　But, with mien of lord or lady, perched above my chamber door—
Perched upon a bust of Pallas just above my chamber door—
　　　Perched, and sat, and nothing more.

Then this ebony bird beguiling my sad fancy into smiling,
By the grave and stern decorum of the countenance it wore,
⁴⁵ "Though thy crest be shorn and shaven, thou," I said, "art sure no craven,
Ghastly grim and ancient Raven wandering from the Nightly shore—
Tell me what thy lordly name is on the Night's Plutonian shore!"
　　　Quoth the Raven "Nevermore."

Much I marvelled this ungainly fowl to hear discourse so plainly,
⁵⁰ Though its answer little meaning—little relevancy bore;
　　For we cannot help agreeing that no living human being
　　Ever yet was blessed with seeing bird above his chamber door—
Bird or beast upon the sculptured bust above his chamber door,
　　　With such name as "Nevermore."

⁵⁵ But the Raven, sitting lonely on the placid bust, spoke only
That one word, as if his soul in that one word he did outpour.
　　Nothing farther then he uttered—not a feather then he fluttered—
　　Till I scarcely more than muttered "Other friends have flown before—
On the morrow he will leave me, as my Hopes have flown before."
⁶⁰ 　　　Then the bird said "Nevermore."

Startled at the stillness broken by reply so aptly spoken,
"Doubtless," said I, "what it utters is its only stock and store
　　Caught from some unhappy master whom unmerciful Disaster

Followed fast and followed faster till his songs one burden bore—
⁶⁵ Till the dirges of his Hope that melancholy burden bore
Of 'Never—nevermore'."

But the Raven still beguiling all my fancy into smiling,
Straight I wheeled a cushioned seat in front of bird, and bust and door;
Then, upon the velvet sinking, I betook myself to linking
⁷⁰ Fancy unto fancy, thinking what this ominous bird of yore—
What this grim, ungainly, ghastly, gaunt, and ominous bird of yore
Meant in croaking "Nevermore."

This I sat engaged in guessing, but no syllable expressing
To the fowl whose fiery eyes now burned into my bosom's core;
⁷⁵ This and more I sat divining, with my head at ease reclining
On the cushion's velvet lining that the lamp-light gloated o'er,
But whose velvet-violet lining with the lamp-light gloating o'er,
She shall press, ah, nevermore!

Then, methought, the air grew denser, perfumed from an unseen censer
⁸⁰ Swung by Seraphim whose foot-falls tinkled on the tufted floor.
"Wretch," I cried, "thy God hath lent thee—by these angels he hath sent thee
Respite—respite and nepenthe from thy memories of Lenore;
Quaff, oh quaff this kind nepenthe and forget this lost Lenore!"
Quoth the Raven "Nevermore."

⁸⁵ "Prophet!" said I, "thing of evil!—prophet still, if bird or devil!—
Whether Tempter sent, or whether tempest tossed thee here ashore,
Desolate yet all undaunted, on this desert land enchanted—
On this home by Horror haunted—tell me truly, I implore—
Is there—is there balm in Gilead?—tell me—tell me, I implore!"
⁹⁰ Quoth the Raven "Nevermore."

"Prophet!" said I, "thing of evil!—prophet still, if bird or devil!
By that Heaven that bends above us—by that God we both adore—
Tell this soul with sorrow laden if, within the distant Aidenn,
It shall clasp a sainted maiden whom the angels name Lenore—
⁹⁵ Clasp a rare and radiant maiden whom the angels name Lenore."
Quoth the Raven "Nevermore."

"Be that word our sign of parting, bird or fiend!" I shrieked, upstarting—
"Get thee back into the tempest and the Night's Plutonian shore!
Leave no black plume as a token of that lie thy soul hath spoken!
¹⁰⁰ Leave my loneliness unbroken!—quit the bust above my door!
Take thy beak from out my heart, and take thy form from off my door!"
Quoth the Raven "Nevermore."

And the Raven, never flitting, still is sitting, *still* is sitting
On the pallid bust of Pallas just above my chamber door;
And his eyes have all the seeming of a demon's that is dreaming,
105   And the lamp-light o'er him streaming throws his shadow on the floor;
And my soul from out that shadow that lies floating on the floor
Shall be lifted—nevermore!

Questions for Discussion:

1. What role do the internal rhymes, the end rhymes, and the repetition of "Nevermore" play in creating the poem's music? What does the poem's use of repetition communicate about the effects of repetition in human psychology?
2. What role does the speaker's own imagination play in developing his relationship with the raven? What is the poet communicating about the effects of grief on people?

"The Lamb"

William Blake

Author Biography: William Blake was born in London in 1757 and died in 1827, meaning he lived through both the American and French Revolutions, events that influenced him greatly. He was considered something of an eccentric during his time, but later critics have appreciated his diverse talents and intellect. He was not only a writer and poet, but also an accomplished artist, painter, and printmaker. Many critics have also noted the influence of his complex relationship with organized religion in his work.

Context: Blake is often considered part of the Romantic movement, which placed focus on individual expression and feeling as well as reverence for the natural world. "The Lamb" is from his work, *Songs of Innocence,* about the "purer" state of childhood as opposed to the corrupt nature of adulthood, which he explores in his collection *Songs of Experience,* in which "The Tyger" is published.

Literary Terms: repetition, rhyming couplets, the four beat line

Little Lamb who made thee?
    Dost thou know who made thee,
Gave thee life & bid thee feed,
By the stream & o'er the mead;
Gave thee clothing of delight,
Softest clothing wooly bright;
Gave thee such a tender voice,
Making all the vales rejoice!
    Little Lamb who made thee
10   Dost thou know who made thee

Little Lamb I'll tell thee,
Little Lamb I'll tell thee!
He is called by thy name,
For he calls himself a Lamb:
He is meek & he is mild,
He became a little child:
I a child & thou a lamb,
We are called by his name.
Little Lamb God bless thee.
20 Little Lamb God bless thee.

Questions for Discussion:

1. Who is the lamb in the poem? (Hint: "Lamb" is used with more than one definition.)
2. Who is the speaker of the poem? Who is the audience? What is their relationship?
3. What is the tone of the poem? How is it appropriate to the speaker-audience relationship and to the subject matter of the poem?

"The Tyger"

William Blake

Literary Terms: repetition, rhyming couplets, the four beat line, art

Tyger Tyger, burning bright,
In the forests of the night;
What immortal hand or eye,
Could frame thy fearful symmetry?

In what distant deeps or skies.
Burnt the fire of thine eyes?
On what wings dare he aspire?
What the hand, dare seize the fire?

And what shoulder, & what art,
Could twist the sinews of thy heart?
And when thy heart began to beat,
What dread hand? & what dread feet?

What the hammer? what the chain,
In what furnace was thy brain?
What the anvil? what dread grasp,

Dare its deadly terrors clasp!
When the stars threw down their spears
And water'd heaven with their tears:
Did he smile his work to see?
Did he who made the Lamb make thee?

Tyger Tyger burning bright,
In the forests of the night:
What immortal hand or eye,
Dare frame thy fearful symmetry?

Questions for Discussion:

1. This poem is a series of questions when most poems are full of statements. What does the use of questions suggest about the relationship between the speaker and the audience?
2. Tigers are not forged in blacksmith shops, so what is the point of pretending they are?
3. "The Lamb" and "The Tyger" are written in nearly identical form, so what makes the tones of the two poems strikingly different?

"The Sick Rose"

William Blake

Literary Terms: symbolism, imagery, allegory, meter

O Rose thou art sick.
The invisible worm,
That flies in the night
In the howling storm:

Has found out thy bed
Of crimson joy:
And his dark secret love
Does thy life destroy.

Questions for Discussion:

1. What could the rose represent?
2. Given what the rose might represent, what, then, could other objects in the poem—the worm, the storm—represent accordingly?

"The Snow-Storm"

Ralph Waldo Emerson

Author Biography: Ralph Waldo Emerson was born in Boston in 1803, and is considered one the foundational writers of American letters. An essayist, poet, and lecturer, Emerson was one of the foremost spokesmen for American Transcendentalism, penning such landmark essays as "Nature," "The American Scholar," "Self-Reliance," and "Experience." Emerson was sometimes critiqued and condemned as a heretic or atheist because of his views on religion, but was well-known and in demand on the lecture circuit even during his time.

Context: Transcendentalism was a cousin to England's Romantic Movement that espoused the primacy and goodness of people and nature, as opposed to the more corrupt state of contemporary society and its institutions. Whereas the nineteenth century saw a rise in the belief of empiricism to create a more perfect world, Transcendentalists like Emerson pushed for people to be more self-reliant, independent, and to rely on intuition over measurement and control of the physical world.

Literary Terms: blank verse, enjambment, number, proportion, imagery

Announced by all the trumpets of the sky,
Arrives the snow, and, driving o'er the fields,
Seems nowhere to alight: the whited air
Hides hills and woods, the river, and the heaven,
And veils the farm-house at the garden's end.
The sled and traveller stopped, the courier's feet
Delayed, all friends shut out, the housemates sit
Around the radiant fireplace, enclosed
In a tumultuous privacy of storm.

Come see the north wind's masonry.
Out of an unseen quarry evermore
Furnished with tile, the fierce artificer
Curves his white bastions with projected roof
Round every windward stake, or tree, or door.
Speeding, the myriad-handed, his wild work
So fanciful, so savage, nought cares he
For number or proportion. Mockingly,
On coop or kennel he hangs Parian wreaths;
A swan-like form invests the hidden thorn;
Fills up the farmer's lane from wall to wall,
Maugre the farmer's sighs; and, at the gate,
A tapering turret overtops the work.
And when his hours are numbered, and the world
Is all his own, retiring, as he were not,
Leaves, when the sun appears, astonished Art

To mimic in slow structures, stone by stone,
Built in an age, the mad wind's night-work,
The frolic architecture of the snow.

1. What does the first verse paragraph about people's being snowed in contribute to the poem?
2. The second verse paragraph begins with an invitation from speaker to reader to "Come see." What is the reader supposed to see about "the North wind's masonry"? Why is masonry an apt (and inapt) image for constructions from snow?
3. What is the poet communicating about the relationship between nature, art, and the artist?

"Aunt Jennifer's Tigers"

Adrienne Rich

Author Biography: Adrienne Rich was born in Baltimore Maryland in 1929. Her father encouraged her literary interests when she was young. After graduating from Radcliffe College, her first work of poetry was chosen by renowned poet W.H. Auden for the Yale Series of Younger Poets Award. Throughout her life, Rich won many awards for her work, including Guggenheim and MacArthur Fellowships and a National Book Award. Rich died in 2012 in California.

Context: Rich was highly involved in the second-wave feminism that swept America in the mid-twentieth century. She was very politically involved, writing and speaking about women's rights and the advancement of rights for homosexual groups. Much of her work deals with the way society is set up to favor heterosexuality, and she explores the consequences for herself and others because of that default.

Literary Terms: form, structure, diction, imagery, metaphor, paradox

Aunt Jennifer's tigers prance across a screen,
Bright topaz denizens of a world of green.
They do not fear the men beneath the tree;
They pace in sleek chivalric certainty.

Aunt Jennifer's finger fluttering through her wool
Find even the ivory needle hard to pull.
The massive weight of Uncle's wedding band
Sits heavily upon Aunt Jennifer's hand.

When Aunt is dead, her terrified hands will lie
Still ringed with ordeals she was mastered by.
The tigers in the panel that she made
Will go on prancing, proud and unafraid.

Questions for Discussion:

1. What could the tigers represent within this poem?
2. What does the persona's word choice suggest about the marriage between the persona's Aunt and Uncle?

"Conjoined"

Judith Minty

Author Biography: Judith Minty is an award-winning essayist, poet, and story writer born in Detroit in 1937. She earned an M.F.A. from Western Michigan University and later a Ph.D. from Michigan Technological University. She has taught at universities all over the U.S., including in Michigan and on the West Coast.

Context: Minty is known for work that investigates the meaning of place, both on the macro and micro level. Though her language is often simple, Minty's work investigates profound themes of life, nature, and place, with the tropes of earth and water playing heavily in her subject matter.

Literary Terms: simile, metaphor, analogy, diction, tone

The onion in my cupboard, a monster, actually
two joined under one transparent skin:
each half-round, then flat and deformed
where it pressed and grew against the other.

An accident, like the two-headed calf rooted
in one body, fighting to suck at its mother's teats;
or like those other freaks, Chang and Eng[1], twins
joined at the chest by skin and muscle, doomed
to live, even make love, together for sixty years.

Do you feel the skin that binds us
together as we move, heavy in this house?
To sever the muscle could free one,
but might kill the other. Ah, but men
don't slice onions in the kitchen, seldom see
what is invisible. We cannot escape each other.

Questions for Discussion:

1. What does the persona's use of metaphors and tone reveal about her attitude toward marriage?
2. Why does the persona begin and end the poem with the image of an onion?

---

1 *Chang and Eng:* The original and most famous Siamese twins, born in 1811. They were never separated but nevertheless fathered twenty-two children. They died in 1874.

"Digging"

Seamus Heaney

Author Biography: Seamus Heaney was born in Northern Ireland in 1939, lived off and on in America for many years, and died in Dublin, Ireland, where he lived during the latter half of his life. Heaney began to publish poetry soon after graduating from college, and was known not only for his verse, but for plays, lectures, and translations. He held a number of academic appointments throughout his life, and was awarded the Nobel Prize in Literature in 1995.

Context: Though Northern Ireland, where Heaney grew up, was more industrialized than Ireland itself, Heaney's father was a farmer, and in "Digging," we see the poet remembering and commenting on those memories of his father's work. Heaney worked a great deal with translation during his life, and so we see in much of his work considerations of what it means to move between languages and experiences, a comparison of differing words and differing lives.

Literary Terms: open form, enjambments, repetition, metaphor

Between my finger and my thumb
The squat pen rests; snug as a gun.

Under my window, a clean rasping sound
When the spade sinks into gravelly ground:
My father, digging. I look down

Till his straining rump among the flowerbeds
Bends low, comes up twenty years away
Stooping in rhythm through potato drills
Where he was digging.

The coarse boot nestled on the lug, the shaft
Against the inside knee was levered firmly.
He rooted out tall tops, buried the bright edge deep
To scatter new potatoes that we picked,
Loving their cool hardness in our hands.

By God, the old man could handle a spade.
Just like his old man.

My grandfather cut more turf in a day
Than any other man on Toner's bog.
Once I carried him milk in a bottle
Corked sloppily with paper. He straightened up
To drink it, then fell to right away
Nicking and slicing neatly, heaving sods
Over his shoulder, going down and down
For the good turf. Digging.

The cold smell of potato mould, the squelch and slap
Of soggy peat, the curt cuts of an edge
Through living roots awaken in my head.
But I've no spade to follow men like them.

Between my finger and my thumb
The squat pen rests.
I'll dig with it.

Questions for Discussion:

1. What words in the poem stimulate each of the five senses? Why does the poet put such a strong emphasis on sensual impressions?
2. In what ways is the persona's analogy between farming and writing both accurate and inaccurate?

" I like to see it lap the Miles "

Emily Dickinson

Author Biography: Emily Dickinson was born in Amherst, Massachusetts in 1830. She lived what some might call a secluded life surrounded by family and friends. Though she was a prolific poet, Dickinson published fewer than a dozen poems and was not publicly recognized for her work during her lifetime. After her death in 1886, her family found over 1,800 poems beautifully hand-bound in forty volumes. These were published posthumously in 1890 and 1955. Though her poems are titled in this reader, she never provided titles. Therefore, we should ignore the title as an important part of the reading.

Context: Dickinson's poetry is influenced by Christianity, Transcendental philosophy, individualism, her family and friends, as well as advances in science and technology and the social forces accompanying the Industrial Revolution of nineteenth-century America. Today, Dickinson is heralded as the first original American female poet.

Literary Terms: form, meter, symbolism, metaphor, sound devices

I like to see it lap the Miles -

And lick the Valleys up -
And stop to feed itself at Tanks -
And then - prodigious step

Around a Pile of Mountains -
And supercilious peer
In Shanties - by the sides of Roads -
And then a Quarry pare
To fit it's sides
And crawl between

Complaining all the while
In horrid - hooting stanza -
Then chase itself down Hill -
And neigh like Boanerges -
Then - prompter than a Star
Stop - docile and omnipotent
At it's own stable door -

Questions for Discussion:

1. What does the "it" represent in this poem?
2. Why does Dickinson capitalize certain words in this poem?

"I heard a Fly buzz – when I died"

Emily Dickinson

Literary Terms: punctuation, symbolism, speaker

I heard a Fly buzz - when I died -
The Stillness in the Room
Was like the Stillness in the Air -
Between the Heaves of Storm -

The Eyes around - had wrung them dry -
And Breaths were gathering firm
For that last Onset - when the King
Be witnessed - in the Room -

I willed my Keepsakes - Signed away
What portion of me be
Assignable - and then it was
There interposed a Fly -

With Blue - uncertain - stumbling Buzz -
Between the light - and me -
And then the Windows failed - and then
I could not see to see -

Questions for Discussion:

1. How does the Fly separate the physical and the spiritual in the poem?
2. How do the dashes affect the reading and the sound of the poem?

"The Burial of the Dead" from *The Waste Land*

T.S. Eliot

Author Biography: T.S. Eliot was born in St. Louis, MO in 1888, but at age 25 became one of the many American expatriate artists who emigrated to Europe and became known as the "Lost Generation" after World War I. Eliot eventually became a British citizen. Eliot was a prolific poet and known as one of the foremost artists of the modern period, earning on Order of Merit from the British Monarchy as well as the Nobel Prize for Literature in 1948.

Context: Eliot was a member of the "Lost Generation," a term coined to describe the generation of citizens and artists that grew up in the aftermath of World War I. The Great War, as it was also known, reigned death and destruction on Europe as had never before been known; the war was the first time the world saw the use of tanks, airplanes, machine guns, and chemical warfare. Like many artistic works of the time period, *The Waste Land* is characterize by a dark mood and destructive subject matter. Like nearly all of Eliot's work, it combines these characteristics with scholarly and literary references throughout.

Literary Terms: paradox, imagery, form, allusion

I. The Burial of the Dead

April is the cruellest month, breeding
Lilacs out of the dead land, mixing
Memory and desire, stirring
5 Dull roots with spring rain.
Winter kept us warm, covering
Earth in forgetful snow, feeding
A little life with dried tubers.
Summer surprised us, coming over the Starnbergersee
10 With a shower of rain; we stopped in the colonnade,
And went on in sunlight, into the Hofgarten,
And drank coffee, and talked for an hour.
Bin gar keine Russin, stamm' aus Litauen, echt deutsch.
And when we were children, staying at the arch-duke's,
15 My cousin's, he took me out on a sled,
And I was frightened. He said, Marie,
Marie, hold on tight. And down we went.
In the mountains, there you feel free.
I read, much of the night, and go south in the winter.

20 What are the roots that clutch, what branches grow
Out of this stony rubbish? Son of man,
You cannot say, or guess, for you know only
A heap of broken images, where the sun beats,
And the dead tree gives no shelter, the cricket no relief,
25 And the dry stone no sound of water. Only
There is shadow under this red rock,

(Come in under the shadow of this red rock),
And I will show you something different from either
Your shadow at morning striding behind you
30 Or your shadow at evening rising to meet you;
I will show you fear in a handful of dust.
    Frisch weht der Wind
    Der Heimat zu
    Mein Irisch Kind,
35   *Wo weilest du?*
"You gave me hyacinths first a year ago;
"They called me the hyacinth girl."
—Yet when we came back, late, from the Hyacinth garden,
Your arms full, and your hair wet, I could not
40 Speak, and my eyes failed, I was neither
Living nor dead, and I knew nothing,
Looking into the heart of light, the silence.
Oed' und leer das Meer.

Madame Sosostris, famous clairvoyante,
45 Had a bad cold, nevertheless
Is known to be the wisest woman in Europe,
With a wicked pack of cards. Here, said she,
Is your card, the drowned Phoenician Sailor,
(Those are pearls that were his eyes. Look!)
50 Here is Belladonna, the Lady of the Rocks,
The lady of situations.
Here is the man with three staves, and here the Wheel,
And here is the one-eyed merchant, and this card,
Which is blank, is something he carries on his back,
55 Which I am forbidden to see. I do not find
The Hanged Man. Fear death by water.
I see crowds of people, walking round in a ring.
Thank you. If you see dear Mrs. Equitone,
Tell her I bring the horoscope myself:
60 One must be so careful these days.
Unreal City,
Under the brown fog of a winter dawn,
A crowd flowed over London Bridge, so many,
I had not thought death had undone so many.
65 Sighs, short and infrequent, were exhaled,
And each man fixed his eyes before his feet.
Flowed up the hill and down King William Street,
To where Saint Mary Woolnoth kept the hours
With a dead sound on the final stroke of nine.
70 There I saw one I knew, and stopped him, crying: "Stetson!
"You who were with me in the ships at Mylae!

"That corpse you planted last year in your garden,
"Has it begun to sprout? Will it bloom this year?
"Or has the sudden frost disturbed its bed?
75 "Oh keep the Dog far hence, that's friend to men,
"Or with his nails he'll dig it up again!
"You! hypocrite lecteur!—mon semblable,—mon frère!"

Questions for Discussion:

1. What effect does Eliot achieve by using French and German expressions in certain lines?
2. Why does Eliot set this poem within spring and winter?

"Jabberywocky"

Lewis Carroll

Author Biography: Lewis Carrol is the pen name of Charles Lutwidge Dodgson, born in England in 1832. Born into a conservative household, Carroll showed promise as a writer at a young age and continued writing through his education at Oxford. His most known work, *Alice's Adventures in Wonderland*, embodies the kind of playful manner in which he wrote.

Context: "Jabberwocky" exhibits Carroll's fantastical and whimsical style well. It is a prime example of a nonsense poem that uses neologisms (made-up words) and other creative licenses. The poem can be found in the sequel to *Wonderland, Alice through the Looking Glass*, where Alice discovers it printed backward on the page so that it only was readable in a mirror.

Literary Terms: imagery, symbolism, wordplay, form, meter

'Twas brillig, and the slithy toves
    Did gyre and gimble in the wabe:
All mimsy were the borogoves,
    And the mome raths outgrabe.

"Beware the Jabberwock, my son!
    The jaws that bite, the claws that catch!
Beware the Jubjub bird, and shun
    The frumious Bandersnatch!"

He took his vorpal sword in hand;
    Long time the manxome foe he sought—
So rested he by the Tumtum tree
    And stood awhile in thought.

And, as in uffish thought he stood,
    The Jabberwock, with eyes of flame,
Came whiffling through the tulgey wood,
    And burbled as it came!

One, two! One, two! And through and through
    The vorpal blade went snicker-snack!
He left it dead, and with its head
    He went galumphing back.

"And hast thou slain the Jabberwock?
    Come to my arms, my beamish boy!
O frabjous day! Callooh! Callay!"
    He chortled in his joy.
'Twas brillig, and the slithy toves
    Did gyre and gimble in the wabe:
All mimsy were the borogoves,
    And the mome raths outgrabe.

Questions for Discussion:

1. Despite Carroll's use of nonsensical words throughout this poem, how do they nonetheless function in the narrative?
2. How do these nonsensical words affect the poem's imagery?

"Metaphors"

Sylvia Plath

Author Biography: Sylvia Plath was born in 1932 in Boston. She was an excellent student, attending Smith College and earning a guest editorship at *Mademoiselle*. There, though, and throughout her life, Plath struggled with severe depression and even underwent electroshock therapy. She later studies in England and met her husband, poet Ted Hughes, with whom she had two children. Despite writing well and earning a good reputation, Plath could not overcome her depression, and committed suicide in 1963 at age 30.

Context: Plath is best known for her autobiographical and confessional style, which leaves just about nothing about the poet and author unsaid. She is well known for both her poetry and her novel *The Bell Jar,* which is about depressive episodes during her college years. "Lady Lazarus" clearly references World War II, an event that no artist of the time escaped.

Literary Terms: symbolism, theme, form, imagery

I'm a riddle in nine syllables,
An elephant, a ponderous house,
A melon strolling on two tendrils.

O red fruit, ivory, fine timbers!
This loaf's big with its yeasty rising.
Money's new-minted in this fat purse.
I'm a means, a stage, a cow in calf.
I've eaten a bag of green apples,
Boarded the train there's no getting off.

Questions for Discussion:

1. How does Plath's choice of metaphors illustrate one woman's perspective on pregnancy?
2. Is this a positive or negative depiction of pregnancy?

"Lady Lazarus"

Sylvia Plath

Literary Terms: metaphor, personification, imagery, irony

I have done it again.
One year in every ten
I manage it——

A sort of walking miracle, my skin
5 Bright as a Nazi lampshade,
My right foot

A paperweight,
My face a featureless, fine
Jew linen.

10 Peel off the napkin
O my enemy.
Do I terrify?——

The nose, the eye pits, the full set of teeth?
The sour breath
15 Will vanish in a day.

Soon, soon the flesh
The grave cave ate will be
At home on me

20 And I a smiling woman.
I am only thirty.
And like the cat I have nine times to die.

This is Number Three.
What a trash
25 To annihilate each decade.

What a million filaments.
The peanut-crunching crowd
Shoves in to see

Them unwrap me hand and foot——
30 The big strip tease.
Gentlemen, ladies

These are my hands
My knees.
I may be skin and bone,

35 Nevertheless, I am the same, identical woman.
The first time it happened I was ten.
It was an accident.

The second time I meant
To last it out and not come back at all.
40 I rocked shut

As a seashell.
They had to call and call
And pick the worms off me like sticky pearls.

Dying
45 Is an art, like everything else.
I do it exceptionally well.

I do it so it feels like hell.
I do it so it feels real.
I guess you could say I've a call.
50 It's easy enough to do it in a cell.
It's easy enough to do it and stay put.
It's the theatrical

Comeback in broad day
To the same place, the same face, the same brute
55 Amused shout:

'A miracle!'
That knocks me out.
There is a charge

For the eyeing of my scars, there is a charge
60 For the hearing of my heart——
It really goes.

And there is a charge, a very large charge
For a word or a touch
Or a bit of blood

65 Or a piece of my hair or my clothes.
So, so, Herr Doktor.
So, Herr Enemy.

I am your opus,
I am your valuable,
70 The pure gold baby

That melts to a shriek.
I turn and burn.
Do not think I underestimate your great concern.

Ash, ash—
75 You poke and stir.
Flesh, bone, there is nothing there——

A cake of soap,
A wedding ring,
A gold filling.

80 Herr God, Herr Lucifer
Beware
Beware.

Out of the ash
I rise with my red hair
85 And I eat men like air.

Questions for Discussion:

1. How does Plath us Biblical allusion in the poem?
2. What does the poem tell the reader about the speaker? What can we understand about her from her monologue?

"My Papa's Waltz"

Theodore Roethke

Author Biography: Theodore Roethke was born near the Saginaw River in Michigan in 1908. He earned both B.A. and M.A. degrees from the University of Michigan, but had to abandon further graduate studies when the Great Depression hit. He taught poetry at many schools throughout his life and influenced many other poets who went on to great success. He won the Pulitzer Prize in 1954 and the National Book Award for Poetry in both 1959 and posthumously in 1965.

Context: Roethke is known primarily for the introspective nature of his poetry—so—much of it is focused on himself, his life, and his emotions, which were perhaps not typical of such an award-winning poet. Roethke was born in a rural area to an immigrant father who died when Roethke was 14. Throughout his life, he struggled with his self-esteem as well as substance abuse issues.

Literary Terms: symbolism, theme, form, imagery

The whiskey on your breath
Could make a small boy dizzy;
But I hung on like death:
Such waltzing was not easy.
We romped until the pans
Slid from the kitchen shelf;
My mother's countenance
Could not unfrown itself.

The hand that held my wrist
Was battered on one knuckle;
At every step you missed
My right ear scraped a buckle.

You beat time on my head
With a palm caked hard by dirt,
Then waltzed me off to bed
Still clinging to your shirt.

Questions for Discussion:

1. What is ironic about the characterization of the persona's relationship with his father as a dance?
2. What tone is created by the poem's imagery?

"Navajo Night Chant"

Translated by John Bierhorst

Literary Terms: repetition, imagery, symbolism, theme

I

House made of dawn.
House made of evening light.
House made of the dark cloud.
House made of male rain.
5 House made of dark mist.
House made of female rain.
House made of pollen.
House made of grasshoppers.

Dark cloud is at the door.
10 The trail out of it is dark cloud.
The zigzag lightning stands high upon it.
An offering I make.
Restore my feet for me.
Restore my legs for me.
15 Restore my body for me.
Restore my mind for me.
Restore my voice for me.
This very day take out your spell for me.

Happily I recover.
20 Happily my interior becomes cool.
Happily I go forth.
My interior feeling cool, may I walk.
No longer sore, may I walk.
Impervious to pain, may I walk.
25 With lively feelings may I walk.
As it used to be long ago, may I walk.

Happily may I walk.
Happily, with abundant dark clouds, may I walk.
Happily, with abundant showers, may I walk.
30 Happily, with abundant plants, may I walk.
Happily on a trail of pollen, may I walk.
Happily may I walk.
Being as it used to be long ago, may I walk.

May it be beautiful before me.
35 May it be beautiful behind me.
May it be beautiful below me.
May it be beautiful above me.
May it be beautiful all around me.
In beauty it is finished.
40 In beauty it is finished.

'Sa'ah naaghéi, Bik'eh hózhó

II
Now Talking God
With your feet I walk.
I walk with your limbs
45 I carry forth your body
For me your mind thinks
Your voice speaks for me
Beauty is before me
And beauty is behind me
50 Above and below me hovers the beautiful
I am surrounded by it
I am immersed in it
In my youth I am aware of it
And in old age I shall walk quietly
55 The beautiful trail.
The mountains, I become part of it . . .
The herbs, the fir tree, I become part of it.
The morning mists, the clouds, the gathering waters,
I become part of it.
60 The wilderness, the dew drops, the pollen . . .
I become part of it.

May it be delightful my house;
From my head may it be delightful;
To my feet may it be delightful;
65 Where I lie may it be delightful;
All above me may it be delightful;
All around me may it be delightful.

'Sa'ah naaghéi, Bik'eh hózhó

III
From the base of the east.
70 From the base of the Pelado Peak.
From the house made of mirage,
From the story made of mirage,

From the doorway of rainbow,
75 The path out of which is the rainbow,
The rainbow passed out with me,
The rainbow rose up with me.
Through the middle of broad fields,
The rainbow returned with me.
80 To where my house is visible,
The rainbow returned with me.
To the roof of my house,
The rainbow returned with me.
To the entrance of my house,
85 The rainbow returned with me.
To just within my house,
The rainbow returned with me.
To my fireside,
The rainbow returned with me.
90 To the center of my house,
The rainbow returned with me.
At the fore part of my house with the dawn,
The Talking God sits with me.
The House God sits with me.
95 Pollen Boy sits with me.
Grasshopper Girl sits with me.
In beauty my Mother, for her I return.
Beautifully my fire to me is restored.
Beautifully my possessions are to me restored.
100 Beautifully my soft goods to me are restored.
Beautifully my hard goods to me are restored.
Beautifully my horses to me are restored.
Beautifully my sheep to me are restored.
Beautifully my old men to me are restored.
105 Beautifully my old women to me are restored.
Beautifully my young men to me are restored.
Beautifully my women to me are restored.
Beautifully my children to me are restored.
Beautifully my wife to me are restored.
110 Beautifully my chiefs to me are restored.
Beautifully my country to me are restored.
Beautifully my fields to me are restored.
Beautifully my house to me are restored.
Talking God sits with me.
115 House God sits with me.
Pollen Boy sits with me.
Grasshopper Girl sits with me.
Beautifully white corn to me is restored.
Beautifully yellow corn to me is restored.

120 Beautifully blue corn to me is restored.
Beautifully corn of all kinds to me is restored.
In beauty may I walk.
All day long may I walk.
Through the returning seasons may I walk.
125 On the trailed marked with pollen may I walk.
With grasshoppers about my feet may I walk.
With dew about my feet may I walk.
With beauty may I walk.
With beauty before me, may I walk.
130 With beauty behind me, may I walk.
With beauty above me, may I walk.
With beauty below me, may I walk.
With beauty all around me, may I walk.
In old age wandering on a trail of beauty, lively, may I walk.
135 In old age wandering on a trail of beauty, living again, may I walk.
It is finished in beauty.
It is finished in beauty.

'Sa'ah naaghéi, Bik'eh hózhó

IV

In the house made of dawn,
140 In the house made of evening twilight,
In the house made of dark cloud,
In the house made of rain and mist, of pollen, of grasshoppers,
Where the dark mist curtains the doorway,
The path to which is on the rainbow,
145 Where the zig-zag lightning stands high on top,
Where the he-rain stands high on top, Oh, Father God!

With your moccasins of dark cloud, come to us,
With your mind enveloped in dark cloud, come to us,
With the dark thunder above you, come to us soaring,
150 With the shapen cloud at your feet, come to us soaring.
With the far darkness made of the dark cloud over your head,
come to us soaring,
With the far darkness made of the rain and the mist over your head,
come to us soaring,
155 With the far darkness made of the rain and the mist over your head,
come to us soaring.
With the zig-zag lightning flung out high over your head,
With the rainbow hanging high over your head, come to us soaring.
With the far darkness made of the dark cloud on the ends of your wings,
160 With the far darkness made of the rain and the mist on the ends of your wings,
come to us soaring,

With the zig-zag lightning, with the rainbow hanging high on the ends of your
wings, come to us soaring.
With the near darkness made of dark cloud of the rain and the mist, come to us,
165 With the darkness on the earth, come to us.
With these I wish the foam floating on the flowing water over the roots
of the great corn,
I have made your sacrifice,
I have prepared a smoke for you,
170 My feet restore for me.
My limbs restore, my body restore,
my mind restore,
my voice restore for me.

Today, take out your spell for me,
175 Today, take away your spell for me.
Away from me you have taken it,
Far off from me it is taken,
Far off you have done it.

Happily I recover,
180 Happily I become cool,
My eyes regain their power,
my head cools,
my limbs regain their strength,
I hear again.
185 Happily for me the spell is taken off,
Happily I walk; impervious to pain,
I walk; light within, I walk; joyous,
I walk.

Abundant dark clouds I desire,
190 An abundance of vegetation I desire,
An abundance of pollen, abundant dew, I desire.
Happily may fair white corn, to the ends of the earth, come with you,
Happily may fair yellow corn, fair blue corn, fair corn of all kinds,
plants of all kinds, goods of all kinds, jewels of all kinds, to the ends of
195 the earth, come with you.
With these before you, happily may they come with you,
With these behind, below, above, around you, happily may they come with you,

Thus you accomplish your tasks.
Happily the old men will regard you,
200 Happily the old women will regard you,
The young men and the young women will regard you,
The children will regard you,
The chiefs will regard you,

Happily, as they scatter in different directions, they will regard you,
Happily, as they approach their homes, they will regard you.

205 May their roads home be on the trail of peace,
Happily may they all return,
In beauty I walk.
With beauty before me, I walk.
210 With beauty behind me, I walk.
With beauty above and about me, I walk.
It is finished in beauty.
It is finished in beauty.

215 'Sa'ah naaghéi, Bik'eh hózhó

Questions for Discussion:

1. Understanding that this is a practiced Native American ceremony, what are the cultural dilemmas for studying it as a poem?
2. As a sacred, historical ceremony, what effect might be achieved by its use of repetition?

"Workshop"

Billy Collins

Author Biography: Billy Collins was born in New York in 1941. From a young age, he was interested in poetry, and went on to earn a Ph.D. in poetry. Since 1968, Collins is a Distinguished Professor at Lehman University and was the United States Poet Laureate from 2001 to 2003.

Context: Collins is well known for poetry that is humorous, lighthearted, and even irreverent, engaging not as often with lofty, literary concepts as much as everyday situations and subjects. There is often a self-aware, wry quality to his poetry that makes reading him very accessible.

Literary Terms: symbolism, theme, characterization, irony, metaphor

I might as well begin by saying how much I like the title.
It gets me right away because I'm in a workshop now
so immediately the poem has my attention,
like the Ancient Mariner grabbing me by the sleeve.

And I like the first couple of stanzas,
the way they establish this mode of self-pointing
that runs through the whole poem
and tells us that words are food thrown down

on the ground for other words to eat.
I can almost taste the tail of the snake
in its own mouth,
if you know what I mean.

But what I'm not sure about is the voice,
which sounds in places very casual, very blue jeans,
but other times seems standoffish,
professorial in the worst sense of the word
like the poem is blowing pipe smoke in my face.
But maybe that's just what it wants to do.

What I did find engaging were the middle stanzas,
especially the fourth one.
I like the image of clouds flying like lozenges
which gives me a very clear picture.
And I really like how this drawbridge operator
just appears out of the blue
with his feet up on the iron railing
and his fishing pole jigging—I like jigging—
a hook in the slow industrial canal below.
I love slow industrial canal below. All those l's.
Maybe it's just me,
but the next stanza is where I start to have a problem.
I mean how can the evening bump into the stars?
And what's an obbligato of snow?
Also, I roam the decaffeinated streets.
At that point I'm lost. I need help.

The other thing that throws me off,
and maybe this is just me,
is the way the scene keeps shifting around.
First, we're in this big aerodrome
and the speaker is inspecting a row of dirigibles,
which makes me think this could be a dream.
Then he takes us into his garden,
the part with the dahlias and the coiling hose,
though that's nice, the coiling hose,
but then I'm not sure where we're supposed to be.
The rain and the mint green light,
that makes it feel outdoors, but what about this wallpaper?
Or is it a kind of indoor cemetery?
There's something about death going on here.
In fact, I start to wonder if what we have here
is really two poems, or three, or four,
or possibly none.

But then there's that last stanza, my favorite.
This is where the poem wins me back,
especially the lines spoken in the voice of the mouse.
I mean we've all seen these images in cartoons before,
but I still love the details he uses
when he's describing where he lives.
The perfect little arch of an entrance in the baseboard,
the bed made out of a curled-back sardine can,
the spool of thread for a table.
I start thinking about how hard the mouse had to work
night after night collecting all these things
while the people in the house were fast asleep,
and that gives me a very strong feeling,
a very powerful sense of something.
But I don't know if anyone else was feeling that.
Maybe that was just me.
Maybe that's just the way I read it.

Questions for Discussion:

1. In what ways does the poem reveal the poet's self-awareness?
2. In what ways is "Workshop" a relevant title for this poem?

"The Writer"

Richard Wilbur

Author Biography: Richard Wilbur was born in New York City in 1921. First published at age 8, Wilbur wrote poetry throughout his time earning a B.A. at Amherst College and two years in the Army during World War II. Wilbur has taught at several major liberal arts colleges, received the Pulitzer Prize for Poetry in both 1957 and 1989, and earned the National Book Award for Poetry in 1957. He teaches at Amherst College.

Context: Wilbur has written much about his experiences in World War II, though perhaps surprisingly, much of his poetry is optimistic in nature. In addition to that work, Wilbur has been compared to poets like Robert Frost for his engagement with everyday, personal situations, although he never became a true confessional poet like Sylvia Plath.

Literary Terms: simile, metaphor, personification, meter, symbolism

In her room at the prow of the house
Where light breaks, and the windows are tossed with linden,
My daughter is writing a story.
I pause in the stairwell, hearing

From her shut door a commotion of typewriter-keys
Like a chain hauled over a gunwale.

Young as she is, the stuff
Of her life is a great cargo, and some of it heavy:
I wish her a lucky passage.

But now it is she who pauses,
As if to reject my thought and its easy figure.
A stillness greatens, in which

The whole house seems to be thinking,
And then she is at it again with a bunched clamor
Of strokes, and again is silent.

I remember the dazed starling
Which was trapped in that very room, two years ago;
How we stole in, lifted a sash
And retreated, not to affright it;
And how for a helpless hour, through the crack of the door,
We watched the sleek, wild, dark

And iridescent creature
Batter against the brilliance, drop like a glove
To the hard floor, or the desk-top,

And wait then, humped and bloody,
For the wits to try it again; and how our spirits
Rose when, suddenly sure,

It lifted off from a chair-back,
Beating a smooth course for the right window
And clearing the sill of the world.

It is always a matter, my darling,
Of life or death, as I had forgotten. I wish
What I wished you before, but harder.

Questions for Discussion:

1. What could the starling represent in this poem?
2. Why does the father wish his daughter a "lucky passage" in the third stanza, and wish it even "harder" in the last stanza?

"Ode on a Grecian Urn"

John Keats

Author Biography: John Keats was born at the very end of the eighteenth century in London. Through much of his professional life, he apprenticed and trained to be a doctor, but was ambivalent about the profession as he increasingly pursued writing and poetry. Even though he eventually dedicated himself to writing, he was not well known during his time and suffered financial and health difficulties throughout the later parts of his life. He died of tuberculosis in 1821 at age 25.

Context: Like his contemporaries, Lord Byron and Percy Shelley, Keats was a Romantic poet who is most known for working with the ode form of poetry and adapting it to his needs. Many of these poets looked back to classic literature and art for inspiration, at a time when the world was changing dramatically due to the Industrial Revolution.

Literary Terms: form, symbolism, imagery, ode, wordplay

Thou still unravish'd bride of quietness,
    Thou foster-child of silence and slow time,
Sylvan historian, who canst thus express
    A flowery tale more sweetly than our rhyme:
What leaf-fring'd legend haunts about thy shape
    Of deities or mortals, or of both,
        In Tempe or the dales of Arcady?
    What men or gods are these? What maidens loth?
What mad pursuit? What struggle to escape?
        What pipes and timbrels? What wild ecstasy?

Heard melodies are sweet, but those unheard
    Are sweeter; therefore, ye soft pipes, play on;
Not to the sensual ear, but, more endear'd,
    Pipe to the spirit ditties of no tone:
Fair youth, beneath the trees, thou canst not leave
    Thy song, nor ever can those trees be bare;
        Bold Lover, never, never canst thou kiss,
Though winning near the goal yet, do not grieve;
    She cannot fade, though thou hast not thy bliss,
        For ever wilt thou love, and she be fair!

Ah, happy, happy boughs! that cannot shed
    Your leaves, nor ever bid the Spring adieu;
And, happy melodist, unwearied,
    For ever piping songs for ever new;
More happy love! more happy, happy love!
    For ever warm and still to be enjoy'd,

For ever panting, and for ever young;
All breathing human passion far above,
        That leaves a heart high-sorrowful and cloy'd,
                A burning forehead, and a parching tongue.

Who are these coming to the sacrifice?
        To what green altar, O mysterious priest,
Lead'st thou that heifer lowing at the skies,
        And all her silken flanks with garlands drest?
What little town by river or sea shore,
        Or mountain-built with peaceful citadel,
                Is emptied of this folk, this pious morn?
And, little town, thy streets for evermore
        Will silent be; and not a soul to tell
                Why thou art desolate, can e'er return.

O Attic shape! Fair attitude! with brede
        Of marble men and maidens overwrought,
With forest branches and the trodden weed;
        Thou, silent form, dost tease us out of thought
As doth eternity: Cold Pastoral!
        When old age shall this generation waste,
                Thou shalt remain, in midst of other woe
Than ours, a friend to man, to whom thou say'st,
        "Beauty is truth, truth beauty,—that is all
                Ye know on earth, and all ye need to know."

Questions for Discussion:

1. What is the poem communicating about the role of art in society?
2. What is the speaker's tone in the poem? Is there more than one? Why?

"The Passionate Shepherd to His Love"

Christopher Marlowe

Author Biography: Christopher Marlowe was born in Kent, England in 1564, the same year as his contemporary, William Shakespeare. Marlowe was a poet, playwright, and translator, responsible for many important plays of the time, including *Doctor Faustus*. Marlowe was stabbed to death in 1593 under speculation that he had worked in some secret capacity for the British government earlier in his life.

Context: Marlowe and Shakespeare are part of the English Renaissance, and this work is a good example of a lyrical style love poem of the time. Famously, Walter Raleigh replied to this poem with his own, in which he implicitly chastises Marlowe for being young and naïve in his views about love.

Literary Terms: imagery, repetition, form, theme

Come live with me and be my love,   *male*
And we will all the pleasures prove,
That Valleys, groves, hills, and fields,
Woods, or steepy mountain yields.

And we will sit upon the Rocks,
Seeing the Shepherds feed their flocks,
By shallow Rivers to whose falls
Melodious birds sing Madrigals.

And I will make thee beds of Roses
And a thousand fragrant posies,
A cap of flowers, and a kirtle
Embroidered all with leaves of Myrtle; *break*
A gown made of the finest wool
Which from our pretty Lambs we pull;
Fair lined slippers for the cold,
With buckles of the purest gold;

A belt of straw and Ivy buds,
With Coral clasps and Amber studs:
And if these pleasures may thee move,
Come live with me, and be my love.

The Shepherds' Swains shall dance and sing
For thy delight each May-morning:
If these delights thy mind may move,
Then live with me, and be my love.

Questions for Discussion:

1. What is the role of nature imagery in the poem?
2. What does the poem reveal about the speaker?

"The Nymph's Reply to the Shepherd"

↗ A fairy (generally female)

Female

Sir Walter Raleigh

Author Biography: Born in England in 1552, Sir Walter Raleigh had a storied and some-times tumultuous life. His experience fighting for England in Ireland (an English colony at the time) earned him a knighthood and the opportunity to settle the colony of Virginia, but his later secret marriage to one of Queen Elizabeth's ladies-in-waiting led to his impris-onment in the Tower of London. Later released, Raleigh set out to explore South America and find the legendary city of gold, El Dorado. Raleigh was later sent back to the Tower of London for his involvement in a plot to kill King James I, but was again released after some time to find El Dorado. During that mission, however, he attacked a Spanish outpost, violating international treaties; he was returned to England and executed for this in 1618.

Context: Raleigh, despite his busy military career, was also a writer and poet. "The Nymph's Reply to the Shepherd" is a response to Christopher Marlowe's lyrical poem "The Passionate Shepherd to His Love." While Marlowe was focused on writing a genuine love poem, however, Raleigh here tries to counter him at every turn.

Literary Terms: symbolism, theme, irony, sound devices

If all the world and love were young,   Female
And truth in every Shepherd's tongue,
These pretty pleasures might me move,
To live with thee, and be thy love.

Time drives the flocks from field to fold,
When Rivers rage and Rocks grow cold,
And *Philomel* becometh dumb,
The rest complains of cares to come.

The flowers do fade, and wanton fields,
To wayward winter reckoning yields,
A honey tongue, a heart of gall,
Is fancy's spring, but sorrow's fall.

Thy gowns, thy shoes, thy beds of Roses,
Thy cap, thy kirtle, and thy posies
Soon break, soon wither, soon forgotten:
In folly ripe, in reason rotten.

Thy belt of straw and Ivy buds,
The Coral clasps and amber studs,
All these in me no means can move
To come to thee and be thy love.

But could youth last, and love still breed,
Had joys no date, nor age no need,
Then these delights my mind might move
To live with thee, and be thy love.

Questions for Discussion:

1. What role do the seasons play in the poem?
2. How does the speaker push against the label of Nymph throughout the poem?

"Phenomenal Woman"

Maya Angelou

Author Biography: Maya Angelou was born in 1928 in St. Louis, MO. She was a prolific writer whose body of work includes essays, plays, poems, and seven biographies that chronicle her extremely rich life. Angelou worked throughout her life as a cook, performer, journalist, and activist, working with both Martin Luther King, Jr. and Malcom X during the Civil Rights movement. Later in her life, she held a lifetime professor position at Wake Forest University and was active on the lecture circuit.

Context: Born in the 1920s, Angelou lived through many tumultuous periods in American and world history—the Great Depression, World War II, and the Civil Rights Movement, among others. Many of these time periods, especially the 1960s, saw increasing concern about the rights of minority and non-dominant groups, such as African Americans and women. Angleou's work, therefore, often explores issues of identity, including gender, race, and family.

Literary Terms: rhyme, theme, form, metaphor

Pretty women wonder where my secret lies.
I'm not cute or built to suit a fashion model's size
But when I start to tell them,
They think I'm telling lies.
5 I say,
It's in the reach of my arms,
The span of my hips,
The stride of my step,
The curl of my lips.
10 I'm a woman

Phenomenally.
Phenomenal woman,
That's me.

I walk into a room
15 Just as cool as you please,
And to a man,
The fellows stand or
Fall down on their knees.
Then they swarm around me,
20 A hive of honey bees.
I say,
It's the fire in my eyes,
And the flash of my teeth,
The swing in my waist,
25 And the joy in my feet.
I'm a woman
Phenomenally.

Phenomenal woman,
That's me.

30 Men themselves have wondered
What they see in me.
They try so much
But they can't touch
My inner mystery.
35 When I try to show them,
They say they still can't see.
I say,
It's in the arch of my back,
The sun of my smile,
40 The ride of my breasts,
The grace of my style.
I'm a woman
Phenomenally.
Phenomenal woman,
45 That's me.

Now you understand
Just why my head's not bowed.
I don't shout or jump about
Or have to talk real loud.
50 When you see me passing,
It ought to make you proud.
I say,

It's in the click of my heels,
The bend of my hair,
55 the palm of my hand,
The need for my care.
'Cause I'm a woman
Phenomenally.
Phenomenal woman,
60 That's me.

Questions for Discussion:

1. What is the tone of the poem? How does repetition inform the tone?
2. What is the poem saying about conventional ideas of beauty and femininity?

"The Negro Speaks of Rivers"

Langston Hughes

Author Biography: Langston Hughes was born in 1902 in Joplin, MO, descended from both slaves and slave owners. After travelling and holding odd jobs around the world, Hughes earned a B.A. from Lincoln University. His lifelong interest in writing came to the fore in the 1920s, when he became one of the leading figures of the Harlem Renaissance, a literary, musical, and cultural movement that sought to celebrate the African-American culture that was unknown by mainstream America.

Context: Hughes composed "The Negro Speaks of Rivers" early in his career; he was just 17 when he wrote it on a train he was taking to Mexico to visit his father. Still, there is a theme here which will run through his future work from the Harlem Renaissance: a preoccupation with—and a pride in—the African roots of black Americans.

Literary Terms: symbolism, theme, allegory, imagery, movement

I've known rivers:
I've known rivers ancient as the world and older than the flow of human blood in human veins.

My soul has grown deep like the rivers.

I bathed in the Euphrates when dawns were young.
I built my hut near the Congo and it lulled me to sleep.
I looked upon the Nile and raised the pyramids above it.
I heard the singing of the Mississippi when Abe Lincoln went down to New Orleans, and I've seen its muddy bosom turn all golden in the sunset.

I've known rivers:
Ancient, dusky rivers.

My soul has grown deep like the rivers.

Questions for Discussion:

1. What is the role of the different rivers in this poem?
2. How does the third section change the tone of the poem?

"The Second Coming"

William Butler Yeats

Author Biography: W.B. Yeats was an Irish poet and, later in his life, a politician who influenced the world of Irish and English literature immensely. Yeats helped found the Abbey Theatre, Ireland's national theater and the first state-sponsored theater in the English-speaking world. He was awarded the Nobel Prize in Literature in 1923.

Context: While Yeats is not always considered part of the "Lost Generation" that included writers like Hemingway, Pound, and Eliot, the events of World War I had a profound impact on him, like so many of those writers and the nations of Europe. Perhaps his most famous work, this poem ruminates on what that massive war and loss of human life means for the world.

Literary Terms: imagery, allegory, blank verse, symbolism, riddle

Turning and turning in the widening gyre
The falcon cannot hear the falconer;
Things fall apart; the centre cannot hold;
Mere anarchy is loosed upon the world,
The blood-dimmed tide is loosed, and everywhere
The ceremony of innocence is drowned;
The best lack all conviction, while the worst
Are full of passionate intensity.

Surely some revelation is at hand;
Surely the Second Coming is at hand.
The Second Coming! Hardly are those words out
When a vast image out of *Spiritus Mundi*
Troubles my sight: somewhere in sands of the desert
A shape with lion body and the head of a man,
A gaze blank and pitiless as the sun,
Is moving its slow thighs, while all about it

Reel shadows of the indignant desert birds.
The darkness drops again; but now I know
That twenty centuries of stony sleep
Were vexed to nightmare by a rocking cradle,
And what rough beast, its hour come round at last,
Slouches towards Bethlehem to be born?

Questions for Discussion:

1. What is the role of the avian metaphors throughout the poem?
2. What could be the reasons why Yeats ends this poem with a question?

"Gentleness Stirred"

Nimah Nawwab

Author Biography: Nimah Nawwab is a Malaysian poet, writer, and activist who became interested in English literature at a young age. Graduating with a B.A. in that subject, Nawwab has taken on a wide array of projects, including speaking, advising, and in 2000, writing poetry.

Context: Nawwab has a keen interest in the politics and culture of the Middle East, especially Saudi Arabia. Her work—fiction and non-fiction—explores the many facets of those cultures and the contemporary issues that surround them, especially for women.

Literary Terms: theme, form, imagery

Striding through the gates of learning,
Wrapped warmly in her black abaya,
Modestly cloaked head to toe,
Not a hair astray, nor skin showing,
Holding her head up high,
Thinking of the future,
Arms laden with books,
Head in the clouds,
Lunch, television, studies, friends,
That is how her day will go
Near future, far future,
Blissful, brimming with expectations.

"Hey, you there!" thunders across the parking lot
"You with the black boots" the tone is raised
Oh, oh, reluctantly she turns,
Fear stirs,

Flinching,
Watches wrath unleashed.
The self-righteous, bushy-bearded figure,
Crashes through the crowds,
Bestriding his narrow world like a Colossus,
As his entourage hurries in his wake,
A raging bull on the rampage,
Seeing red as the girl flouts 'convention.'

Necks crane to watch,
The crowds are in on the show.
He thunders on,
The police by his side
"Stop, your scarf has slipped."
The tirade begins, gains momentum.

Head cast down,
Eyes to the ground,
Shoulders drooping
She listens,
Afraid,
Confused,
Cringing,
Burrowing into her deepest self.

Has she missed a prayer?
Has she been a disobedient daughter?
Cheated, lied, stolen,
Beaten a child, an animal, been cruel to another soul?
What did she do?
Her scarf slipped,
An unforgivable transgression,
In the eyes of the Controllers.
Is that her sin,
Her ever-lasting humiliation,
Her major fall from grace,
Her offense?

The mind is strange, the spirit stranger yet,
The rebellion begins.

Questions for Discussion:

1. How do the short sentences add to the speed of the poem and what does that accomplish?
2. How does the last line of the poem shape a second reading differently than a first?

"Sonnet XVIII"

William Shakespeare

Author Biography: Born in 1564 in Stratford-upon-Avon, England, William Shakespeare is perhaps the best-known writer in the English language. He married Anne Hathaway, 8 years his senior, when he was 18, and the couple had three children, though one, Hamnet, died at the age of 11. Shakespeare began his career as an actor and writer and co-owned a theater company called the King's Men, patented by King James I. He was later part of a group that founded and owned the Globe Theater, an endeavor that brought him wealth throughout his life.

Context: Shakespeare is best known for his plays, of course, but he was also an accomplished poet, producing some long-form poetry as well as 154 sonnets, a poetical form invented in Italy in the thirteenth century. Shakespeare's sonnets deal with topics we might traditionally expect of poetry—beauty, love, and life and death.

Literary Terms: Shakespearean sonnet, metaphor, form

Shall I compare thee to a summer's day?
Thou art more lovely and more temperate:
Rough winds do shake the darling buds of May,
And summer's lease hath all too short a date:
Sometime too hot the eye of heaven shines,
And often is his gold complexion dimm'd;
And every fair from fair sometime declines,
By chance, or nature's changing course, untrimm'd;
But thy eternal summer shall not fade
Nor lose possession of that fair thou ow'st;
Nor shall Death brag thou wander'st in his shade,
When in eternal lines to time thou grow'st;
So long as men can breathe or eyes can see,
So long lives this, and this gives life to thee.

Questions for Discussion:

1. In what ways is this a love poem and in what ways is it more than just that?
2. What is the speaker providing his muse in the line, "When in eternal lines to time thou grow'st"?

"Sonnet CXVI"

William Shakespeare

Literary Terms: Shakespearean sonnet, metaphor, form

Let me not to the marriage of true minds
Admit impediments. Love is not love
Which alters when it alteration finds,
Or bends with the remover to remove.
O no! it is an ever-fixed mark
That looks on tempests and is never shaken;
It is the star to every wand'ring bark,
Whose worth's unknown, although his height be taken.
Love's not Time's fool, though rosy lips and cheeks
Within his bending sickle's compass come;
Love alters not with his brief hours and weeks,
But bears it out even to the edge of doom.
If this be error and upon me prov'd,
I never writ, nor no man ever lov'd.

Questions for Discussion:

1. What ideal of love is the speaker addressing in this poem?
2. How does the final couplet shape the reading of the poem and our view of the speaker?

"Childe Roland to the Dark Tower Came"

Robert Browning

Author Biography: Robert Browning was one of the more prolific poets and playwrights of Victorian England. His life and career spanned most of the nineteenth century. While his prominence rose and fell while he was alive, often due to the complexity and obscurity of his work, he is now one of the most enduring English poets.

Context: Like many writers, Browning borrows from those who have gone before him. Indeed, the title for this work comes from a line from Shakespeare's *King Lear*. Like much of Shakespeare's works, Browning here is interested in the idea of the journey, both a literal journey for a character and the internal journey they face, each fraught with danger.

Literary Terms: theme, symbolism, dramatic monologue, imagery, metaphor

My first thought was, he lied in every word,
  That hoary cripple, with malicious eye
  Askance to watch the working of his lie
On mine, and mouth scarce able to afford
5 Suppression of the glee, that purs'd and scor'd
  Its edge, at one more victim gain'd thereby.

What else should he be set for, with his staff?
  What, save to waylay with his lies, ensnare
  All travellers who might find him posted there,
10 And ask the road? I guess'd what skull-like laugh
  Would break, what crutch 'gin write my epitaph
  For pastime in the dusty thoroughfare,
  If at his counsel I should turn aside
  Into that ominous tract which, all agree,
15 Hides the Dark Tower. Yet acquiescingly
I did turn as he pointed: neither pride
Nor hope rekindling at the end descried,
  So much as gladness that some end might be.

For, what with my whole world-wide wandering,
20 What with my search drawn out thro' years, my hope
  Dwindled into a ghost not fit to cope
With that obstreperous joy success would bring,—
I hardly tried now to rebuke the spring
  My heart made, finding failure in its scope.

25 As when a sick man very near to death
  Seems dead indeed, and feels begin and end
  The tears and takes the farewell of each friend,
And hears one bid the other go, draw breath
Freelier outside, ("since all is o'er," he saith,
30 "And the blow fallen no grieving can amend;")

While some discuss if near the other graves
  Be room enough for this, and when a day
  Suits best for carrying the corpse away,
  With care about the banners, scarves and staves,
35 And still the man hears all, and only craves
  He may not shame such tender love and stay.

Thus, I had so long suffer'd, in this quest,
  Heard failure prophesied so oft, been writ
  So many times among "The Band"—to wit,
40 The knights who to the Dark Tower's search address'd
  Their steps—that just to fail as they, seem'd best.
  And all the doubt was now—should I be fit?

So, quiet as despair, I turn'd from him,
That hateful cripple, out of his highway
45 Into the path the pointed. All the day
Had been a dreary one at best, and dim
Was settling to its close, yet shot one grim
Red leer to see the plain catch its estray.

For mark! no sooner was I fairly found
50 Pledged to the plain, after a pace or two,
Than, pausing to throw backward a last view
O'er the safe road, 't was gone; gray plain all round:
Nothing but plain to the horizon's bound.
I might go on; nought else remain'd to do.

55 So, on I went. I think I never saw
Such starv'd ignoble nature; nothing throve:
For flowers—as well expect a cedar grove!
But cockle, spurge, according to their law
Might propagate their kind, with none to awe,
60 You'd think; a burr had been a treasure trove.

No! penury, inertness and grimace,
In the strange sort, were the land's portion. "See
Or shut your eyes," said Nature peevishly,
"It nothing skills: I cannot help my case:
65 'T is the Last Judgment's fire must cure this place,
Calcine its clods and set my prisoners free."

If there push'd any ragged thistle=stalk
Above its mates, the head was chopp'd; the bents
Were jealous else. What made those holes and rents
70 In the dock's harsh swarth leaves, bruis'd as to baulk
All hope of greenness? 'T is a brute must walk
Pashing their life out, with a brute's intents.

As for the grass, it grew as scant as hair
In leprosy; thin dry blades prick'd the mud
75 Which underneath look'd kneaded up with blood.
One stiff blind horse, his every bone a-stare,
Stood stupefied, however he came there:
Thrust out past service from the devil's stud!

Alive? he might be dead for aught I know,
80 With that red, gaunt and collop'd neck a-strain,
And shut eyes underneath the rusty mane;
Seldom went such grotesqueness with such woe;

I never saw a brute I hated so;
   He must be wicked to deserve such pain.

⁸⁵ I shut my eyes and turn'd them on my heart.
   As a man calls for wine before he fights,
   I ask'd one draught of earlier, happier sights,
  Ere fitly I could hope to play my part.
  Think first, fight afterwards—the soldier's art:
⁹⁰   One taste of the old time sets all to rights.

Not it! I fancied Cuthbert's reddening face
   Beneath its garniture of curly gold,
   Dear fellow, till I almost felt him fold
  An arm in mine to fix me to the place,
⁹⁵ That way he us'd. Alas, one night's disgrace!
   Out went my heart's new fire and left it cold.

Giles then, the soul of honor—there he stands
   Frank as ten years ago when knighted first.
   What honest man should dare (he said) he durst.
¹⁰⁰ Good—but the scene shifts—faugh! what hangman hands
   Pin to his breast a parchment? His own bands
   Read it. Poor traitor, spit upon and curst!

Better this present than a past like that;
   Back therefore to my darkening path again!
¹⁰⁵   No sound, no sight as far as eye could strain.
  Will the night send a howlet of a bat?
  I asked: when something on the dismal flat
   Came to arrest my thoughts and change their train.

A sudden little river cross'd my path
¹¹⁰   As unexpected as a serpent comes.
   No sluggish tide congenial to the glooms;
  This, as it froth'd by, might have been a bath
  For the fiend's glowing hoof—to see the wrath
   Of its black eddy bespate with flakes and spumes.

¹¹⁵ So petty yet so spiteful All along,
   Low scrubby alders kneel'd down over it;
   Drench'd willows flung them headlong in a fit
  Of mute despair, a suicidal throng:
  The river which had done them all the wrong,
¹²⁰   Whate'er that was, roll'd by, deterr'd no whit.
   Which, while I forded,—good saints, how I fear'd
   To set my foot upon a dead man's cheek,

Each step, or feel the spear I thrust to seek
For hollows, tangled in his hair or beard!
125 —It may have been a water-rat I spear'd,
But, ugh! it sounded like a baby's shriek.

Glad was I when I reach'd the other bank.
Now for a better country. Vain presage!
Who were the strugglers, what war did they wage
130 Whose savage trample thus could pad the dank
Soil to a plash? Toads in a poison'd tank,
Or wild cats in a red-hot iron cage—

The fight must so have seem'd in that fell cirque.
What penn'd them there, with all the plain to choose?
135 No foot-print leading to that horrid mews,
None out of it. Mad brewage set to work
Their brains, no doubt, like galley-slaves the Turk
Pits for his pastime, Christians against Jews.

And more than that—a furlong on—why, there!
140 What bad use was that engine for, that wheel,
Or brake, not wheel—that harrow fit to reel
Men's bodies out like silk? with all the air
Of Tophet's tool, on earth left unaware,
Or brought to sharpen its rusty teeth of steel.

145 Then came a bit of stubb'd ground, once a wood,
Next a marsh, it would seem, and now mere earth
Desperate and done with; (so a fool finds mirth,
Makes a thing and then mars it, till his mood
Changes and off he goes!) within a rood—
150 Bog, clay, and rubble, sand and stark black dearth.

Now blotches rankling, color'd gay and grim,
Now patches where some leanness of the soil's
Broke into moss or substances like thus;
Then came some palsied oak, a cleft in him
155 Like a distorted mouth that splits its rim
Gaping at death, and dies while it recoils.

And just as far as ever from the end,
Nought in the distance but the evening, nought
To point my footstep further! At the thought,
160 A great black bird, Apollyon's bosom-friend,
Sail'd past, nor beat his wide wing dragon-penn'd
That brush'd my cap—perchance the guide I sought.

For, looking up, aware I somehow grew,
  Spite of the dusk, the plain had given place
165 All round to mountains—with such name to grace
Mere ugly heights and heaps now stolen in view.
How thus they had surpris'd me,—solve it, you!
  How to get from them was no clearer case.

Yet half I seem'd to recognize some trick
170 Of mischief happen'd to me, God knows when—
  In a bad perhaps. Here ended, then,
Progress this way. When, in the very nick
Of giving up, one time more, came a click
  As when a trap shuts—you 're inside the den.

175 Burningly it came on me all at once,
  This was the place! those two hills on the right,
  Couch'd like two bulls lock'd horn in horn in fight,
While, to the left, a tall scalp'd mountain … Dunce,
Dotard, a-dozing at the very nonce,
  After a life spent training for the sight!

180
What in the midst lay but the Tower itself?
  The round squat turret, blind as the fool's heart,
  Built of brown stone, without a counter-part
In the whole world. The tempest's mocking elf
Points to the shipman thus the unseen shelf
185
  He strikes on, only when the timbers start.

Not see? because of night perhaps?—Why, day
  Came back again for that! before it left,
  The dying sunset kindled through a cleft:
The hills, like giants at a hunting, lay,
190 Chin upon hand, to see the game at bay,—
  "Now stab and end the creature—to the heft!"

Not hear? when noise was everywhere! it toll'd
  Increasing like a bell. Names in my ears
  Of all the lost adventurers my peers,—
195 How such a one was strong, and such was bold,
And such was fortunate, yet each of old
  Lost, lost! one moment knell'd the woe of years.

There they stood, ranged along the hill-sides, met
  To view the last of me, a living frame
200 For one more picture! in a sheet of flame
I saw them and I knew them all. And yet
Dauntless the slug-horn to my lips I set,
  And blew *"Childe Roland to the Dark Tower came."*

Questions for Discussion:

1. What could this poem be arguing about success and failure?
2. How does the poems use of iambic pentameter affect our reading?

"Sisters of Mercy"

Leonard Cohen

Author Biography: Born in 1934, Leonard Cohen began his career as a poet and novelist, only later turning to music, which he is perhaps most known for now. Much of Cohen's work explores religion, politics, and many other belief systems, which he explored and pursued widely throughout his life.

Context: Cohen has been variously known as a practicing Jew, Buddhist, and more. Throughout his life, he sought to understand many disparate philosophies and religions.

Literary Terms: theme, analogy, form, repetition, imagery, song

Oh, the sisters of mercy, they are not departed or gone
They were waiting for me when I thought that I just can't go on
And they brought me their comfort and later they brought me this song
Oh, I hope you run into them, you who've been travelling so long
Yes, you who must leave everything that you cannot control
It begins with your family, but soon it comes around to your soul
Well, I've been where you're hanging, I think I can see how you're pinned
When you're not feeling holy, your loneliness says that you've sinned
Well, they lay down beside me, I made my confession to them
They touched both my eyes and I touched the dew on their hem
If your life is a leaf that the seasons tear off and condemn
They will bind you with love that is graceful and green as a stem
When I left they were sleeping, I hope you run into them soon
Don't turn on the lights, you can read their address by the moon
And you won't make me jealous if I hear that they sweetened your night
We weren't lovers like that and besides, it would still be all right
We weren't lovers like that and besides, it would still be all right

Questions for Discussion:

1. What do the sisters of mercy provide the speaker?
2. How does the biblical image of confession contribute to the poem?

"Cold Summer"

Charles Bukowski

Author Biography: Charles Bukowski was born in Germany in 1920, but his family immigrated to Los Angeles when we was three years old. Bukowski wrote early and often in his life, with much of his work published in underground or small publications. His work focuses largely on the everyday man, poor families, addiction, and the often seedy side of modern life.

Context: Much of Bukowski's work focuses on the plight of everyday people and their various hardships. Bukowski himself became addicted to alcohol and throughout his life was in and out of hospitals.

Literary Terms: direct language, free verse

not as bad as yours, Fante,
but bad enough: in and out
of the hospital, in and out of
the doctor's office, swinging
by the thread: you're in
remission…no, wait, 2 new
cells here…and your
platelets are way down…
you been drinking?
we'll probably have to take
another bone marrow…
we'll probably…

the doctor is busy, the
waiting room in the cancer
ward is crowded: people
reading *Time*, people reading
People…

the nurses are pleasant, they
joke with me.
I think that's nice, joking in the
shadows of death.
my wife is with me.
I am sorry for my wife, I am
sorry for everybody's
wife.

then we are down in the
parking lot.
I drive sometimes.
I drive then.
it's been a cold summer.

Questions for Discussion:

1. How does dialogue help the reader understand the situation of the poem?
2. What does the speaker mean in the line, "the bill has come due?" What is the "final payment"?

"Love Sonnet XVII"

Pablo Neruda

Author Biography: Pablo Neruda was born in Chile in 1904. Encouraged by teachers—though discouraged by his father—Neruda wrote early in his life, publishing at the age of 13. He wrote throughout his life, while also working as a diplomat off and on throughout his career. He first worked for the communist government, and was then exiled in 1948 when a new government banned communism. He later returned to work in a new communist government, but died after he was injected with a mysterious substance while in the hospital, probably at the order of dictator August Pinochet, who had just risen to power after a coup d'état. Before his death, he was awarded the Nobel Prize in Literature.

Context: Neruda is perhaps best known as a writer for his love poetry, which is often described as "sensuous" and involves much physical interaction between characters.

Literary Terms: sonnet, repetition, imagery

I do not love you as if you were salt-rose, or topaz,
or the arrow of carnations the fire shoots off.
I love you as certain dark things are to be loved,
in secret, between the shadow and the soul.

I love you as the plant that never blooms
but carries in itself the light of hidden flowers;
thanks to your love a certain solid fragrance,
risen from the earth, lives darkly in my body.

I love you without knowing how, or when, or from where.
I love you straightforwardly, without complexities or pride;
so I love you because I know no other way

than this: where I does not exist, nor you,
so close that your hand on my chest is my hand,
so close that your eyes close as I fall asleep.

Questions for Discussion:

1. What is the goal of the repetition in the poem?
2. How does the speaker use cliché and surprising imagery to show his love?

"Ozymandias"

Percy Bysshe Shelley

Author Biography: Percy Bysshe Shelley was born in 1792 in Sussex, England. He is one of the most influential English poets to have ever lived. Shelley was revered more after his life, having courted a good deal of controversy during his life; he was kicked out of Oxford for writing a pamphlet entitled *The Necessity of Atheism*, and was disliked by many in the British government for his writing about and to the Irish, which suggested they were being persecuted and oppressed by the English. Surrounded by other great artists throughout his life, he was part of a circle that included Lord Byron, and his own second wife Mary authored *Frankenstein*.

Context: "Ozymandias" was the Greek name for the Egyptian pharaoh Ramesses II. In 1817, the British Museum brought in a large section of a statue of the Pharaoh, which inspired Shelley and his friend Horace Smith to write competing poems of the same title. Shelley's poem is a rumination of time and decay, and how power and renown diminish with time.

Literary Terms: sonnet, meter, sound, imagery

I met a traveller from an antique land
Who said: 'Two vast and trunkless legs of stone
Stand in the desert. Near them, on the sand,
Half sunk, a shattered visage lies, whose frown,
And wrinkled lip, and sneer of cold command,
Tell that its sculptor well those passions read
Which yet survive, stamped on these lifeless things,
The hand that mocked them and the heart that fed.
And on the pedestal these words appear —
"My name is Ozymandias, king of kings:
Look on my works, ye Mighty, and despair!"
Nothing beside remains. Round the decay
Of that colossal wreck, boundless and bare
The lone and level sands stretch far away.'

Questions for Discussion:

1. How does the poem portray the title character?
2. How does the iambic pentameter shape a reading of this poem? (Read the poem out loud for ideas.)

"The Indian Burying Ground"

Philip Freneau

Author Biography: Born in New York City in 1752, it was probably inevitable that as Freneau became interested in writing, his themes and causes leaned toward the patriotic as he lived through the American Revolution. Nearly dying on a British Prison Ship after his capture during the War, Freneau lived to be recruited by Thomas Jefferson to edit *The National Gazette*, a partisan newspaper that dived quite directly into political debates of the time. Later in his life, Freneau retired to more rural enclaves, writing increasingly about nature and the natural world.

Context: Freneau was a prolific writer, covering politics, wars, Native Americans, and nature. Though less known than Emerson or Thoreau, Freneau was an early precursor to American Romanticism, writing often lyrical works that hint toward the direction of works to come. "The Indian Burying Ground" combines the topic of Native Americans and the lyrical style we see in much of his work.

Literary Terms: romance, symbolism, alternate rhyme, nature

In spite of all the learned have said,
  I still my old opinion keep;
The posture, that we give the dead,
  Points out the soul›s eternal sleep.

Not so the ancients of these lands—
  The Indian, when from life released,
Again is seated with his friends,
  And shares again the joyous feast.

His imaged birds, and painted bowl,
  And venison, for a journey dressed,
Bespeak the nature of the soul,
  Activity, that knows no rest.

His bow, for action ready bent,
  And arrows, with a head of stone,
Can only mean that life is spent,
  And not the old ideas gone.

Thou, stranger, that shalt come this way,
  No fraud upon the dead commit—
Observe the swelling turf, and say
  They do not lie, but here they sit.

Here still a lofty rock remains,
　　On which the curious eye may trace
(Now wasted, half, by wearing rains)
　　The fancies of a ruder race.

Here still an aged elm aspires,
　　Beneath whose far-projecting shade
(And which the shepherd still admires)
　　The children of the forest played!

There oft a restless Indian queen
　　(Pale Shebah, with her braided hair)
And many a barbarous form is seen
　　To chide the man that lingers there.

By midnight moons, o'er moistening dews;
　　In habit for the chase arrayed,
The hunter still the deer pursues,
　　The hunter and the deer, a shade!

And long shall timorous fancy see
　　The painted chief, and pointed spear,
And Reason's self shall bow the knee
　　To shadows and delusions here.

Questions for Discussion:

1. How does the poem portray death? How is this different than modern culture?
2. How is the Native American portrayed in the poem?

"On the Amtrak From Boston To New York City"

Sherman Alexie

Author Biography: Sherman Alexie is a Spokane-Coeur d'Alene writer who was born on the Spokane Indian Reservation in Washington in 1966. He has written novels, short stories, poetry, and screenplays. His collection of short stories, *The Lone Ranger* and *Tonto Fistfight in Heaven*, was adapted into the film *Smoke Signals*. Alexie has won numerous awards for his writing and now lives in Seattle.

Context: Throughout his body of work, Alexie's interest is in exploring and informing others about the issues facing contemporary Native American populations; he often does so through comparison and contrast between modern American culture and Native American history and tradition (which you will see in this poem). In Alexie's hands, these comparisons are often humorous, ironic, and satirical, illustrating the extremely complex situations that modern Native Americans face.

Literary Terms: race, tone, verse, imagery

The white woman across the aisle from me says 'Look,
look at all the history, that house
on the hill there is over two hundred years old,'
as she points out the window past me

into what she has been taught. I have learned
little more about American history during my few days
back East than what I expected and far less
of what we should all know of the tribal stories

whose architecture is 15,000 years older
than the corners of the house that sits
museumed on the hill. 'Walden Pond,'
the woman on the train asks, 'Did you see Walden Pond?'

and I don't have a cruel enough heart to break
her own by telling her there are five Walden Ponds
on my little reservation out West
and at least a hundred more surrounding Spokane,

the city I pretended to call my home. 'Listen,'
I could have told her. 'I don't give a shit
about Walden. I know the Indians were living stories
around that pond before Walden's grandparents were born

and before his grandparents' grandparents were born.
I'm tired of hearing about Don-fucking-Henley saving it, too,
because that's redundant. If Don Henley's brothers and sisters
and mothers and father hadn't come here in the first place

then nothing would need to be saved.'
But I didn't say a word to the woman about Walden
Pond because she smiled so much and seemed delighted
that I thought to bring her an orange juice

back from the food car. I respect elders
of every color. All I really did was eat
my tasteless sandwich, drink my Diet Pepsi
and nod my head whenever the woman pointed out

another little piece of her country's history
while I, as all Indians have done
since this war began, made plans
for what I would do and say the next time

somebody from the enemy thought I was one of their own.

Questions for Discussion:

1. What is the tone of the speaker throughout the poem, and how does it shape the reading?
2. What does the speaker's interaction with "the white woman" tell us about his character?

History of Writers @ Work

In 2011, the Chattanooga State Community College Humanities Department founded Writers @ Work (W@W) to enhance literary analysis in its Composition II classes through the reading of a common novel with a focus on Southern culture and people. It quickly transformed into an arts experience that touches the lives of so many in the greater Chattanooga area.

W@W chooses Southern authors with works centered on life in this region; the effect is that participants are able to gain a new understanding and appreciation for the culture and arts offered in the South, in their own city, and through the community college that serves them. In a media-driven world that shows a limited view of the South, W@W actively works to showcase and celebrate the diversity and rich culture of the Southern people.

Since its inception, W@W has expanded to provide more opportunities for public interaction with selected authors through dynamic events that are always free to attendees. These take place in various locations across the city such as the Chattanooga Aquarium, Bessie Smith Cultural Center, and the Hunter Museum of American Art, where the community can interact with the authors in settings that highlight the best of Chattanooga.

W@W has featured:

2012   Terry Kay's *To Dance With the White Dog*

2013   Ishmael Reed's *New and Collected Poems*

2014   Jill McCorkle's *Creatures of Habit*

2015   Rick Bragg's *All Over But the Shoutin'* and Lila Quintero Weaver's *Darkroom: A Memoir in Black and White*

2016   Ron Rash's *Serena* and selected poems from Robert Morgan

2017   Tayari Jones's *Silver Sparrow* (a National Endowment for the Arts Big Read selection)

Reading on the River | 273

Excerpt from
To Dance with the White Dog

Terry Kay

Terry Kay was born in 1938 in Royston, Georgia. A prolific and award-winning author, Kay has written fiction and screenplays, as well as a children's book and a collection of nonfiction prose. His novel *To Dance with the White Dog* became a best-seller that was dramatized by the Hallmark Hall of Fame in a televised production.

Kay received the Southeastern Library Association Outstanding Author of the Year Award in 1991 for *To Dance with the White Dog*, which was twice nominated for the American Booksellers Association's Book of the Year. Kay also won an Emmy in 1990 for his original teleplay *Run Down the Rabbit*. In 1999 LaGrange College awarded him an Honorary Doctor of Humane Letters, and in 2006 he was inducted into the Georgia Writers Hall of Fame. The following year Kay received the Stanley W. Lindberg Award, sponsored by the Georgia Center for the Book and named for Stanley Lindberg, former editor of the *Georgia Review*. In 2009 he received a Governor's Award in the Humanities, and in 2011 he received the Lifetime Achievement Award from the Georgia Writers Association.

It was now an obsession with the sisters and they talked constantly to one another over the telephone about their father.

Kate: "You know what's going to happen, don't you? Somebody's going to stop in to pay him a visit, to pay their respects because of Mama—somebody like the preacher—and Daddy's going to start bragging about some white dog that's not even there, and it'll get out that he's crazy like old man Bobo Ward. You wait. Every time we go somewhere there'll be people looking at us pitiful-like, like the whole lot of us have lost our senses."

Carrie: "I know it. I keep thinking the same thing. Poor old man Bobo Ward. Last time I saw him he was walking down the road in his long-handle underwear with the bottom unbuttoned and his butt showing. I told you about that. Poor old man. I saw that daughter of his later, up in town. She was in the drugstore buying him some medicine, and I couldn't even look at her, I felt so sorry. When she left, they were saying it took the sheriff to get old man Bobo home. Said he was about to drive everybody in the family up the walls. They just don't know what to do with him."

Kate: "That's what they're going to be saying about us."

Carrie: "At least Daddy's not walking around in his long handles with his butt-flap down."

Kate: "Not now, but he may be before long. I've read stories about how people go crazy. They do it a little bit at a time. One day, it's almost nothing. They're talking along like they always do, and then they start saying things that don't make the first bit of sense, like they were trying to tell a joke, but nothing's funny about it. Next thing you know, they're down on all fours, making out like they're a goat or something."

Carrie: "Oh, Lord, don't say that."

Kate: "Happened that way to that old woman down in Elberton a few years ago. Mama told me about it. Said she was a pillar of the community, even taught school—home economics, Mama said. Then one day they found her on her front porch, in the swing, sitting on a quilt and clucking away like a chicken. Mama said she'd put a dozen eggs on the quilt and was trying to hatch them. Broke every last one of them."

Carrie: "I hope to heaven we won't find Daddy that way, trying to crawl around on all fours, making out like he's a dog."

Kate: "Why'd you say that, Carrie? Oh, Lord, now I'll be worried to death. Maybe that's what's happened—and we don't know it. Maybe he's looking in the mirror and seeing a dog instead of himself. I wish you hadn't said that. I remember reading something about how lots of crazy people get to thinking they're some kind of animal."

Carrie: "I don't even want to talk about it. Makes me want to cry just thinking about it. Every time I think about him patting the air like he was patting a dog's head, saying I was blind because I couldn't see his dog, I can't help but cry."

Kate: "Did Lois call you this morning?"

Carrie: "We talked for a minute. She wanted to know if we'd been able to see the dog yet, and I told her I couldn't even talk about it, it bothered me so much. She sounded put off."

Kate: "I told her the same thing yesterday. I know she thinks we're making it up. I can hear it in her voice. She calls me two or three times a day, like all I've got to do is talk about Daddy."

Carrie: "Sam Junior sounds the same way. He told me last night that we must be making more of it than was needed. Said it may be Daddy's way of keeping everything in balance and we ought not to worry if he wanted to make up having a dog."

Kate: "Well, Sam Junior and Lois and the rest of them don't know what it's like, watching it every day. All they got to do is call up and talk, and a lot of good that does."

Carrie: "I know it."

Kate: "Have you seen Daddy today?"

Carrie: "I was about to go out there."

Kate: "Call me when you get back."

Noah did not mean for the comment to be taken seriously—had said it, in fact, more to tease them than to inspire them—but he knew immediately from their uplifted faces and from the way their eyes flashed with revelation that he had provided them with a plan of action.

"Now, wait a minute," Noah said quickly. "All I said was you ought to put a lookout on your daddy early in the morning. I didn't mean nothing by that. I was just talking."

"What'd you say it again for?" Kate asked indignantly.

"I know that look," Noah told her. "I know you got it in your head. You and Carrie both."

Carrie pushed back the empty coffee cup. Her eyes moistened slightly, and she sniffed softly. She said, "I just came back from watching him sitting out there in his rocking chair with a hairbrush in his hand, brushing thin air, saying he was brushing that white dog's hair. That's what he calls it: White Dog. I couldn't even go back to the house, it scared me so much. I had to come on out here. You ask me, it's a good idea to find out the truth."

"Damn it," Noah sighed. "I don't know why I ever open my mouth around the two of you, especially when Holman's not here to take my side."

"We just want to know if Daddy's going crazy," protested Kate.

"Your daddy's not the one that's crazy. It's the two of you," Noah said bluntly.

"I resent you saying that," Kate replied angrily. "You're not around here in the daytime. You didn't see what Carrie saw."

"I stopped by there on the way in," Noah argued. "Your daddy was sitting in his rocking chair reading the paper. He didn't say nothing about a dog."

"Well, I guess he'd already finished when you got there, Mr. Smartbutt," Kate hissed cynically.

"Good Lord, Kate, don't you know your daddy better'n that? The two of you are aggravating him to death. All he's doing is paying you back. He's putting you on. You know he likes to do that."

"When's he ever done that?" snapped Kate.

Noah stared at Kate in disbelief. "Well, what about last year when he got you going about buying a mule?"

"He was serious about that," Carrie said. "Dead serious. Said he was going to put in his garden with one."

"Come on, Carrie, you know better than that," Noah said. "Mr. Sam can't even walk without using his walker. He knows he can't plow anymore, but he got pure joy out of the two of you fretting over it."

"He drug his plows out," Kate argued.

"He had to make you believe it, didn't he? All he wanted to do was touch them again. The trouble with the two of you is you don't know how a man feels when he can't do something anymore."

"Well, you think what you want to, mister. He was going to buy a mule, before Mama stopped him," Kate said defiantly.

"Your Mama didn't even try to stop him," corrected Noah. "In fact, she said she'd make the call for him. She knew he was putting the two of you on. He's always doing that, and y'all just don't know it."

Carrie rolled her eyes and got up from the kitchen table and poured more coffee into their cups. After a moment, she said, "But the white dog's different, Noah, and you know it."

Noah nodded reluctantly. "I guess that's right. He must think it's there, or he wouldn't've wanted me to kill it."

"But you said it can't be there," Kate said.

"Don't see how," admitted Noah. "Old Red would be barking his fool head off if there was another dog around. Your dogs, too, Carrie."

Carrie sat again at the table. "He keeps saying the dog shows up early every morning to be fed, before we get up and get going."

Kate narrowed her eyes on her sister and said in a low voice, "We could hide out in the ditch, behind that boxwood hedge."

"Good Lord," Noah whispered in desperation.

"You can see the back of the porch clear as day from there," continued Kate.

"If we got out there before sunup, we'd be able to see anything that showed up," Carrie said.

"I don't believe this," Noah moaned. He got up and opened the kitchen door leading to the outside of the house. "I swear, I feel sorry for Mr. Sam. I'm going out to see Holman." He left the house.

"If Daddy sees us, he'll have a fit," Carrie warned.

"He won't see us," promised Kate.

When she left her house the following morning in the soot cloud of night, slipping out the back door, using only the beam of her flashlight, Kate was dressed in jeans and a dark sweater. She had a stocking cap pulled over her hair and the top of her forehead. Her face was smudged with ashes taken from the fireplace. She stood for a moment, letting her eyes adjust to the night, then she raised her flashlight and, partly covering its beam with her fingers, flashed a signal in the direction of Carrie's house. She saw a return light. At least she didn't oversleep, Kate thought. She crouched over and began moving across the lawn, following the familiar path to her father's house.

Carrie was already kneeling behind the boxwood hedge when Kate arrived. Carrie was also dressed in dark clothes, with a stocking cap unfolded down over her hair. She looked at Kate in astonishment.

"What's that you got all over your face?" Carrie whispered.

"Ashes. I got some for you," Kate said. She handed Carrie a small glass jar half-filled with ash.

"I don't want to put that stuff on me," Carrie mumbled.

"Noah said it was what they used to do in the Army. He said it was easy to see a white face from a distance."

"Well, Noah can kiss my foot."

"If Daddy sees you, it won't be a foot-kissing."

"My Lord," sighed Carrie. She opened the jar and dumped the ash out in her hand and rubbed it over her face. "I feel like a fool," she complained. "I hope none of the kids see me like this. They do, they'll be covered up in this stuff."

"It washes off, for crying out loud, Carrie. No reason to take chances. You put up the dogs in the house?"

"I told you I would. You put Red up?"

"Stupid dog didn't even move when I left the house. He was asleep under the kitchen table."

"Is Noah up?" Carrie asked.

"Wadn't when I left, but he was awake. I could tell. He was trying to make me think he was asleep. I could hear him giggling when I left the room."

"Holman was the same," Carrie said. "He thinks we're crazy."

"I don't give a flip what they think," Kate declared in an angry whisper. "It's not their daddy."

"What I say," agreed Carrie. "How long you think we'll have to wait?"

"Don't matter."

"What if he sleeps late?"

"He won't. He went to bed early last night. I saw the lights go out."

"He was hurting some yesterday. Maybe he'll sleep late," Carrie said.

"If he does, we'll come back tomorrow. If he's got a dog, I plan on seeing it."

"Watch out," Carrie said quickly. "That's my foot you're on."

"I thought it was a rock," Kate said.

The two sisters squatted in the ditch behind the boxwood hedge and peered anxiously through the limbs, two dark sentries in the dark of night, and waited for a white dog they did not believe existed. Behind them, in the east, the still-deep frost of morning began to coat the sky.

"He's sleeping late, like I said," Carrie whispered. "It's going to be light before long."

"Let's give him a little more time," Kate said.

A mockingbird began to sing noisily in a nearby tree. A rooster crowed from the farm of Herman Morris, far across the creek on the Goldmine ridge.

And then a light snapped on in Sam Peek's house.

"He's up," Kate said excitedly.

They watched as the bathroom light went on and, a few minutes later, the kitchen light. They could see their father at the kitchen window, hobbling slowly about on his walker.

"He's making biscuits," Kate guessed.

"Looks like it," Carrie said.

They spied impatiently as their father cooked his breakfast and then disappeared from their view to eat. In a few minutes they saw him again at the sink behind the window. They watched him lift something and, turning, make his way across the room. The light to the back porch snapped on. They heard a door open and saw him at the steps of the porch, bending to place a bowl on the steps. They heard his soft voice: "Come on, girl. Breakfast time."

"Oh, my Lord," Carrie said in a soft voice. She bit her lip to stop the surge of pity.

"Sssssh," Kate commanded. She moved closer to the hedge and pushed aside a boxwood limb.

"You see anything?" Carrie asked.

"Nothing yet," answered Kate.

Suddenly, from behind them, a dog barked sharply.

"Good Lord," Kate exclaimed, leaping to her feet.

A short, shrill scream spit from Carrie's throat. She grabbed Kate.

The dog sprinted across the road, barking happily, wagging his tail. He nudged playfully against Kate.

"Red," Kate said angrily. "How did you get—?" She heard a roll of laughter from beneath the black canopy of a pecan tree.

"Noah," Carrie snapped. "And Holman."

"Damn you, Noah," Kate yelled.

From across the yard, Sam Peek called, "What's going on out there?"

"Daddy," Carrie whispered fearfully. She dropped to her knees below the hedge. Kate dropped beside her.

"Who's out there?" he called again.

Noah and Holman stepped from the shadows of the pecan tree.

"It's just us, Mr. Sam," Noah said in a loud voice.

"Who?"

"Noah and Holman," Noah said again. He paused and smiled at the hiding Kate and Carrie. "And the girls," he added cheerfully.

"What're you doing?"

"The girls were out taking a walk," Noah called back. He began to laugh uncontrollably.

"Yes sir," Holman sang out. "The girls were out taking a walk and—and me and Noah heard a dog barking and we came out looking for them." He laughed hard, bending over, swallowing the sound.

"Where're the girls?" he asked harshly.

"Right here," Noah said.

"I don't see them," he said.

Kate and Carrie stood slowly. They glared at their husbands.

"Right here, Daddy," Kate called. She held the flashlight up.

"Here, Daddy," echoed Carrie.

"Come on up here," their father ordered.

"Damn," Kate muttered. She turned to Noah. "I'll get you for this if it takes the last breath in my body, Noah," she sputtered in a low, menacing voice.

"Come on, Kate," Carrie said.

He watched his daughters approach the house, followed by Noah and Holman. His daughters looked absurd, dressed in dark clothing, their heads covered with stocking caps, their faces smudged.

"Good God," he said. "What're you doing out this time of morning, looking like that?"

His daughters stood sheepishly before him, their faces lowered in shame.

"Well, like I said," Noah replied confidently, "the girls got it in their heads they ought to be out walking for exercise. There was something on television about it a couple of nights ago." He turned to Holman. "That's when it was, wadn't it, Holman?"

"Seems to me that's right," Holman said. A smile broke in his face like a light. He turned away.

"Anyway, it said early morning was the best time of day for it. We tried to talk them out of it, but you know how they can get, Mr. Sam."

"What's that you got all over your face?" he asked suspiciously.

"Uh," Kate muttered.

"Ah, it's—" Carrie said.

"Well, that's our doing, Mr. Sam," Noah said quickly. "Me and Holman were just pulling their legs. Told them it'd keep the bugs off them. All it is, is fireplace ashes."

"Good God," he said sorrowfully. He looked at his daughters and shook his head.

"It was Holman and Noah, Daddy," Carrie said defensively. "They were just trying to scare us. We were just—just walking."

"You want to walk, you do it in the daytime, so you can be seen," he said. "I could of shot you."

"Yes sir," Carrie whined.

"Probably scared off my dog, with all that racket," he said. "She likes to eat this time of morning."

Kate could feel tears welling in her eyes. It was sad, watching him like that, standing in the porch light, leaning heavily on his walker, looking for an imaginary dog. "We'll go home now, Daddy," she said. Then: "We won't walk any more this time of the morning."

He did not see his daughters for the rest of the day. The day was warm and clear, and he went out among his pecan trees for a short time before retiring to his padded rocking chair to rest his aching hip. At lunch he made a peanut butter sandwich and ate it and then went to the front porch to sit and watch for his white dog. The dog had been driven away, he believed, by the early-morning nonsense of his daughters. It didn't matter. She was not gone, only hiding.

In the afternoon, he napped fitfully, dreaming a nightmarish dream of his daughters wandering ethereally in their strange dress, with gray-black faces like mourners. When he awoke, the pain in his hip had increased, and he took aspiring. In early evening, he went to the front door and called for the white dog, and the dog appeared out of the tangle of the shrubbery and trotted into the house.

"Been keeping out of sight, have you?" he said to the dog. "Don't blame you. You ought to be hiding from some folks." He thought of his daughters and smiled. "Lord, they're enough to hide from sometimes."

He fed his dog and watched television and then went into the middle room to sit at his desk and write in his journal.

> Not much to say today. Kate and Carrie caused a ruckus this morning by wanting to get out and go walking when it was still dark. Noah and Holman made a joke of it but I could tell Kate and Carrie did not think it was funny. They were both spirited children and they still are. Sometimes I think they have too much spirit. My hip has hurt worse today than it has in a long time. I fixed White Dog some food, but didn't eat much myself. I hope I sleep tonight.

"Chattanooga"

Ishmael Reed

Born in Chattanooga, Tennessee, in 1938, Ishmael Reed grew up in Buffalo, New York, where he graduated from the University of Buffalo. Reed has published 28 books that include novels, plays, poetry, and essays. He is known for his thought-provoking, pugilistic satire focused primarily on the hypocrisies of American society and the African-American experience. His experimental style in both language and theme has been praised by critics and his work has been nominated for both the National Book Award and the Pulitzer Prize. In addition to writing, Reed is a teacher and commentator having taught at numerous institutions across the country including Harvard, Yale, and the University of California at Berkeley.

1

Some say that Chattanooga is the
Old name for Lookout Mountain
To others it is an uncouth name
Used only by the uncivilised
5 Our a-historical period sees it
As merely a town in Tennessee
To old timers of the Volunteer State
Chattanooga is "The Pittsburgh of
The South"
10 According to the Cherokee
Chattanooga is a rock that
Comes to a point

They're all right
Chattanooga is something you
15 Can have anyway you want it
The summit of what you are
I've paid my fare on that
Mountain Incline #2, Chattanooga
I want my ride up
20 I want Chattanooga

2

Like Nickajack a plucky Blood
I've escaped my battle near
Clover Bottom, braved the
Jolly Roger raising pirates
25 Had my near miss at Moccasin Bend
To reach your summit so
Give into me Chattanooga
I've dodged the Grey Confederate sharpshooters
Escaped my brother's tomahawks with only
30 Some minor burns
Traversed a Chickamauga of my own
Making, so
You belong to me Chattanooga

3

I take your East Ninth Street to my
35 Heart, pay court on your Market
Street of rubboard players and organ
Grinders of Haitian colors rioting
And old Zip Coon Dancers
I want to hear Bessie Smith belt out
40 I'm wild about that thing in
Your Ivory Theatre
Chattanooga
Coca-Cola's homebase
City on my mind

4

45 My 6th grade teacher asked me to
Name the highest mountain in the world
I didn't even hesitate, "Lookout Mountain"
I shouted. They laughed
Eastern nitpickers, putting on the
50 Ritz laughed at my Chattanooga ways
Which means you're always up to it

To get to Chattanooga you must
Have your Tennessee
"She has as many lives as a
55 cat. As to killing her, even
the floods have failed
you may knock the breath out of
her that's all. She will re-
fill her lungs and draw
60 a longer breath than ever"

From a Knoxville editorial—
1870s

5

Chattanooga is a woman to me too
I want to run my hands through her
65 Hair of New Jersey tea and redroot
Aint no harm in that
Be caressed and showered in
Her Ruby Falls
That's only natural
70 Heal myself in her
Minnehaha Springs
58 degrees F. all year
Around. Climb all over her
Ridges and hills
75 I wear a sign on my chest
"Chattanooga or bust"

6

"HOLD CHATTANOOGA AT ALL HAZARDS"—Grant to Thomas
When I tasted your big juicy
Black berries ignoring the rattle-
80 Snakes they said came to Cameron
Hill after the rain, I knew I
Had to have you Chattanooga
When I swam in Lincoln Park
Listening to Fats Domino sing
85 I found my thrill on Blueberry
Hill on the loudspeaker
I knew you were mine Chattanooga
Chattanooga whose Howard Negro
School taught my mother Latin
90 Tennyson and Dunbar
Whose Miller Bros. Department
Store cheated my Uncle out of
What was coming to him
A pension, he only had 6
95 Months to go
Chattanoooooooooooooooooooooga
Chattanoooooooooooooooooooooga
"WE WILL HOLD THIS TOWN TILL WE STARVE"-Thomas to Grant

7

To get to Chattanooga you must
100 Go through your Tennessee

I've taken all the scotsboros
One state can dish out
Made Dr. Shockley's "Monkey Trials"
The laughing stock of the Nation
105 Capt. Marvel Dr. Sylvanias shazam
Scientists running from light-
ning, so
Open your borders. Tennessee
Hide your TVA
110 DeSota determined, this
Serpent handler is coming
Through

Are you ready Lookout Mountain?

"Give all of my Generals what he's
115 drinking," Lincoln said, when the
Potomac crowd called Grant a lush

8
I'm going to strut all over your
Point like Old Sam Grant did
My belly full of good Tennessee
120 Whiskey, puffing on
A.05 cigar
The campaign for Chattanooga
Behind me
Breathing a spell
125 Ponying up for
Appomattox!

"Cats"
from *Creatures of Habit*

Jill McCorkle

A member of the Fellowship of Southern Writers, McCorkle has the distinction of having published her first two novels on the same day in 1984. Since then, she has published three other novels and three collections of short stories. Five of her eight books have been named New York Times notable books. Her stories have appeared in *The Atlantic, Ploughshares, Oxford American, Southern Review* and *Bomb Magazine,* among others. Two of her stories have appeared in Best American Short Stories and several have been collected in New Stories from the South. Her story, "Intervention," is in the most recent edition of the Norton Anthology of Short Fiction.

McCorkle has received the New England Book Award, The John Dos Passos Prize for Excellence in Literature and the North Carolina Award for Literature. Aside from published fiction, her essays and reviews have appeared in *The New York Times Books Review, The Washington Post, The News & Observer, Southern Living, Real Simple* and the *American Scholar.* Jill McCorkle was born in 1958 in Lumberton, North Carolina. She is a noted and acclaimed southern writer and a professor in the MFA Creative Writing at NC State. McCorkle has taught at UNC-Chapel Hill, Tufts, and Brandeis where she was the Fannie Hurst Visiting Writer. She was a Briggs-Copeland Lecturer in Fiction at Harvard for five years where she also chaired Creative Writing. She is a core faculty member of the Bennington College Writing Seminars and is a frequent instructor in the Sewanee Summer Writers Program.

A member of the Fellowship of Southern Writers, McCorkle has the distinction of having published her first two novels on the same day in 1984. Since then, she has published three other novels and three collections of short stories. Five of her eight books have been named New York Times notable books. Her stories have appeared in *The Atlantic, Ploughshares,* and *Oxford American,* among others. Two of her stories have appeared in Best American Short Stories and several have been collected in *New Stories from the South.* Her story, "Intervention," is in the most recent edition of the Norton Anthology of Short Fiction.

In addition to numerous awards in literature, her essays and reviews have appeared in *The New York Times Books Review, The Washington Post, The News & Observer, Real Simple,* and the *American Scholar.*

A

bbott is out there again and when Anne hears his feeble attempts with his key at a lock long changed, she freezes, holds her breath, hopes that this time something will occur to him, some glimpse of something will snap him back into present time and his life with the woman he left her for one April afternoon twelve years ago. The kitchen was blue then, Wedgwood blue, the place mats were straw, a wedding present from a friend in her college dorm, someone she hasn't seen since the day she married Abbott and everyone threw rice and blew kisses. As he told her the news "I'm leaving," she thought of the friend who'd given her the mats all those years ago, and about how she had no idea where she was living or what she was doing. How we let people slip from present to past, rarely looking back.

"Anne," he said. "Did you hear what I just said?"

She remembers nodding as he told her what she had been waiting to hear. There was someone else. Though, he added, the someone was not, of course, the reason he was leaving. Their marriage would be ending even if there weren't another woman. She wanted to ask a simple *then why?* but couldn't get the words up and over her tongue. Their sons had been at school and the noon sun streamed through the very window that had made her want to buy the house to begin with, a big bay window—big enough for hanging plants—casting a warm patch of light in the center of the room. The boys were eight and ten then, and when they got home that day, they found her sitting in the kitchen, a pile of unraveled straw on the table in front of her. They told her she looked just like the girl in "Rumpelstiltskin" and then they made awful faces and begged her to guess their names. She missed their big fat cat, who used to curl up in the sunshine and sleep through the day. She missed the ease with which she could pacify the boys when they were babies, how she had once had the power to make everything in their lives okay.

Now the boys are twenty and twenty-two, both in college, both with girlfriends. Now the divorced CEO of the hospital where she works as a physical therapist occasionally shares her bed. He would move in if she invited him. He would marry her in a second if she gave him the go-ahead, and her friends all issue warnings that she better not keep him waiting too long, that he is bound to give up one of these days and find another house in which to take up residence. Everyone thinks she is holding out so that Abbott has to keep sending money. The new wife tells anyone who will listen how Anne is intentionally bleeding them dry. That's not true. Sometimes she isn't sure what is true.

Though she lives on in the same house, she sleeps in a different room, an addition she worked and saved to build after Abbott had left and moved in across town and started a whole new family. Anne herself had been the new younger wife and the newest was even younger.

She turned their old bedroom into a rumpus room and let it evolve along with the boys: puppet theater and LEGO blocks, pool table and stereo speakers. She painted it azure; they painted it black. And during each incarnation she remained aware of its original status; her mind never released the position of the bed, the way the light bathed the room in the late afternoon, a time they had often—whenever life permitted—allowed themselves the luxury of a nap. It was during those times she felt—if only for a second—the satisfied reassurance that she had made no mistake when she agreed to marry him.

People from far away who loved her began calling as soon as word reached them that Abbott had left. They called to say *come home come home*, and she was tempted. The home of her childhood was waiting just a few hours down the interstate. Sometimes at night she got herself to sleep picturing the town—flatland and tobacco barns, billboards calling her to the coast. She thought of those summer nights when she was a kid and had nothing to do but ride her bike through the streets of her hometown.

But by then home needed to be where her children were at home. Home had become the Japanese maple she planted and when they bought the house and the roses she had trained up a trellis by the garage. So she had changed what she could afford to change. The sheets. The paint. She adopted a kind old yellow Lab to replace the cat in their marriage, Possum, on whom she had completely doted until Abbott was ready to have a child. The cat's death, twelve years after their wedding, coincided with Abbott's straying, and the two events were forever linked in her mind. The old Lab lived long enough to help her through the transition.

"Probably coyote or raccoon chow," he had said and shaken his head as she and the children wept over Possum's disappearance. "After twelve years, old Possum is nothing but a cheap lunch."

That comment and the scent on his face and neck when he came home from God knows where—he said golf, he said baseball, he said auto show, places she never went with him—told her that he was not who she had thought he was. He had become a stranger. This was what she was thinking as she picked her way through the wooded strip of land that separated their yard from the yards of yet another new neighborhood. In these woods the wild creatures had their own lairs, their own food supply. She could feel them watching her from their dark holes and caves as they waited for night to fall. That there had been no sign of Possum had made her feel hopeful even though deep down she knew better.

And now Abbott is back, twisting and turning the knob with his own persistent optimism. She dries her hands and opens the door to his tired bewildered face. His wife always comes to lead him away like a confused child. Her appearance, however fraught with anger and frustration, seems to call him back into his present life, but until she shows up, he is back in their marriage. He asks where the boys are. He leans in and kisses her lips, pulls her close before she can catch her breath and step aside. He picks up on a conversation they had over a dozen years ago. How he's thinking about opening his own business. How he's thinking he should buy all the little drive-through buildings left behind by a defunct bank. How he will stock them with late-night necessities: milk and aspirin, diapers and toilet paper, beer and tampons. Twenty-four-hour service. Drive right through. People don't have to get dressed; they don't have to lift the baby out of the car. WHATEVER GETS YOU THROUGH THE NIGHT. The slogan was hers. The dream was his, one of fast fortune. There were many nights when she was all alone and believed more than ever that they had devised a brilliant plan. Necessities: those wee hours of the morning when a kid's fever spiked and not a drop of Tylenol in the house, or times when she realized that there would be no milk for her morning coffee.

In all the years since Abbott left, Anne has not slept a whole night through. Usually she wakes at two, sometimes three. Even with her CEO lying beside her, she often can't keep herself from playing through the nights she lay there with Abbott, the tension between them so thick she felt she might strangle on it, so thick it forced her awake, the beginnings of the chronic habit. There is a time in a woman's life when being a mother may be all that she can successfully be, with her mind so fragmented by thoughts of fevers and stitches and homework and Little League. Laundry and cleaning, shopping and cooking. A bath is a luxury. Sleep, the greatest luxury of all. He kept commenting on how she had changed. She knew what was going on was what had changed. She could almost pinpoint the day he came home with a different look about him. She could smell the deception, but she didn't have proof. Night after night, she had lain beside him wanting anything he could give her: a confession, an apology, a profession of his love even with the admission of his inability to remain faithful. Now she hated the part of herself that over the years still refused to let go of a love that he refused to return. She hated the part of herself that delighted in the fate of the young unencumbered women that so many men who stray manage to find. A year, maybe two and then *that* woman is also encumbered, only this time he has someone who is too young to share his memories. She was disgusted with the part of herself that pictured Abbott in such a state of aloneness.

Her great-aunt Rosemary was fond of saying that by and large marriage is an unnatural state. Anne resisted the notion and clung to the natural history of certain rare monogamous creatures in the wild—the prairie vole, the purple martin, geese—even while she secretly believed Rosemary was probably right. Why else do women so easily settle in with their litters and nests; why do the females in nature blend into the background while the males remain flashy and continue life as sexual predators? Why was man created to continue giving life while women ran out of time, ran out of eggs?

I am indispensable, she thought one night when the coyotes' blood-chilling cries kept her awake. *A temporary shelter, a brief stop on a very long journey.*

Now she slips the cordless phone into her pocket and goes into the bathroom to call Abbott's wife while he murmurs to himself about how great everything looks, how neat and clean. She closes the bathroom door, leaving just enough of a crack that she can see his shadow, hear his footsteps. She plans to once again whisper into the receiver *He's here, I have him*, but then there is no answer, and his voice—strong and coherent—on the answering machine startles her and she hangs up.

Over a year ago, her sons had told her there were problems. At first they thought he had had a stroke of some kind. Then a brain tumor. There had been a CAT scan, all kinds of tests. He was just that unlucky person, a man barely sixty in the throes of dementia.

"But isn't he too young for this?" she had asked his young wife.

"Yes," she said, her eyes lined and weary. Their children—a boy and a girl—were barely in junior high.

"And *I'm* too young for this," the wife added, then she caught herself and softened. She spoke then as if reciting from a medical textbook, spoke of her support group and how most of the others were a lot older and yet it did happen. One in a zillion. "Lucky huh?" she asked. "And think about genetics, will you? Your children and my children." She said all of this with Abbott right there in the next room. She said, "*your* children and *my* children," the business of women.

"I'll be there soon," the wife had said last time. She hesitated. "Maybe if you stopped letting him in…"

But he might get lost. He might get hit by a car. He might get mugged, she wanted to say.

When Anne was a child her great-aunt Rosemary had had a cat who wandered, a gigantic yellow-and-white tom named Pumpkin Pie who regularly came home beaten and battered. Nobody got their male cats fixed back then. They were allowed to go about their business, spraying and screwing and prowling the streets. Everyone in the neighborhood knew Pumpkin Pie by name. They would feed and pet him; sometimes in the winter he'd be invited in to snooze by a fire. Sometimes the call of nature and a female cat in heat was more than he could bear and some well-intentioned neighbor would have to turn a hose on him. Rosemary painted his battle wounds with Mercurochrome, bright orange splotches on his silky white fur. In winter, Pumpkin Pie used to climb up and snuggle down near the engine of a recently driven car. But one night he wound up riding all the way across town. When he climbed out and ran away, Anne's great-uncle, a man too old for running, tried to follow and catch him. In vain. They mourned and blamed one another; Rosemary locked herself in the bathroom and sobbed. Then three weeks to the day, there he was again, clawing on the screen door and crying, one ear ripped and bleeding.

"Marriage goes against nature," Rosemary had said. She sat stroking the big tom, the white of his throat bright orange with Mercurochrome. "The tom wants to roam while the missus stays home with the little ones until they pull her old teats to death. Then she just wants to stay home. I myself have always just wanted to stay at home."

Anne had told the boys about Pumpkin Pie and his trip across town, stoking any lingering hopes that Possum had met a similar fate, or that some well-meaning neighbor had let her in and would soon read her tag and call to say that she was fine. "Unless she lost her tag," Abbott added, giving all three of them hard leveled stares. "Then we may never learn what happened. If so, it can't be helped. It can't be changed."

He was right, of course. It could have been an animal, could have been a car. Anyway, someone was nice enough to take the body to a veterinarian. They had her in the freezer if Anne would like to come and claim the body. They had some Polaroids so she could make a positive ID; the tag was close by but not on the cat's neck at the time it was found. They strongly advised that she not look at the body. "Better to remember her as she was," the teenage attendant recited handing Anne the box.

She built Possum a little mausoleum, easy enough on that frigid February afternoon. A little spit for mortar and the bricks froze solid. Without ever looking under the wrappings, she put the body into her biggest Tupperware and sealed the lid; she could not stand the thought of some hungry creature digging up what little bit remained. And then she just sat there. Anne had a lot in common with Possum. Black hair with the occasional streak of gray, voluntary sterilization. (She liked to believe that is what Possum—at least in those later years—would have chosen for herself as well.) They both appreciate fine wool fabrics and warm spots in front of windows.

She had put the Tupperware down into the little brick cave just as Abbott was about to go out that dark late afternoon. His breath formed a cloud as he called out to her. He had a dinner meeting, hoped it wouldn't go on too long, but he never knew. He was wearing a new shirt, a shade of green that brought out the green of his eyes. She'd bought him a sweater that shade one Christmas that he had refused to wear, clinging staunchly to a wardrobe of khaki and navy, the occasional burgundy or gray. "Men don't wear this kind of color," he'd said. She thought about that as she watched him drive away. *Men don't primp and preen and wear that kind of color unless there is someone new out there asking for it, someone waiting for a sign.*

By that springtime afternoon when he broke the news in the kitchen, she was almost relieved, she had waited so long for him to tell her the truth. Anything is better than the waiting, she told herself as she stared out the window where Possum's brick tomb had thawed and toppled to one side. And after he left with most of his personal belongings already piled on the backseat of his car, and before the boys got home, she did what she was not supposed to do. She looked. She peeled back the soggy layers of towel and stared down at what had once been Possum. There was absolutely nothing familiar left.

Every time the wife came after him, her eyes seemed to say *This is supposed to be your life.* Did her eyes also say *Do you want him back?*

The wife looked all around Anne's house, maybe looking for old traces of her husband, or maybe in awe of the order a single woman with grown children can bring to a home. A calm. A peacefulness. The wife was drawn to a framed photograph of Anne and her CEO and then to a small picture of Anne and Abbott at the beach with the boys—a picture taken three years before the end; it was the one photo of him that she had never managed to put away. It reminded her of a time when trust and faith meant everything.

But today, Anne lets time pass before calling again. Abbott is standing in the doorway of her room looking at the bed.

"Okay," he finally says. "Something's different."

"No," she says, "nothing's changed."

"C'mon, you can say." He goes and stands by the window. "Anne?" He calls her name as if testing it over his tongue, then repeats it. "Anne, how many years..." he pauses, shakes his head.

"Since we moved in?" she asks, and he nods, still clearly unsure of his question.

"Almost twenty years," she answers him. It's not a lie.

"It's good." He leans his face against the glass pane. His shoulders are slightly hunched, thinner than she remembers, his corduroys loose through the hips.

"Yes, I think so, too." She goes and puts her arm around his waist and he returns the gesture while still staring out at the small backyard. In a few minutes she really will have to call his wife. She may already be driving over, frantic and worried, just blocks away, coming once again to claim him. But for now Anne can't seem to move away from the warm afternoon light that fills her room.

"Here, lie down." She leads him over to the bed and then stretches out beside him. When he rolls over to take her in his arms, she sees the change in his eyes, faint traces of what she once knew. He pulls her closer, burying his face in her neck, his breath warm, his heart beating against her chest. Same heart. Same rhythm. It is the most natural thing in the world.

"Rest," she whispers, her hand stroking the hair back from his forehead, then slowly moving to the warmth of his neck. She moves her hand down his back and then inches her fingers under his belt and along the edge of his pants, teasing only to then pop the elastic of his boxers. It was an old joke; it was *their* old joke and her need to repeat it seems an involuntary act, one that makes him laugh and hug her tighter. And then in the very next second, he is on the verge of crying. "What will we do now?" he asks and shakes his head, a look of total defeat washing over him. "What can we do?"

"Rest," she says. "Just rest." She waits for him to close his eyes and for his breath to fall into rhythm of sleep, his fingers still linked through her own. She knows she needs to call. She knows he is not hers to keep even though she would like nothing better than to believe that at the end of his long journey, after all was said and done, that what he wanted more than anything in the world was to come home.

Student Essay on *Creatures of Habit:* (The student essay below is based on another story from Jill McCorkle's *Creatures of Habit* called "Billy Goats.")

Richard Norwood

Professor

ENGL 1020

February 13, 2014

False Face: The Sinister Reputation of a Small Town

All communities may harbor dark secrets: dismal myths of appalling crime and painful loss. Within a small town, such secrets may be known to all who live there. In Jill McCorkle's "Billy Goats," an example of a small community's secrets and their associated stories is revealed. Through the locations and people identified by each different story, a setting like this illustrates an idea of the power of rumor, and how it may encapsulate and influence the day-to-day lives of its inhabitants. Within McCorkle's small town of Fulton, North Carolina, a number of ominous tales have rooted themselves in the minds of the locals. Places with tragic tales of the past, children's frightening rumors of the present, and fearful whispers of gossip are but a few of the dark ideas that quickly spread within this small setting.

Throughout "Billy Goats," many locations within the town are connected with an often sinister story. Houses are defined by "histories of death, divorce, [and] disaster," and parking lots are said to be the sites of many shocking rendezvous (2). One house is described as the "murder-suicide house," said to be the site of a gruesome tragedy which involved a couple who agreed to commit suicide together (5). At another house, even something as menial and insignificant as an iron fence takes on a haunting image, still associated with its gory role in a horrible car accident long past (7). Every different place has its own distinct tale, and because of this, the town and its many locales take on a life of their own. These rumors have the power to take hold of the hearts, minds, and fears of the town's inhabitants. All through the story, the narrator is consistently speaking in a dark manner that is indicative of the lasting effects of these rumors and experiences. An appropriate illustration of this is when the narrator states that she and her friends "learned a lot about murder that year," and that they "did have to wonder about death" (7,8,9). The town's locations and their stories hold significant amounts of power on the mind. They spread and grow, and soon became the dominant subject of conversation at social gatherings (7).

Children in this small town are revealed to be also quite capable of spreading fearful rumors themselves. Groups of friends sit together, telling their own sinister stories of accidents, murders and suicides in hushed voices (5). From there the children could leave and spread their stories even further, quickly infecting the small town with these tales. Whether they deal with reports of brutal images from the local hospital, or unspoken fears surrounding a neighborhood storm drain, the business of rumor is theirs (3). One child, described as "the freckled boy," even develops a reputation as the one they "counted on to bring [them] the kind of news that left [them] weak in the knees and too nervous to sleep" (3,4). Without a doubt, the children of this town in "Billy Goats" further prove that such a small community can quickly become a breeding ground of grim tales and rumors.

In a town like Fulton, certain citizens may become the prey of these rumors. The size of the city makes it easy for this to happen, with gossip quickly moving from place to place and home to home. One such citizen is Hank Carter, described as a "genius who 'crossed the line'" (5). The local children sometimes stand around, attempting to catch a glimpse of the man the rumors make him out to be (12). In reality, a character like Hank is an example of how a small town can shape the image of its citizens. He is a part of the community, and his life is a part of its story. The small town made him who he was, and whether they be about his once promising future or lost loves, rumors of his past follow him wherever he goes (14). In the end, it is not until after his death that the townsfolk realize how essential he was to their home, " . . .helping at accidents or collecting litter along the highway or just riding his motorbike through town" (17). This small town setting reveals that a single person can become an icon to many.

McCorkle's "Billy Goats" is more than an appropriate illustration of a small American town. It intensifies the plot of the story by creating a setting where rumors may quickly spread and grow. A place where each location has a history, local children spread shady reports and rumors from around town, and gossip shapes the images of its citizens. In conclusion, though the town may be small, the secrets and stories it holds are far greater and more powerful than they would be in a large city.

Work Cited

McCorkle, Jill. "Billy Goats." *Creatures of Habit.* New York: Algonquin, 2001.

Excerpt from
All Over But the Shoutin'

Rick Bragg

Rick Bragg won the Pulitzer Prize for Feature Writing in 1996 for his work at The New York Times. Born in Piedmont, Alabama, in 1959, Mr. Bragg is the author of two best-selling memoirs, *All Over But the Shoutin'* and *Ava's Man*, as well as *The Prince of Frogtown* and a biography, *Jerry Lee Lewis: His Own Story.* His most recent book is *My Southern Journey.* Bragg credits his writing ability to the oral storytelling of family and friends in his childhood in the Appalachian foothills of Alabama. Bragg has told stories and taught writing at Harvard University, the Poynter Institute for Media Studies, Boston University, the University of South Florida, and many other colleges.

Bragg attended Harvard University as a Nieman Fellow from 1992 to 1993 ("the only real college I ever had") and in addition to his Pulitzer Prize, he is the recipient of the American Society of Newspaper Editors Distinguished Writing Award and 31 other national, regional and state writing awards. He has had stories included in Best Newspaper Writing 1991, Best of the Press 1988, and two journalism textbooks on good writing and foreign reporting.

He now works as a writing professor at the University of Alabama's journalism program in its College of Communications and Information Sciences.

I used to stand amazed and watch the redbirds fight. They would flash and flutter like scraps of burning rags through a sky unbelievably blue, swirling, soaring, plummeting. On the ground they were a blur of feathers, stabbing for each other's eyes. I have seen grown men stop what they were doing, stop pulling corn or lift their head out from under the hood of a broken-down car, to watch it. Once, when I was little, I watched one of the birds attack its own reflection in the side mirror of a truck. It hurled its body again and again against that unyielding image, until it pecked a crack in the glass, until the whole mirror was smeared with blood. It was as if the bird hated what it saw there, and discovered too late that all it was seeing was itself. I asked an old man who worked for my uncle Ed, a snuff-dipping man named Charlie Bivens, why he reckoned that bird did that. He told me it was just its nature.

This is not an important book. It is only the story of a strong woman, a tortured man and three sons who lived hemmed in by thin cotton and ragged history in northeastern Alabama, in a time when blacks and whites found reason to hate each other and a whole lot of people could not stand themselves. Anyone could tell it, anyone with a daddy who let his finer nature slip away from him during an icebound war in Korea, who allowed the devil inside him to come grinnin' out every time a sip of whiskey trickled in, who finally just abandoned his young wife and sons to the pity of their kin and to the well-meaning neighbors who came bearing boxes of throwaway clothes.

Anyone could tell it, anyone who had a momma who went eighteen years without a new dress so that her sons could have school clothes, who picked cotton in other people's fields and ironed other people's clothes and cleaned the mess in other people's houses, so that her children didn't have to live on welfare alone, so that one of them could climb up her backbone and escape the poverty and hopelessness that ringed them, free and clean.

Anyone could tell it, and that's the shame of it. A lot of women stood with babies on their hips in line for commodity cheese and peanut butter. A lot of men were damaged deep inside by the killing and dying of wars, then tried to heal themselves with a snake oil elixir of sour mash and self-loathing. A lot of families just came to pieces in that time and place and condition, like paper lace in a summer rain. You can walk the main street in any small town, in any big one, and you will hear this story being told behind cigarette-scarred bars, before altars, over fresh-dug ground in a thousand cemeteries. You hear it from the sixty-five-year-old woman with the blank eyes who wipes the tables at the Waffle House, and by the used-up men with Winstons dangling from their lips who absently, rhythmically swing their swingblades at the tall weeds out behind the city jail.

This story is important only to me and a few people who lived it, people with my last name. I tell it because there should be a record of my momma's sacrifice even if it means unleashing ghosts, because it is one of the few ways I can think of—beyond financing her new false teeth and making sure the rest of her life is without the deprivations of her past—to repay her for all the suffering and indignity she absorbed for us, for me. And I tell it because I can, because it is how I earn my paycheck, now at the *New York Times*, before at so many other places, telling stories. It is easy to tell a stranger's story; I didn't know if I had the guts to tell my own.

This is no sob story. While you will read words laced with bitterness and killing anger and vicious envy, words of violence and sadness and, hopefully, dark humor, you will not read much whining. Not on her part, certainly, because she does not know how.

I have been putting this off for ten years, because it was personal, because dreaming backwards can carry a man through some dark rooms where the walls seem lined with razor blades. I put if off and put it off until finally something happened to scare me, to hurry me, to make me grit my teeth and remember.

It was death that made me hurry, but not my father's. He died twenty years ago, tubercular, his insides pickled by whiskey and beer. Being of long memory, my momma, my brothers and I did not go to the cemetery to sing hymns or see him remanded to the red clay. We placed no flowers on his grave. Our momma went alone to the funeral home one night, when it was just him and her.

No, the death that made me finally sit down to write was that of my grandmother, my mother's mother, Ava, whom we all called by her pet name, Abigail. Miss Ab, who after enduring eighty-six years of this life and a second childhood that I truly believed would last forever, died of pneumonia two days before Thanksgiving, 1994. The night her grown children gathered around her bed in the small community hospital in Calhoun County, Alabama, I was in New Orleans, writing about the deaths of strangers.

I was sitting in a cramped living room in a crumbling housing project, listening to a hollow-eyed and pitiful young woman tell how her little boy had been killed one morning by a stray bullet as he stood in the doorway, his book satchel in his hand, like a little man going to work. She told me how the Dr. Seuss and Winnie the Pooh just fell out on the stoop, how the boy looked up at her after the bullet hit, wide-eyed, wondering. And as she talked, her two surviving children rode tight circles around the couch on their bicycles, because she was afraid to let them play outside in the killing ground of the project courtyard. As I left, shaking her limp hand, she thanked me. I usually just nod my head politely and move on, struck anew every time by the graciousness of people in such a soul-killing time. But this time, I had to ask why. Why thank me for scribbling down her hopeless story for the benefit of people who live so far and safely away from this place where the gunfire twinkles like lightning bugs after dark? She answered by pulling out a scrapbook of her baby's death, cut from the local newspaper. "People remembers it," she said. "People forgets if it ain't wrote down."

I reckon so.

The next morning, one of those hotel mornings when it takes you a few uneasy seconds to remember where you are and what you are doing there, the phone shook me awake. You always look at it a second before you reach for it, because it is often the slingshot that sends you hurtling toward a place like Oklahoma City, where you walk quietly and respectfully among the rubble and blood and baby shoes scattered by a monster's bomb, or to some obscure dateline like Union, South Carolina, and into the mind of a young mother who drowned her two sons in a dark lake. And the monstrous thing is that you secretly hope that it is something like that, not something dull.

But this time the summons, the death I was called to, was personal. My grandmother, who fried me whole boneyards of chicken, who got mildly drunk on her prescriptions, played "Boilin' Cabbage Down" on the banjo and stomped so hard on the planks it sounded like Jehovah pounding at the door, was gone. All her songs and sayings, all the beautiful things that filled her, warmed her, were quiet.

I had known she was sick. But my kin, hopeful she would recover, told me not to come home yet, told me she would be there when I came home Thanksgiving. But I came home to a coldly modern funeral home, to the people of our community sitting quietly in their pews, white socks peeking out from under black dress pants. There were not a lot of people, but the ones who came would have been important to her. There were third-cousins who had not seen her in years but gave up half a day's pay at the mill to be there; an old drunk who sobered up for her out of respect and sat pale and quietly shaking in the back pew; an ancient, hawk-nosed, hard-eyed man who had not seen her since he was young, but remembered she had once poured him a glass of buttermilk, or was it coffee? and old women who used to sit beside her on the porch, cutting okra, holding grandbabies, telling lies. These were people who remembered the weight of the cotton sack, people with grease under their fingernails that no amount of Octagon soap would ever scrub away, people who built redwood decks on their mobile homes and have no idea that smart-aleck Yankees think that is somehow funny. People of the pines. My people.

I came home to a pale and elegant body in an open coffin, her thin hands crossed on her breast. As I said, I have made my living in graveyards of spirit, in the blasted-out, crack-infested streets of Miami's Liberty City, in the insane hallways of Manhattan's welfare hotels, in the projects in Birmingham and the reeking oceanfront slums of Port-au-Prince and on death rows in three states. I have seen so many horrible things in so many horrible places that I have suspicions about God and doubts about heaven, but in that funeral home, I found myself wishing for it, envisioning it. I bet even God, unless He is an Episcopalian, likes a little fais-do-do every now and then, and I like to think of her Up There, blowing a hurricane on her harmonica and singing a little too loud.

A million sights and sounds rang through my head as I stared down at her. I thought about the times when I was still a little boy, no more than five, when she would let me sleep at the foot of her bed so we could listen to her Philco, how I drifted off to sleep with the tinny voices of Faron Young, Little Jimmy Dickens, Bill Monroe and Mother Maybelle Carter in chorus inside my head. It was one of the benefits of being old, she told me: "You can play your radio all damn night long if you want to, and no one can do a damn thing about it." Like everyone in that part of the world, she had been enraptured by a young, thin man from Mount Olive, Alabama, who sang with a twisted spine and a tortured spirit, and she would whirl the dial, over and over, searching for his words.

I've never seen a night so long
When time goes crawling by
The moon just went behind the clouds
To hide his face and cry

She told me she saw Hank Williams once, back before he died. But she was flying pretty high on her medicine that night and might had told a lie, since she felt that another benefit of old age was that it gave you license to lie like a Republican. But it was then, as that dead man's poetry ran through my mind, as I stared down at that old woman I had seen for just a few hours a year on Thanksgiving and Christmas because I wrongly believed I was doing more important things, that I knew I should not wait any longer to write some of this down, whether anyone ever read it or not.

It is not something I can go look up in a book. Poor people in the South do not make many historical registers unless we knock some rich man off his horse. It is not something I can research standing over the silence of graves. My mother is only sixty, but I cannot take the chance of squandering the knowledge and the stories that she and my people hold inside them, even if—as in the case of my father—some of it is sad and dark as the darkest night.

I miss my grandma most when I drive the back roads of the Deep South, the radio tuned to fiddle music on the Cotton States Network down around Troy, or to some wall-rattling black choir on the AM dial outside Hattiesburg. It is when I have long hours to look, think, remember. I know that any time I want to hear the rest of that haunted song, all I have to do is put on the record. But I want her to sing it to me. After all the dying I have seen, I finally understand what death is: simple wanting. My grandma would have added some happiness to this book, and although her mind had clouded considerably in the past few years—she would ask me how my wife was, and I haven't been married for ten years—she would have remembered for me, set me straight on some things. Maybe, if I tell it right, she will live again in these pages, that all the things she could have shared about who we are, who I am, will not be so badly missed. I like to believe that.

I already know a good bit about my history, stories that were seldom written down, only passed from one to another of us over cones of strawberry ice cream in the gravel parking lot of the tiny store owned by a one-legged man named Tillison. I heard them over the ring of guitar strings on the front porch, over the endless, beautiful, hateful rows of cotton that I still dream about even today, even though the fields lie in trash and weeds.

I know I was born during one of those periods when my father had abandoned my mother or driven her away, that—I still do not know whether to laugh or cry about this—he did not bother to come and see me until I was almost two years old. I know he brought a stuffed panda bear as big as God, and I dragged it around by one leg until he was one-eared and his cotton stuffing leaked out and his eyes fell off. And I remember running with it, too heavy, when I was a few years older, running down a road in the night, from him.

I know I grew up in the time when a young man in a baggy suit and slicked-down hair stood spraddle-legged in the crossroads of history and talked hot and mean about the colored, giving my poor and desperate people a reason to feel superior to some-body, to anybody. I know that even as the words of George Wallace rang through my Alabama, the black family who lived down the dirt road from our house sent fresh-picked corn and other food to the poor white lady and her three sons, because they knew their daddy had run off, because hungry does not have a color.

I know that a few weeks later he whirled through our house in a drunken rage, and as always our momma just absorbed it, placing herself like a wall between her husband and sons. I know that later my brother Sam and I lay in the dark safety of our bedroom and tried to figure out a way to kill a grown man, before he hurt her any more.

I know that I had a third brother, an infant who died because we were left alone and with no money for her to see a doctor, that he did not live long enough to have a name. I know his gravestone just reads Baby Bragg and my momma never mentioned him to us, for thirty years, but carried his memory around deep inside her, like a piece of broken glass.

I know that my grandfather on my momma's side, Abigail's husband, was a strong and good man, who tried the last years of his life to protect her from him, and the fact I never knew my grandfather, never saw his face, is one of the great regrets of my life. I know he was a hardworking roofer who made a little whiskey now and then in a still that sent a perfume into the pines that could knock sparrows from the sky. I know he once was forced to shoot a big woman through both buzzoms with a .410 deer slug because she and her brothers came at him with butcher knives, and that when I inquired as to whether the woman died, my aunt Gracie Juanita only said: "Lord no, hon. Went clean through."

I know that I was surrounded in that later part of my childhood by the love of aunts and uncles, that my aunt Gracie Juanita used to feed me tea cakes and tell me that the chicken cooking in her kitchen was buzzard, and then we would sit and eat and talk about how, *mmmm-mmmm*, that buzzard sure was tasty; that every Friday my aunt Mary Jo would haul us to PeeWee Johnson's Dixie Dip for a foot-long hot dog that is still the best thing I have ever had, better'n anything in New York, crème brûlée or no crème brûlée. I know my aunt Edna fried crappie for us and picked the bones out so we would not choke. I know my aunt Sue rocked and walked me to sleep, but lost her grip on me once and I fell headfirst on the fireplace stones, which could explain a lot of things.

I know that my mother's brother, Uncle Jimbo, once won a twenty-dollar bet by eating a bologna sandwich while sitting on a dead mule. I know he drove a Nash Rambler with a naked lady hood ornament, that my aunt Gracie Juanita was so mortified that she painted a bathing suit over the chromed body. I know that you never ever traded cars with my uncle Bill unless you wanted to walk home.

I know that my mother was not afraid of much—I watched her do in a four-foot rattlesnake with a broken-handled rake and a Red Ryder BB gun—and that she could have handled life with my father, if it had just been him and her, without the ghosts. They came from him in the winter, mostly. I could see them only in my father's almost pathological fear of cold, in his hatred of ice. I saw them on a winter day in 1965, when my little brother stepped through the ice on a tiny, shallow pond, when my daddy snatched him up and ran all the way to the house, his face white as frost.

I know that my father had not always been the tortured man of my childhood, that when he started courting my momma, a tall, serenely beautiful woman who looked like a 1940s movie star, he had worn black penny loafers with dimes in them and pants with creases sharp enough to slice bologna. I know he had once been just a slight, dark, part Cherokee man who had a reputation for being a little too quick to pull his knife, who could not hold his liquor, but who consumed life in great gulps. I know he liked to hear his brother-in-law pick the guitar, that he liked to see dogs and chickens fight, and a pretty woman dance.

And I know that something happened to him in those years when he was a marine in Korea, something involving a bitter cold night in a place he could not spell or even pronounce. And I know that after that he was too often mean and cold, and kept a secret that he only talked about when he was either knee-walkin' drunk or scared of dying, like he was at the end, when he called me to his side and told it.

I know a good bit. But one of the best men I have ever known told me once that to tell a story right you have to lean the words against each other so that they don't all fall down, and I needed more words, more facts. I spent a year just talking to the people close to me, filling in the holes in my memory.

I would not have written it at all if my momma had said no. I asked if I should, and I warned her that for every smile it evoked it would bring an equal number of tears. She was quiet a minute, staring out the window of the car. "Write it," she said. "I sat quiet, for fifty years."

The biggest reason for writing this story is to set one thing straight from now on. My momma believes that she failed, that her three sons, being all she has ever had, did not get enough of the fine things in life because she was our mother. My older brother, Sam, has worked like a dog his whole life, in the coal yard and clay pits when he was eleven, with a pick and shovel and yard rake when he was a young man, and now in the cotton mill. If he has ever had a full day of rest in his life, I cannot remember when. She blames herself for that.

My younger brother, Mark, has known the inside of jails. He is a hard drinker and fighter who bears the long scars of knife wounds on his body and still carries a bullet in one arm, who seems to have somehow absorbed the spirit of the father he cannot even remember. She blames herself for that.

Then there is me, the newspaperman who, through the leg-up that she gave him and a series of happy accidents, wound up at the temple of this profession, working under legends. I am no better, no worse than my brothers; in fact, they are both smarter than me. But the truth is that I am proud of who and what I am, just as proud of being the son of a woman who picked cotton and took in ironing as I am of working for a place like the *New York Times*. I have always believed that one could not have been without the other. My job has carried me to see things seldom seen by a country boy, without a white-trash, first-pick draft notice, to the other side of the world and into the same columned mansions where my momma used to clean bathrooms. When I was a man of thirty-three they even let me into Harvard, and I was not holding a mop. When I was thirty-six, I won the highest honor our professions bestows.

I hope she blames herself for that, too.

I hope she sees some of her backbone in me, because without it I would have been more accepting of the words of others, of the editor who once looked me dead in the eye and told me I was not sophisticated enough to cover the Anniston, Alabama, city council, of one or two Yankee reporters who allowed that I was mildly talented in a quaint Southern way, of a high school teacher who said a boy like me ought to think about a good trade school. It was my momma who said, "Don't never take nothin' off nobody." And while it was my daddy who taught me to fight dirty, she was the one who taught me not to give a damn when it hurt.

I hope she sees some of her gentleness and sensitivity in my words, because if there is any of that in me still, it came from her. In an important way, her sadness is in every story I write. I have written mostly about people whose lives came and went on tides of whim, apathy and cruelty. Some reporters know Washington. I know this. I have, heaven help me, a talent for it. I have never felt so at home as I did in Haiti, where little girls with dead eyes hold your hands and whisper about fathers who were shot in the back of the head by grinning soldiers. I walked through neighborhoods in my own country where the killing is done with laughter, acting like I was ten feet tall and bulletproof even as my legs trembled, because I believe that if we are going to write about life and death, we should not do it from the cheap seats.

I believe I was drawn to those stories because of her; because of all the lessons my mother tried to teach me, the most important was that every life deserves a certain amount of dignity, no matter how poor or damaged the shell that carries it. The only time I ever made her truly ashamed of me was the day I made fun of a boy from a family that was even poorer than us. His daddy had shaved his head to cheat the lice, and I laughed at him, made fun of him, until I saw the look in my momma's eyes.

So, this story is for her, as have been, in smaller ways, all the stories I have ever told and the method in which I told them. I would like to be able to say, with trite and silly melodrama, that I am sorry that my father did not live to see his son's name on a book. But that would be a bigger lie than I can tell, sober. I will not track the muck of cheap sentimentality into this story by saying that it will be in any way an instrument for healing. I understand him better now, understand the pounding his character endured in that defining time overseas. But somewhere between understanding and forgiveness there is another wall, too wide to get around.

The errors in this book that I know of are omissions, not fabrications, intended to spare people who have enough pain in their lives, a little more.

After my grandmother's funeral I strolled over to his tiny headstone in a corner of the cemetery in Jacksonville. I still wonder sometimes to whom the Marines handed the triangle of American flag that had draped his coffin. I do not want it. I only wonder. I noticed that someone had cared enough to come by and pluck the weeds and wild onions from the grave, to put a pink silk flower in a vase, and I wondered about that, too. But if there was any real regret in me, I could not find it. There was no pain to speak of, I think because the dead place inside me where my father resides is shiny and slick and perfectly symmetrical, polished by a lifetime. It is not pain so much as a sculpture of it. It is hard to the touch, but smooth.

No, this is not an important book. The people who know about books call it a memoir, but that is much too fancy a word for me, for her, for him. It is only a story of a handful of lives, in which one tall, blond woman, her back forever bent by the pull of that sack, comes off looking good and noble, and a dead man gets to answer for himself from deep in the ground. In these pages I will make the dead dance again with the living, not to get at any great truth, just a few little ones. It is still a damn hard thing to do, when you think about it.

God help me, Momma, if I am clumsy.

A page from
Darkroom: A Memoir in Black and White

Lila Quintero Weaver

Lila Quintero Weaver is the author-illustrator of a debut graphic novel that explores the connections between immigration and race, *Darkroom: A Memoir in Black and White* (The University of Alabama Press, 2012). Darkroom is the story of Weaver's family's immigration to the American South from Argentina in 1961 when she was five years old. Their arrival in Alabama coincided with significant developments in the Civil Rights Movement, including a the dismantling of Jim Crow laws, a night of racial violence that exploded one block from the family's back door, and a tense and protracted period of public school desegregation. Because Weaver is also a lifelong dabbler in the visual arts, she created *Darkroom* as a graphic novel through her own hand-drawn images.

A native of Buenos Aires, Argentina, Lila Quintero Weaver grew up in Alabama, where she still resides with her husband. She holds a Bachelor's degree from the University of Alabama. *Darkroom*, her first book, was named a finalist in the Small Press Expo's Ignatz 2012 award for "Promising New Talent" and listed in Notable Books for a Global Society by the Children's Literature & Reading Special Interest Group of the International Reading Association. In addition to writing and making art, her passions are social justice and hunger alleviation.

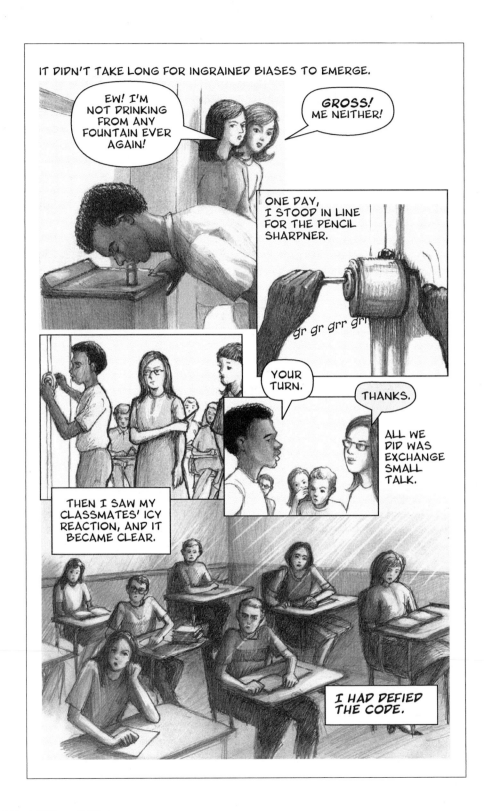

Excerpt from
Serena

Ron Rash

American poet and novelist Ron Rash was born in Chester, South Carolina, in 1953. He grew up on the family farm in western North Carolina where his ancestors had lived since the mid-1700s. After completing his degrees, he later became a college professor at Gardner-Webb University in Boiling Springs. Rash currently holds the John Parris Chair in Appalachian Studies at Western Carolina University. He is the author of 9 books including short stories, poetry and novels. In addition to many other awards, Rash has been awarded an NEA Poetry Fellowship, and he has won the Sherwood Anderson Prize. Rash's *One Foot in Eden* was also named Appalachian Book of the Year. Ron Rash's poetry and fiction have appeared in over one hundred journals, magazines, and anthologies.

Photo Credit: Ulf Anderson

The meeting with the park delegation was set for eleven on Monday morning, but by ten o'clock Pemberton, Buchanan and Wilkie had already gathered in the office's back room, smoking cigars and discussing the payroll. Harris also sat at the table, reading the morning's *Asheville Citizen* with visible ire. Campbell stood in the corner until Pemberton checked his watch and nodded it was time to get Serena.

"They're early," Buchanan said minutes later when the office door opened, but it was Doctor Cheney and Reverend Bolick instead. They came into the back room, and Cheney settled into the closest chair. Bolick held his black preacher's hat in his hand, but he sat down without being asked and placed his hat on the table. Pemberton couldn't help but admire the man's brazenness.

"Reverend Bolick wishes to have a word with you," Doctor Cheney said. "I told him we were busy but he was insistent."

The morning was warm and the preacher dabbed his forehead and right temple with a cotton handkerchief, not touching the left side of his face where the skin was withered and grainy, thinner seeming, as if once shaved with a planer. Caused by a house fire during his childhood, Pemberton had heard. Bolick placed the handkerchief in his coat pocket and set his clasped hands before him.

"As you have guests arriving soon, I'll be brief," Reverend Bolick said, addressing them all but looking specifically at Wilkie. "It's about the pay raise we've discussed. Even half a dollar more a week would make a huge difference, especially for the workers with families."

"Have you not seen all those men on the commissary steps?" Wilkie asked, his voice quickly shifting from annoyance to anger. "Be grateful your congregation has work when so many don't. Save your proselytizing for your congregation, Reverend, and remember you serve here at our indulgence."

Bolick glared at Wilkie. The fire-scarred side of the preacher's face appeared to glow with some lingering of that long-ago violence.

"I serve only at God's indulgence," he said, reaching for his hat.

Pemberton had been looking out the window and now he spoke.

"Here comes my wife," he said, and the others turned and looked out the window as well.

Serena paused at the ridge crest before her descent. Lingering fog laid a thick mist on the ground and the ridge, but the morning's brightness broke full on the summit. Threads of sunlight appeared to have woven themselves into Serena's cropped hair, giving it the appearance of shone brass. She sat upright on the gelding, the eagle perched on the leather gauntlet as if grafted to her arm. As Bolick pushed back his chair to rise, Wilkie turned his gaze from the window and met Bolick's eyes.

"There's a true manifestation of the godly," Wilkie said admiringly. "Such an image gave the Greeks and Romans their deities. Gaze upon her, Reverend. She'll never be crucified by the rabble."

For a few moments no one spoke. They watched Serena descend into the swirling fog and vanish.

"I'll listen to no more of this blasphemy," Bolick said.

The preacher put on his hat and quickly walked out of the room. Doctor Cheney remained seated until Pemberton told him his services were no longer needed.

"Of course," Cheney said dryly as he got up to leave. "I forgot my input is needed only in matters of life and death."

Pemberton went to the bar and brought a bottle of cognac to the table, went back and got the crystal tumblers. Buchanan looked at the bottle and frowned.

"What?" Pemberton asked.

"The liquor. It could be perceived as a provocation."

Harris looked up from his newspaper.

"I was under the impression we were meeting the Secretary of the Interior, not Eliot Ness."

The park delegation was twenty minutes late, by which time Wilkie had gone to the commissary for a bromide. Everyone shook hands, the visitors unsurprised when Serena offered hers. Pemberton surmised they'd been told she was not a woman of deference, and that it might help their cause to acknowledge as much. Except for Kephart, who was dressed in a clean flannel shirt and dark wool pants, the visitors wore dark suits and ties, lending the meeting a formal air despite the room's rusticity. Albright and Pemberton sat at opposing ends of the table. Davis, Rockefeller's lawyer, seated himself to the right of Albright, Kephart and Webb near the table's center. Cuban cigars and cognac were passed around. Several of the late arrivals took a cigar, but all in the visiting contingent politely declined the alcohol except Kephart, who filled his tumbler. Gunmetal-blue streams of cigar smoke soon rose, raveled into a diaphanous cloud above the table's center.

Harris folded the newspaper and laid it on the table.

"I see you've folded the paper to my most recent editorial, Mr. Harris," Webb said.

"Yes, and as soon as my constitution allows, I plan to wipe my ass with it."

Webb smiled. "I plan to write enough articles on this park to keep you well supplied, Mr. Harris. And I won't be alone. Secretary Albright informs me a *New York Times* reporter will arrive this weekend to write about what land has already been purchased, as well as complete a profile on Kephart's role in the park's creation."

"Perhaps the article will discuss Mr. Kephart's desertion of his family," Serena said, turning to Kephart. "How many children were left in Saint Louis for your wife to raise alone, was it four or five?"

"This is not really relevant," Albright said, looking at the table as if for a gavel.

"It's very relevant," Serena said. "My experience has been that altruism is invariably a means to conceal one's personal failures."

"Whatever my personal failings, I'm not doing this for myself," Kephart said to Serena. "I'm doing it for the future."

"What future? Where is it?" Serena said sarcastically, looking around the room. "All I see is the here and now."

"With all respect, Mrs. Pemberton," Albright said, "we are here to discuss a reality, the creation of a national park, not engage in sophistry."

"The sophistry is on your side," Harris said. "Even with the land you've bought, this park is still nothing more than a fairy dream on a goat hill."

"Rockefeller's five million dollars is real enough," Webb countered. "This country's eminent domain law is real enough also."

"So the threats begin," Harris said.

The door opened and Wilkie entered. He apologized profusely to all though Pemberton note the old man's eyes were on Secretary Albright as he spoke. Albright stood and offered his hand.

"No need to apologize, Mr. Wilkie," Albright said as they shook. "It's good to finally meet you in person. Henry Stimson speaks highly of you as both a businessman and a gentleman."

"That's kind of him to say," Wilkie replied. "Henry and I go back many years, all the way to Princeton."

"I'm a Princeton man myself, Mr. Wilkie," Davis said, offering his hand as well.

Pemberton spoke before Wilkie could respond.

"We are very busy, gentlemen, so please tell us about your proposition."

"Very well, then," Albright said as Wilkie took his seat. "The initial price we offered Boston Lumber Company for its thirty-four thousand acres was, I admit, too low, and with the generous help of Mr. Rockefeller we can make a far more substantial offer."

"How much?" Pemberton asked.

"Six hundred and eighty thousand."

"Our price is eight hundred thousand," Pemberton said.

"But the land has been appraised at six hundred and eighty thousand," Davis objected. "This country is in a potentially long-term depression. In this market our offer's more than fair."

"What about my eighteen thousand acres?" Harris asked.

"Three hundred and sixty thousand, Mr. Harris," Davis said. "That's twenty dollars an acre, and, as with Boston Lumber, a substantial increase on our initial offer."

"Not nearly good enough," Harris replied.

"But think how much you already have profited here," Webb said with exasperation. "Can't you give something back to the people of this region?"

Serena raised her index finger to her chin, held it there a moment as if bemused.

"Why is this pretense necessary, gentlemen?" she said. "We know what's going on with these land grabs. You've already run two thousand farmers off their land—that's according to your own census. We can't make people work for us and we can't buy their land unless they want to sell it, yet you force them from their livelihood and their homes."

Davis was about to speak but Albright raised his hand. The Secretary's visage achieved a profound solemnity Pemberton suspected was an innate talent of undertakers as well as career diplomats.

"An unfortunate aspect of what has to be done," Albright said. "But like Mr. Webb, I believe it's ultimately for the common good of all people in these mountains."

"And therefore all should sacrifice equally, correct?" Serena said.

"Certainly," Albright agreed, and as he did so Davis grimaced.

Serena took a sheaf of papers from her pocket and placed them on the table.

"This is part of the bill passed by the Tennessee legislature. In it are provisions stating that a number of wealthy landowners will be exempt from eminent domain. They get to keep their land, even though it's inside your proposed park. Perhaps your *New York Times* reporter can do an article about that."

"We had to have their support at that time," Davis replied. "If we hadn't, the park would have been doomed from the start. That was 1927, not today."

"We expect nothing more than to be treated like other wealthy landowners," Serena said.

"That just can't be done now," Davis said, shaking his head.

"Can't or won't?" Harris jeered.

"We'll get this land either way," Davis said, his voice now strident, "and if it's by eminent domain you'll be lucky to get half what we're offering now."

Albright gave a deep sigh and leaned back.

"No final answer is needed today," he said, looking at Buchanan and Wilkie, who'd been silent during the exchange. "Discuss it among yourselves. And consider the fact that Mr. Rockefeller is a businessman like all of you, yet he has given five million dollars. Think about how little in comparison we're asking of Boston Lumber Company."

Buchanan nodded. "We'll certainly discuss the matter."

"Yes," Wilkie said. "We appreciate your coming all this way to talk to us personally."

"My pleasure," Albright said, and raised his hands, palms open in a gesture of mollification. "As I said, nothing need be decided today. We'll be in Tennessee this weekend but back in Asheville Monday. We're beginning negotiations with your fellow timberman, Colonel Townsend. His Elkmont tract has more virgin hardwoods than any land in the Smokies, yet we're offering you the same price per acre as him."

"He's taking your offer seriously?" Serena said.

"Very much so," Davis said. "He's smart enough to know a small profit is better than a big loss."

Secretary Albright stood and the rest of the delegation rose as well. Wilkie and Buchanan accompanied them as they walked back to the train.

"A total waste of time," Harris complained on the office porch.

"I disagree, Mr. Harris," Serena said. "We may have learned about a tract we can invest in together."

"Ah," the older man said, his smile broadening enough to show glints of gold. "That would be something, wouldn't it? Buying Townsend's land out from under them would really throw a monkey wrench in this park business."

Harris paused and watched as the train pulled out and headed back to Waynesville. He took out his car keys, jangled them loosely in his palm before enclosing them in his fist, mimicking a throw of the dice.

"Let's get in touch with Townsend. They've minded copper on that tract. I don't know how much, but I can find out. This could be a boon for both of us, virgin hardwoods for you and copper for me."

Harris walked out to his Studebaker and drove off. As Pemberton and Serena walked toward the stable, Pemberton saw that Buchanan and Wilkie lingered beside the tracks though the train had disappeared over McClure Ridge.

"I believe Buchanan's wavering."

"No, he's not wavering," Serena said. "He's already decided."

"How do you know?"

"His eyes. He wouldn't look our way, not once." Serena smiled. "You men notice so little, Pemberton. Physical strength is your gender's sole advantage."

Pemberton and Serena stepped inside the stable, pausing a moment to let their eyes adjust. The Arabian stamped his foot impatiently at Serena's approach. She unlatched the wooden door and led the gelding out.

"Wilkie wasn't as resolute as he usually is either," Pemberton said.

"Hardly," Serena said. "They stroked him like a housecat and he purred."

She paused and lifted the saddle, placed it below the horse's withers.

"So if Buchanan sides against us," Pemberton said, "you believe Wilkie could be swayed as well?"

"Yes."

"So what should we do?"

Serena led the Arabian to the mounting block and handed the reins to Pemberton.

"We'll rid ourselves of Buchanan."

She strapped the gauntlet on her right forearm and opened the adjacent stall, where the eagle waited quiet and unmoving as a soldier at attention. It's a Berkute, Serena had told Pemberton the week after the creature arrived, much like the golden eagles she and her father hunted with in Colorado, only bigger and stronger, more fierce. The Kazakhs hunted wolves with them, and Serena had claimed Berkutes attacked even snow leopards given the opportunity. Looking at the eagle's huge talons and muscled keel, Pemberton believed it possible.

Serena emerged from the stall, the bird on her arm. She stepped onto the mounting block, then slipped her left foot in the stirrup and swung onto the saddle. Serena's legs and hips clinched the horse's saddled midsection as she balanced herself. It was a deft maneuver, equal parts strength and agility. The eagle raised its wings a moment, resettled them as if also balancing itself.

"Are you still hunting with Harris Sunday?" Serena said.

"Yes."

"Ask Buchanan to come along as well. Tell him it'll give the two of you a chance to discuss the Secretary's offer. On the way out there, talk to Harris some more about the Townsend land, maybe also mention the Jackson County tract Luckadoo called you about. You probably won't have a chance to talk afterward."

Because? Pemberton almost asked, but then understood. Serena stared fixedly at Pemberton, her pupils waxing in the barn's muted light.

"I need to get that second skidder up and running Sunday morning, but I could join you in the afternoon. I can do it, if you want me to."

"No, I'll do it."

"Another time for me, then," Serena said.

Student essay on *Serena*:

Joy Baxendell

Professor

ENGL 1010-55

3 March 2016

The Power of Perspective

Why do people make choices that hurt them? The answer is because of the perspective of the person. Perspective influences decisions, what people care about, and it defines who they are. A perspective that can lead to ruin is that something to be gained is worth more than any pain caused. Shakespeare's 73rd sonnet describes a tree being "Consum'd with that which it was nourish'd by" (line 8). The tree was destroyed by what defines it: the changing seasons. Destruction determined by definition is explored in Ron Rash's *Serena* in several ways. It is developed through main characters like Serena and Pemberton, but Rash explores the idea through minor characters too. Despite the focus on the Pembertons, Rash shows how characters like McDowell, Snipes' logging crew, and Cheney are ultimately destroyed by what motivated them.

McDowell is consumed with his mission to stop the Pembertons, and his mission costs him his life. In the beginning, McDowell can only do so much like forcing Pemberton to pay a fine and to write a statement after Pemberton kills Harmon in self-defense (12). As the novel progresses, McDowell's perspective changes. His need to stop the Pembertons increases, and as a result, he is more and more willing to go further. McDowell plans to stop them using the law, but that option is taken away from him. He tells Rachel he was fired, but "there's ways to beat [the Pembertons] that don't need a sheriff's badge" (295). Having lost his job, he no longer believes the law works. Once Rachel is nearly killed by Galloway, McDowell decides he must act (313). After the house fire, Pemberton sees a "man [watching] the flames... on the ground next to the chair was an empty ten-gallon canister of kerosene... it was McDowell" (317). He commits arson and stays around afterwards, knowing they will kill him. His perspective changes and leads him to his destruction. He is reckless and pays for it with his life without seeing his goal finished.

Snipes' logging crew has a contrasting perspective from McDowell's, but both pay for their choices. They are not obsessive or noble; their need for work motivates them. At one point, the crew talks about how miserable they are and how "there can't be a worser job in the world," but because of the Great Depression, "there's folks wanting [the job]" no matter how awful it is (176, 177). Later, Pemberton sends Snipes crew out even though the area is dangerous and the trees of little value (184). Snipes knows it is too dangerous, but the crew could not refuse (184). He is proven right when a crew member is killed by a falling tree limb (187). There are plenty of men around the camp looking for a position, and they are desperate enough to take their place even if they might die. The crew has no loyalty to Pemberton. Snipes says that if he wanted to kill the Pembertons, he would "[plant] a wooden stake in their hearts," but his statement contrasts with their inaction (322). The reason they do not act is because of perspective. They value their employment too much to risk the consequences that would follow any action, unemployment at best and death at worst. It keeps them from taking action, quitting, or trying to stop the deforestation of the land. After all the trees have been cut, the crew discusses how "there's been so much killed and destroyed it can't ever be alive again" (335). They believe what they see "is what the end of the world will be like" (336). The crew acknowledges "what was in part their handiwork," and it weighs on them (336). Their job destroys their lives and leaves them thinking they have had a hand in the end of the world.

Doctor Cheney is defined both by his job and his prejudice against Serena, and both cost him his life. In one of the earliest interactions, Cheney told Serena that women tend to lack the same intellectual skills men have, but she has "somehow compensated for that weakness" (34). Serena responds by telling him he's ignorant because of where he grew up, sparking a mutual disdain for each other (34). He makes several derogatory comments about her throughout the story. He says Serena catches rattlesnakes so she can "[milk] the fangs and [coat] her tongue with the poison" (102). Cheney knows Serena is dangerous, but he still mocks her when she claims Galloway will be loyal to her (181). His belittlement of Serena and her thoughts is what causes his death. When Serena is in pain, they bring Cheney in to examine her. His perspective is there is nothing seriously wrong with her and she will recover by the next day; however, that delay causes Serena to lose the baby (203, 208). Cheney's mistake was foreshadowed from the beginning. Buchanan tells Serena "the good doctor's patients rarely recover" (32). Serena is able to recover only through Pemberton's blood donation and skill of the doctors at the hospital; the baby does not recover like Buchanan said. Because of his wrong diagnosis, the Pembertons kill him. His skepticism of Serena's pain, influenced by the prejudice that defines him, is what destroys him.

"By-and-by black night doth take away" life, peace of mind, and the will to live (3). Cheney was defined by his view of Serena which misleads him in his diagnosis, costing him his life. Snipes' logging crew is motivated to keep their heads down so they can keep their jobs even when their lives are at stake, and those who live are haunted by what they have done. McDowell's perspective of his mission to stop the Pembertons radically changes, and when he tries to kill them, he stays around, knowing they will kill him for what he did. Like Shakespeare's tree, each character loses something priceless because it defined them. Their choices consumed until there was next to nothing left.

Works Cited

Rash, Ron. *Serena*. New York: HarperCollins Publishers, 2008. Print.

Shakespeare, William. "Sonnet 73." *Shakespeare-Online*. Amanda Mabillard, n.d. Web. 15 Feb. 2016.

"Church Dust"

Robert Morgan

Robert Morgan is an American poet, short story writer, and novelist born in 1944. He grew up in Hendersonville, a small town in the Blue Ridge Mountains of North Carolina, on the family farm. Morgan is the author of 14 books of poetry and 9 volumes of fiction including *Gap Creek*, a *New York Times* bestseller. He has been awarded the James G. Hanes Poetry Prize by the Fellowship of Southern Writers, and the Academy Award in Literature by the American Academy of Arts and Letters, among many others. He was inducted into the North Carolina Literary Hall of Fame in 2010. Morgan has taught since 1971 at Cornell University, where he is a Kappa Alpha Professor of English. His newest book is *Chasing the North Star*.

The oldest wooden churches have
a sediment between the planks
of floor and altar, under pews,
a stive so fine it soaks into
the grain, or flies away before
the broom can touch it to the lip
of pan. The dry mist wrestles in
a beam of light, a shiver dance
that shows the air is troubled in
the stillest house, the quietest room.
The salts and silts from human hope
and human sweat and human mourning,
the bits of hair and flakes of skin,
wash up in corners, lodge in cracks
until a passing step or breath
of weather stirs them up again,
and pieces swirl away like words
from long-forgotten sermons, hymns
once raised at hot revival's end.
A spider works its artistry
beneath the pulpit catching flies.
A mouse hunts through the must for crumbs
beneath the service table, finds
a feast of consecrated lint,
a hornet like a bullet spent,
as time goes cooly counting dust.

Excerpt from
Silver Sparrow

Tayari Jones

Tayari Jones is the author of three novels and numerous short stories, non-fiction, and essays of literary criticism. Jones was born in Atlanta, GA, on November 30, 1970. She received her B.A. from Spelman College, an M.A. from University of Iowa, and an M.F.A. from Arizona State University. She has won numerous awards, including the Martindale Foundation Award for Fiction, the Zora Neale Hurston/Richard Wright Foundation Award, and the Voices of Our Nation Arts Foundation scholarship as well as various fellowships and other recognition.

Jones's first novel, *Leaving Atlanta*, is a coming of age story set during the city's infamous child murders of 1979-81. *Leaving Atlanta* received several awards and accolades including the Hurston/Wright Award for Debut Fiction. It was named "Novel of the Year" by *Atlanta Magazine* and "Best Southern Novel of the Year," by *Creative Loafing Atlanta*. The *Atlanta Journal Constitution* and *The Washington Post* both listed it as one of the best of 2002. Bookpage lists it among the best debuts of the decade. Her second novel, *The Untelling*, published in 2005, is the story of a family struggling to overcome the aftermath of a fatal car accident. *Silver Sparrow* was recently added to the NEA Big Read Library, a selection of contemporary classics. *The Village Voice* wrote that "Tayari Jones is fast defining black middle class Atlanta the way that Cheever did for Westchester." The American Booksellers chose *Silver Sparrow* as the #1 Indie Next pick for June 2011. *Library Journal, O Magazine, Slate* and *Salon* all selected the novel among the best of the year.

My father, James Witherspoon, is a bigamist. He was already married ten years when he first clamped eyes on my mother. In 1968, she was working at the gift-wrap counter at Davison's downtown when my father asked her to wrap the carving knife he had bought his wife for their wedding anniversary. Mother said she knew that something wasn't right between a man and a woman when the gift was a blade. I said that maybe it means there was a kind of trust between them. I love my mother, but we tend to see things a little bit differently. The point is that James's marriage was never hidden from us. James is what I call him. His own daughter, Chaurisse, the one who grew up in the house with him, she calls him Daddy, even now.

Copyright Acknowledgments

Alexie, Sherman. "On the Amtrak From Boston to New York City" from *First Indian On the Moon*. Copyright © 1993 by Sherman Alexie. Reprinted by permission of Hanging Loose Press. All rights reserved.

Angelou, Maya. "Phenomenal Woman" from *And Still I Rise: A Book of Poems*. Copyright © 1978 by Maya Angelou. Used by permission of Random House, an imprint and division of Penguin Random House LLC. All rights reserved.

Bierhorst, John. "Navajo Night Chant" a translation by John Bierhorst, from *Four Masterworks of American Indian Literature*, University of Arizona Press. Copyright © 1984 John Bierhorst. Reprinted with permission of the author. All rights reserved.

Bradbury, Ray. "The Veldt" from *The Illustrated Man*. Original copyright © 1948 by Ray Bradbury. Reprinted with permission. All rights reserved.

Bragg, Rick. Excerpt(s) from *All Over but the Shoutin'*. Copyright © 1997 by Rick Bragg. Used by permission of Pantheon Books, an imprint of the Knopf Doubleday Publishing Group, a division of Penguin Random House LLC. All rights reserved.

Bukowski, Charles. "Cold Summer" from *Poetry Magazine*, July 1994.

Cisneros, Sandra. Excerpt(s) from *Woman Hollering Creek: And Other Stories*. Copyright © 1991 by Sandra Cisneros. Used by permission of Vintage Books, a division of Penguin Random House LLC. All rights reserved.

Cohen, Leonard. "Sisters of Mercy" from the album *Songs of Leonard Cohen*. Copyright © 1967 by Leonard Cohen. Reprinted with permission of Columbia Records. All rights reserved.

Collins, Billy. "Workshop" from *The Art of Drowning*. Copyright © 1995 by Billy Collins. Reprinted by permission of the University of Pittsburg Press. All rights reserved.

Earle, Steve. "A Death in Texas" reprinted from *Utne Reader*. All rights reserved.

Faulkner, William. "Barn Burning" from *Collected Stories of William Faulkner*. Copyright © 1950 by Random House, Inc. Copyright © renewed 1977 by Jill Faulkner Summers. Used by permission of Random House, an imprint and division of Penguin Random House LLC. All rights reserved.

Heaney, Seamus. "Digging" from *Death of a Naturalist*. Copyright © 1966 by Seamus Heaney. Reprinted with permission. All rights reserved.

Hemingway, Ernest. "Hills Like White Elephants" from *The Short Stories of Ernest Hemingway*. Reprinted with the permission of Scribner, a division of Simon & Schuster, Inc. Copyright © 1927 by Charles Scribner's Sons. Copyright © renewed 1955 by Ernest Hemingway. All rights reserved.

Hughes, Langston. "The Negro Speaks of Rivers" from *The Collected Poems Of Langston Hughes*, edited by Arnold Rampersad with David Roessel, Associate Editor. Copyright © 1994 by the Estate of Langston Hughes. Used by permission of Alfred A. Knopf, an imprint of the Knopf Doubleday Publishing Group, a division of Penguin Random House LLC. All rights reserved.

Jackson, Shirley. "The Lottery" originally appeared in *The New Yorker*. Copyright © 1948 by Shirley Jackson. Reprinted with permission. All rights reserved.

Kay, Terry. Excerpt(s) from *To Dance with the White Dog*. Copyright © 1990 by Terry Kay. Reprinted with permission of Peachtree Publishers, Ltd. All rights reserved.

McCorkle, Jill. Excerpt(s) from *Creatures of Habit*. Copyright © 2003 by Jill McCorkle. Reprinted by permission of Algonquin Books of Chapel Hill. All rights reserved.

Minty, Judith. "Conjoined" from *In the Presence of Mothers*. All rights reserved.

Morgan, Robert. "Church Dust" from *The Strange Attractor: New and Selected Poems*. Copyright © 2004 by Robert Morgan. Reprinted with permission. All rights reserved.

Nawwab, Nimah. "Gentleness Stirred" from *The Unfurling*. Copyright © 2004 by Nimah Nawwab. Reprinted with permission of the author and Selwa Press. All rights reserved.

Neruda, Pablo. "Love Sonnet XVII" from *100 Love Sonnets: Cien Sonetos De Amor*. Translated by Stephen Tapscott. Copyright © 1959 by Pablo Neruda and Fundacion Pablo Neruda, copyright © 1986 by the University of Texas Press. Reprinted with permission of the University of Texas Press. All rights reserved.

O'Connor, Flannery. "Revelation" from *Everything that Rises Must Converge*. Copyright ©1956 by Mary Flannery O'Connor, and renewed 1993 by the Estate of Mary Flannery O'Connor. Reprinted with permission of Farrar, Straus, and Giroux. All rights reserved.

Paterniti, Michael. "11:20" from *Esquire Magazine*, Jan. 29, 2007.

Plath, Sylvia. "Lady Lazarus" and "Metaphors" from *The Collected Poems of Sylvia Plath*. Copyright © 1960, 1965, 1971, 1981 by the Estate of Sylvia Plath. Reprinted with permission of HarperCollins. All rights reserved.

Quatro, Jamie. "1.7 to Tennessee" from *I Want to Show You More*. Copyright © 2013 by Jamie Quatro. Reprinted with permission of Grove Press. All rights reserved.

Rash, Ron. Excerpt(s) from *Serena*. Copyright © 2008 by Ron Rash. Reprinted with permission of HarperCollins. All rights reserved.

Reed, Ishmael. "Chattanooga" from *New and Collected Poems, 1964-2007*. Copyright © 1988, 2000, 2006 by Ishmael Reed. Reprinted with permission of Lowenstein-Yost Associates, Inc. All rights reserved.

Rich, Adrienne. "Aunt Jennifer's Tigers" from *The Collected Poems: 1950-2012*. Copyright © 2016 by the Adrienne Rich Literary Trust, copyright © 1951 by Adrienne Rich. Reprinted with permission of W.W. Norton and Co. All rights reserved.

Roethke, Theodore. "My Papa's Waltz" from *Collected Poems*. Copyright © 1942 by Hearst Magazines, Inc. Used by permission of Doubleday, an imprint of the Knopf Doubleday Publishing Group, a division of Penguin Random House LLC. All rights reserved.

Saunders, George. "Sticks" originally appeared in *Harper's Magazine*. Copyright © 1993 by George Saunders. Reprinted with permission of ICM Partners. All rights reserved.

Stark, Peter. "As Freezing Persons Recollect the Snow: Hypothermia" from *Last Breath: The Limits of Adventure*. Copyright © 2001 by Peter Stark. Used by permission of Ballantine Books, an imprint of Random House, a division of Penguin Random House LLC. All rights reserved.

Tan, Amy. "Mother Tongue" first appeared in *The Threepenny Review*. Copyright © 1989 by Amy Tan. Reprinted by permission of the author and the Sandra Dijkstra Literary Agency. All rights reserved.

Walker, Alice. "Everyday Use" from *In Love and Trouble*. Copyright © 1973 by Alice Walker. Reprinted with permission of Houghton Mifflin Harcourt. All rights reserved.

Weaver, Lila Quintero. Excerpt(s) from *Darkroom: A Memoir in Black and White*. Copyright © 2012 by Lila Quintero Weaver. Reprinted with permission of the author. All rights reserved.

Welty, Eudora. "A Worn Path" from *A Curtain of Green and Other Stories*. Copyright © 1941 by Eudora Welty. Reprinted with permission of Houghton Mifflin Harcourt. All rights reserved.

Wilbur, Richard. "The Writer" from *The Mind-Reader*. Copyright ©1971 and renewed by Richard Wilbur. Reprinted with permission of Houghton Mifflin Harcourt Publishing Co. All rights reserved.